# COLORIMETRIC
# METHODS OF ANALYSIS

## Including Some Turbidimetric and Nephelometric Methods

*By*

FOSTER DEE SNELL, Ph.D.

*and*

CORNELIA T. SNELL, Ph.D.

---

*THIRD EDITION*

---

VOLUME I

THEORY—INSTRUMENTS—pH

1948

D. VAN NOSTRAND COMPANY, Inc.

TORONTO    NEW YORK    LONDON

NEW YORK

D. Van Nostrand Company, Inc., 250 Fourth Avenue, New York 3

TORONTO

D. Van Nostrand Company (Canada), Ltd., 228 Bloor Street, Toronto

LONDON

Macmillan & Company, Ltd., St. Martin's Street, London, W.C. 2

QA
113
.S62

PRINTED IN THE UNITED STATES OF AMERICA

*Press of*
GEO. S. FERGUSON CO.
Philadelphia Pa.

# PREFACE TO THE THIRD EDITION

BECAUSE of the tremendous volume of material published on colorimetric methods—and particularly on photometric methods—during the ten years which have elapsed since publication of the second edition, the size and scope of the present edition have necessarily been increased. Nephelometric and turbidimetric methods—minor in number but still important—are included.

As in the second edition, the aim has been completeness, but even so, much condensation was found necessary. Many of the older references given in the second edition have been deleted; policy has been to cite the majority of new references. Description of new equipment designs is necessarily limited to the commercially more important types. Some unusual modifications are outlined briefly. Expansion of text necessitated a change from two to three volumes, covering in Volume I Theory, Instruments, pH; Volume II Inorganic; and Volume III Organic Applications.

Alternative methods are still given, since that which is satisfactory for one purpose may be unsuited to another. Because the preparation of different types of samples is often the most difficult and troublesome part of a determination, much space has been devoted to this.

In this revision, in addition to study of the extensive journal literature, careful attention has been given to various related volumes which have appeared, particularly *Organic Reagents in Inorganic Analysis* by Ibert Mellan (1941); *Kolorimetrische Analyse* by Bruno Lange (1941); *Photelometric Clinical Chemistry* by William S. Hoffman (1941); *Optical Methods of Chemical Analysis* by T. R. P. Gibb, Jr. (1942); *Colorimetric Determination of Traces of Metals* by E. B. Sandell (1944); *Metallurgical Analysis by Means of the Spekker Absorptiometer* by F. W. Haywood and A. A. R. Wood (1944); *Colorimetry for Chemists* by M. G. Mellon (1945); *Colorimetric Analysis* by Noel L. Allport (1945); and others.

iii

Reviews of the previous edition were studied for guidance in meeting constructive criticisms. Also many helpful letters from readers relating experiences with specific methods were given due consideration; our gratitude is expressed here to these people.

The authors wish to express appreciation to Leonard C. Cartwright for help with Chapters 2 and 19, to Sally Cohen for careful editorial aid, and to Anne Burdé for painstaking preparation of manuscript.

FOSTER DEE SNELL

CORNELIA TYLER SNELL

New York, N. Y.
September, 1947

# CONTENTS

# TABLES

# ILLUSTRATIONS

# CHAPTER I

# COLORIMETRIC METHODS

A COLORIMETRIC method as applied to chemical analysis fundamentally consists of treating a solution of a substance with a reagent in such a way as to produce a color which is proportional in intensity to the amount of the substance present in the solution. It is desirable but not essential that the proportionality be linear. The methods are applicable to the determination of many metals, radicals and organic compounds, often after elimination of interfering ions or radicals. The unknown is spoken of in this general discussion as the test substance. After the color has been produced, the solution containing an unknown amount of test substance is compared with a standard solution by one of five methods and the result read either by eye or photoelectrically. The older methods involve a simple comparison of sample versus standard, but modern technics tend to measure the color of the sample in absolute terms and compare with predetermined numerical absorption standards. Whichever method is applied gives a comparison by color as distinguished from the physical analysis of color.

**Measurement.** The intensity of color of a sample may be read by the eye, by a photoelectric cell, by a thermopile or by the record on a photographic plate, the last two being seldom used. The instrument used is not the color meter implied in the term "colorimeter," since only in the spectrophotometer is intensity of color measured quantitatively. That instrument as applied to colorimetry records the absorption of a given band of wave lengths of light.

Colorimetric methods for at least iron and cobalt are more than a century old. The importance of colorimetry has been promoted by rapid improvement in recent years in apparatus for measurement of the absorption of light by aqueous solutions.[1] That improvement has been quite largely in photoelectric methods which has in turn led to the development of superior methods of test. This is indicated by the trend of several ASTM committees to change to photoelectric methods.[2] Accur-

---

[1] G. E. F. Lundell, *Proc. Am. Soc. for Testing Materials,* **44,** 709 (1944).

[2] J. J. Stumm, *Ibid.,* **44,** 749-53 (1944); V. A. Stenger, *Ibid.,* 754-61; C. Zischkau, *Ibid.,* 762-8; Arba Thomas, *Ibid,* 769-78.

acy of visual methods ranges downward from 5 per cent and rarely exceeds 2 per cent. Photoelectric methods are often reproducible to 0.2 per cent but that does not mean necessarily that degree of precision is obtainable. Whether such is the case depends on other factors in the determination, prior to the instrumental reading.

The methods of colorimetric chemical analysis do not include physical color analysis. Thus, the term "colorimetric analysis," as used by the chemist and the physicist, has a different meaning. Chemical methods are applicable to a reasonably limited number of materials; physical methods analyze the wave-length distribution of any transparent or opaque colored substance. Colorimetric chemical analysis finds a matched transmittance by test solution and standard, sometimes indirectly through a comparison curve; colorimetric physical analysis reports quantitatively the transmittance or reflectance. To integrate related optical methods as applied in chemistry, photometric analysis in the general use of the term is measurement of the intensity of transmittance of the entire spectrum; specrophotometric analysis is measurement of the same factor as applied to limited wave lengths, usually narrow bands; abridged spectrophotometry differs from spectrophotometric analysis only in that the wave band is less accurately restricted. Abridged spectrophotometry and spectrophotometric analysis are applied in colorimetric analysis for measurement of absorption or the reciprocal transmittance.

**Series of Standards.** The sample, diluted to a definite volume, is compared with a series of standards of the same volume, in which the amount of test substance is known. The value of the unknown is either taken to be that of the standard to which it most nearly conforms or estimated from that standard. In this way the amount of test substance present is obtained without calculation, since, if the volume and color of the unknown and the standard are the same, their contents of test substance will be identical. Beer's law need not apply and diehromatism can be tolerated.

**Absorption.** This is closely related to the series-of-standards method. The transmittance of a series of developed standards is measured, ordinarily with a restricted wave band, and plotted on a calibration chart. The developed samples are similarly read and the analytical values read from the chart. The chart normally reads either in transmittance, which is a logarithmic curve, or in $-\log_{10}$ of the transmittance known as extinction, which is linear. Beer's law need not apply to the system;

if it does, the transmittance curve will be smooth and the log curve will be a straight line.

**Dilution.** The standard and sample are placed in graduated tubes of similar diameter, and the darker diluted with the same concentration of reagents as is present in sample and standard. The end point is when the color of one viewed horizontally through the tube after mixing is the same as that of the other. When this point is reached, if all necessary conditions have been observed, each unit volume of one solution must contain the same amount of test substance as each unit volume of the other and the amount in the unknown is to the amount in the known directly as their volumes. Beer's law need not hold for the system.

**Balancing.** A sample solution is placed in a flat-bottom graduated tube and a standard solution added to a similar tube, until the color intensities, when observed through the lengths of the columns of liquid, are identical. The amount of test substance in each tube will then be the same, and, since the quantity per unit volume in the standard is known, the total amount in the standard may be calculated. This is identical with the quantity in the sample. If the tubes are not of the same cross section, the amount of test substance per unit of cross section is the same, and the concentrations are to each other inversely as the depths of solution. More briefly, their concentrations are inversely proportional to their depths. This is the method employed with many commercial instruments. Beer's law must hold for the system.

**Duplication.** The sample is made up to a definite volume, and nearly that volume of water in a similar container is treated with the same reagents for bringing out the color of the solution, as were used with the sample. A concentrated solution of standard is added to the blank from a buret, drop by drop when the end point is near. The volume of the blank is then brought up by addition of more water until the two colors and volumes are identical. The amount of standard used in making the duplicate is a measure of the amount of test substance in the sample. Because of its resemblance to usual titration methods this is sometimes called colorimetric titration. Beer's law need not hold for the system but reaction must be practically instantaneous.

**Extent of Use.** The significance of chemical colorimetry is indicated by a conservative estimate of about 25,000 colorimeters in use in 1939,[3]

[3] Ralph H. Müller, *Ind. Eng. Chem., Anal. Ed.*, **11**, 1-17 (1939).

a figure which must have been multiplied by a large whole number since the estimate was made. This cannot include the many laboratories where sets of Nessler tubes or test tubes are used for occasional determinations.

Colorimetric methods often give results in 5 minutes to 1 hour from the time the determination is begun, which is in many cases a small fraction of the time in which similar determinations could be made by other methods. It may be said for colorimetry in general that its methods are rapid and reasonably accurate.

A broad field of usefulness of colorimetry is the determination of impurities in substances easily soluble in water, alkali or acid. The methods are very sensitive, usually determining 0.5-10 ppm., and on rare occasions detecting one part per billion. In many of its applications, chemical colorimetry is a part of microanalysis.[4] When applicable the methods are usually simpler, more convenient, and at least as accurate as alternative methods. As a matter of correlation between the various methods the quantities are referred to in fractions of a milligram rather than in $\gamma$, micrograms, the 0.001 mg. unit in which microchemistry is often expressed. In general, in giving weights, one more numeral than is really significant has often been cited as a guide to the analyst.

The methods are seldom used to determine amounts much greater than one per cent. In control work where limited accuracy is acceptable they are more widely applicable for determination of major constituents. For example, determination of copper up to 22 per cent in ores with an accuracy of 0.1 per cent has been described.[5] By use of monochromatic light as many as four substances have been determined in the same solution[6] and, by proper calculation, overlapping bands can be determined.[7] The importance of colorimetric methods is further indicated by the periodic appearance of reviews of new instruments and their applications.[8]

[4] Albert E. Sobel, *Ind. Eng. Chem., Anal. Ed.,* **17**, 242-5 (1945).

[5] J. P. Mehlig, *Ind. Eng. Chem., Anal. Ed.,* **7**, 387-9 (1935).

[6] Fritz Weigert, *Ber.* **49**, 1496-1532 (1916).

[7] Harold W. Knudson, Villiers W. Meloche, and Chancey Juday, *Ind. Eng. Chem., Anal. Ed.,* **12**, 715-19 (1940).

[8] Ralph H. Müller, *Ind. Eng. Chem., Anal. Ed.,* **7**, 223-6 (1935); *Ibid.,* **12**, 571-630 (1940); *Ibid.,* **13**, 667-754 (1941); S. A. Thiel, *Ber.,* **66B**, 1015-23 (1935); K. S. Gibson, *Instruments,* **9**, 309, 335 (1936); *J. Soc. Motion Picture Engrs.,* **28**, 388 (1937); P. Krumholz, *Scientia Pharm,* **7**, 103-6 (1936); M. G. Mellon, *Ind. Eng. Chem., Anal. Ed.,* **9**, 51-6 (1937); *Ibid.,* **11**, 80-5 (1939); N. Strafford, *Chem. Soc. Annual Repts.,* **33**, 456-65 (1936); G. Kortüm, *Angew. Chem.,* **50**, 193-204

**Development of a Colorimetric Method.** In general, in the development of a new colorimetric procedure, only the method by a series of standards can be assumed to be applicable, the standards containing the same amounts of the same reagents as the unknown and prepared at the same time. Absorption may be measured as a method of recording the intensity of the series of standards and as previously indicated will show whether the system conforms to Beer's law. Even if Beer's law is not found to be applicable to the reaction, the dilution method may usually be applied within limits. If Beer's law holds, the method of balancing is applicable within the limits in which the law has been found to apply. If the color is permanent and develops nearly instantaneously, the method of duplication is applicable.

If the color develops over a wide range of wave bands, then the eye with reasonable accuity over the entire range will respond to the intensity with greater accuracy than an instrument reading a restricted wave band. If, on the other hand, the color change developed by the reagent lies almost entirely in a restricted wave band, the use of filter methods will be definitely preferred. The first condition corresponds with a dull and nonspecific color or, in the extreme case, with a gray; the latter with a bright color.

Frequently, the product obtained from the test substance precipitates above a definite concentration, in which case that sets a limit. The lower limit is usually that at which the color is just perceptible but the absolute accuracy becomes less as this lower limit is approached. In many cases, before precipitation is reached, the substance becomes colloidal rather than dissolved, and sometimes, but not always, the methods become nephelometric under these conditions. The formation of particles large enough to make the method nephelometric can sometimes be avoided by addition of a protective colloid, such as a water-dispersible gum.

(1937); Edwardo Coffari, *Chim. Industria*, (Italy) **19**, 255-6 (1937); S. E. Q. Ashley, *Ind. Eng. Chem., Anal. Ed.*, **11**, 72-9 (1939); W. D. Wright, *Repts. Progress Physics*, **7**, 36-40 (1940); Manfred Richter, *Arch. tech. Messen., No.* **111**, T99-100, No. 113, T123-4 (1940); G. Kortüm and J. Grambow, *Angew. Chem.*, **53**, 183-7 (1940); O. H. Weber, *Ibid.*, **54**, 56-7 (1941); D. L. Tilleard, *J. Oil Colour Chem. Assoc.*, **25**, 227-39 (1942); R. P. MacFate, *Am. J. Clin. Path., Tech. Sect.*, **7**, 55-65 (1943); W. Kluge et al, *Die Chemie*, **55**, 362-6 (1942); **56**, 183-4 (1943); Maria I. Ardao, *Ph.*, **1943**, No. 2, 11-14, No. 3-4, 28-30, No. 5, 3-6; A. L. Davydov, *Trudy Vsesoyuz, Konferentsii Anal. Khim.*, **2**, 233-51 (1943); J. S. Fawcett, *Proc. Phys. Soc.*, (London) **56**, 8-21 (1944); E. I. Stearns, *Am. Dyestuff Reptr.*, **33**, 1-6 (1944); M. G. Mellon, *Proc. Am. Soc. for Testing Materials*, **44**, 735-9 (1945).

**Conditions for a Colorimetric Method.**[9] Although there are many desirable features which can be cited for the ideal colorimetric method such as the following, about the only one that is followed in practice is that a color must be developed. Even then the absorption is occasionally in the ultraviolet so that it is invisible to the naked eye, and therefore does not conform to the classical definition of color (p. 000).

(1) It is desirable that the color developed from a small amount of the test subbstace be intense. This permits operation at or near an optimum of light transmission by dilution, concentration, modification of solvent, addition of excess reagent or in other ways. Such an optimum gives the maximum sensitivity.

(2) The color developed should be stable so that the determination need not be completed rapidly, and so that natural standards will be reasonably permanent. Causes of instability are often air oxidation or photoelectric effects that when recognized can be controlled.

(3) The color is desirably but little affected by change in pH. If so affected, the pH should be controllable by adding a simple buffer or a known amount of acid or alkali, or adjusting to a desired level with a glass electrode or colorimetric indicator.

(4) For visual reading the transmission is preferably between 475 and 625 m$\mu$. For reading photoelectrically a broader range is permissible, depending on the range of sensitivity of the photocell.

(5) It is advantageous that color formation proceed at room temperature, and that variation in temperature have slight effect. Variation from this makes the procedure more complex.

(6) If the system conforms to Beer's law, the standards and calibration curves may be much simplified.

(7) If the color develops quickly, waiting for completion of equilibrium in a reaction is avoided.

(8) When a reagent can be used that is not itself colored, the complications of excess reagent are lessened but by no means avoided. If the reagent is colored, the total visual effect is the sum of that due to the test substance, and the excess reagent. In measurement of transmittance the color due to excess reagent may often be screened out.

(9) In the ideal case, approached but never realized, the reagent would react solely with the test substance and not give a color with any

---

[9] Largely taken from M. G. Mellon, *Proc. Am. Soc. for Testing Materials*, **44**, 733-9 (1944); *Colorimetry for Chemists*, pp. 8-10, G. Frederick Smith Chemical Co., Columbus, O. (1945).

interfering substance. This calls for a specific reaction whereas high selectivity is all that can be anticipated.

(10) The color developed is preferably independent of excess reagent; alternatively, a large excess of reagent should give substantially a constant effect.

(11) The nature of the reaction should be known in order to permit better control of conditions. Conventionally, it is by oxidation, reduction, formation of a complex ion or coupling with a large molecule.

(12) The test substance and reagent are desirably in the same solvent so that excess reagent will neither precipitate nor cause precipitation of other substances.

(13) For simplicity, the colored solution should require no special treatment, such as extraction with an organic solvent.

(14) The order of mixing should not be critical.

**Definition of Terms.** The Colorimetry Committee of the Optical Society of America [10] has defined the terms of physical colorimetry. So far as these apply to chemical colorimetry or photometry their definitions follow and have been used.

*Color* is the general name for all sensations arising from the activity of the retina of the eye and its attached nervous mechanisms, this activity being, in nearly every normal individual, a specific response to radiant energy of certain wave lengths and intensities. It is fundamentally psychological and cannot be synonymous with wave length. It may be defined in terms of the three fundamental attributes of brilliance, hue and saturation.

*Brilliance* is that attribute of any color which classes it as equivalent to some member of a series of grays ranging between black and white. Synonyms are luminosity, brightness, tint, value and visual brightness.

*Hue* is that attribute of certain colors in which they differ characteristically from the gray of the same brilliance and which permits them to be classed as reddish, yellowish, greenish or bluish.

*Saturation* is that attribute of all colors possessing a hue which determines their degree of difference from a gray of the same brilliance. Synonyms are purity and chroma. In chemical colorimetry or photometry, hue and saturation are assumed to have a fixed ratio to each other and brilliance is measured. This is complicated by the use of a mixture of colors, each assumed to meet these conditions.

---

[10] L. T. Troland et al., *J. Optical Soc. Am.*, **6**, 527-96 (1922).

*Spectrophotometry* is the measurement of relative radiant energy as a function of wave length.[11]

*Sensitivity* of a color reaction has been defined as the reciprocal of the weight in milligrams ($\Delta$) of the test substance that produces a change in color that can be differentiated with certainty.[12]

In the examples which have been investigated, mg. present/mg. present $+ \Delta = 0.89-0.96$. Strictly speaking, this is true only over a limited range since Weber's law applies. This is $\Delta R/R = K$ which states that the additional stimulus required to produce a minimum perceptible difference in a sensation bears a constant relation to the original stimulus.

**Illumination.** This is desirably standard, which means the use of artificial light. It is approximated in conventional colorimetry by use of north daylight, or some reasonably duplicable source of indirect illumination. This may be a built-in or separate colorimeter lamp or a general light such as is shown in Figure 1. The variation in quality of daylight between urban and suburban districts or between seasons is a source of some errors. It is easily possissble that two solutions would compare at different levels when the ratio of red to blue light differed, as between bright and cloudy days. The distribution of natural light need not be as accurately duplicable when filters are used with the colorimeter; it need be constant only in the bands passed by the filters. This is one reason for the trend toward the use of color filters with visual colorimeters. For spectrophotometry, artificial light is nearly always used. The subject receives more detailed consideration in Chapter 16.

**Color vs. Wave Length.** The quality of color usually can be maintained at a definite standard of distribution of wave lengths by observing the following precautions given in detail with the particular method. These are designed to accomplish the following:

(1) Insure the same concentration of all reagents in the standard and sample.

---

[11] Optical Soc. Am., Progress Committee, *J. Optical Soc. Am.*, **10**, 169 (1925).

[12] John H. Yoe and William L. Hill, *J. Am. Chem. Soc.*, **50**, 2395-2407 (1927); John H. Yoe and Floyd H. Wirsing, *Ibid.*, **54**, 1866-76 (1932); John H. Yoe and Robert T. Hall, *Ibid.*, **59**, 872-9 (1937); John H. Yoe, *J. Chem. Education*, **14**, 170-2 (1937).

(2) Avoid more than a moderate variation in concentration of test substance between standard and sample.

(3) Insure absence of all materials other than the test substance which are of themselves colored or will produce a color with the reagents used.

In full or abridged spectrophotometric methods only a selected band of wave lengths is used and conformity is necessary only over that

FIG. 1. Artificial skylight. (*Macbeth Daylighting Corp.*)

range. For convenience of reference, the data in Table 1 indicate not only the color transmitted at a given wave length but also the complementary hue.[14] Data are shown in Chapter 12 as to the wave-length distribution of filters available commercially. For correlation, the human eye is sensitive over the range 400-700 m$\mu$, ordinary photographic film over 250-500 m$\mu$, panchromatic film over 250-700 m$\mu$ and various photocells over 200-850 m$\mu$.

[14] Thomas R. P. Gibb, Jr., *Optical Methods of Chemical Analysis*, p. 71, McGraw-Hill Book Co., New York, N. Y. (1942).

TABLE 1.  RELATION OF VISIBLE COLOR, WAVE LENGTH AND
COMPLEMENTARY COLOR

| Wave Length Millimicrons | Color Transmitted | Complementary Color |
|---|---|---|
| 400-435 | Violet | Yellowish-green |
| 435-480 | Blue | Yellow |
| 480-490 | Greenish-blue | Orange |
| 490-500 | Bluish-green | Red |
| 500-560 | Green | Purple |
| 560-580 | Yellowish-green | Violet |
| 580-595 | Yellow | Blue |
| 595-610 | Orange | Greenish-blue |
| 610-750 | Red | Bluish-green |

**Color Intensity.** In general, in colorimetric analysis only the apparent effect is measured. As an example, a dandelion and a sodium flame have the same apparent color. The dandelion reflects all colors except blue, thus giving rise to a sensation of yellow. The sodium flame emits only yellow of sharply defined wave lengths. In spectrophotometry the analysis of the two would be radically different; in comparison colorimetry they would be the same. Conditions are controlled in colorimetric analysis so that the wave-length distribution will be the same in sample and standard with that end in view. The major exception where the two may be radically different yet appear the same visually, is when artificial standards are used.

**Origin of Methods.** The colorimetric method is a logical development from the estimation by eye of the laboratory analyst. In looking at the permanganate solution resulting from a bismuthate determination of manganese one can almost guess the amount of manganese in the sample. The development of methods which would measure such color where it is reasonably stable might well be expected. The attention which has been devoted to this is clearly indicated by the apparatus developed for the purpose.

Such a development of methods is also logical from the trend in qualitative analysis where a student is expected not only to report the elements present but, in addition, determine whether they are in large or small amounts. In their individual ranges of application, the comparison methods are usually accurate to better than 5 per cent. The spectrophotometric methods vary in accuracy from 2 per cent downward to a few tenths of a per cent. Thus, by care, they approach the same degree of accuracy as gravimetric or volumetric methods, except for very small amounts. Then they are frequently much more accurate than any method other than spectrographic or polarographic analysis.

Tacit classification as glorified qualitative analysis gives a fair picture of the possible field of new methods. A new reagent for a qualitative test, especially if it gives a color reaction proportional to the amount of the test substance present, would be expected to lead to development from a qualitative test into a method of estimation. There are doubtless hundreds of qualitative tests giving color reactions which are in use in private laboratories for quantitative colorimetric estimation but of which no details have been published. If one wanted to determine the amount of water in absolute alcohol, could not a tightly stoppered sample be shaken with a few permanganate crystals and then the intensity of pink compared quickly with suitable nonalcoholic permanent standards? Probably such a method is in use but unpublished. With very few exceptions qualitative color reactions are potential colorimetric methods of analysis by application of a suitable technic.

**Concentration by Extraction.** In a limited number of cases the colored substance may be much more soluble in an organic solvent than in water—the ferric thiocyanate complex is an old example. In those cases the color can be concentrated to a substantial extent. Thus, if extracted from 100 ml. of colored solution by 10 ml. of organic solvent the color, all other things being equal, will be concentrated 10 times. This has definite limitations; for example, the color could hardly be efficiently extracted from 100 ml. with 1 ml. of organic solvent. Nevertheless, the technic has permitted the extension of several methods to a region of accuracy previously unattainable. The parallel is an attempt to lengthen the column indefinitely to obtain increased sensitivity, which also has obvious limitations.

**Apparatus in General.** Each of the types of colorimetric determination has its special apparatus, simple or complex. Development has progressed to such a degree that only that available commercially will be described in a series of chapters. Many special designs must be indicated only by reference. This is the more necessary because the eye has been replaced, successfully or otherwise, in almost every type of instrument by the photoelectric cell.

# CHAPTER II

## THEORY

THE essential theory behind colorimetric methods of analysis consists of physical laws of light. Successively, this has consisted of Bouguer's law, Beer's law, and Lambert's law. According to Bouguer's law each layer of equal thickness and composition absorbs an equal fraction of the light which traverses it. Therefore, the light transmitted decreases exponentially as the thickness of the absorbing medium increases arithmetically. Another way of putting this fundamental law is that absorption varies directly as the logarithm of the thickness. Transmittance is the converse of absorption. This has been integrated into the later laws. Simply expressed, Beer's law states that at constant depth the color intensity is directly proportional to concentration. In similar terms, Lambert's law states that at constant concentration the color intensity is directly proportional to depth. As a matter of convenience, both Beer's law and Lambert's law are conventionally referred to as Beer's law.

**Beer's Law.**[1] Visible light, or a selected band of wave lengths, in passing through any medium is absorbed in part. The variation with different media is very great. In passing through water the absorption is small. Deviations in the absorption by two columns of water, one 30 mm. deep, the other 40 mm. deep, would be inappreciable for colorimetric purposes. Only very accurate measurements would show such a difference. For the purposes of colorimetric comparison the variation in absorption is usually assumed to be entirely due to the test substance dissolved. Thus, although Beer's law is often referred to as applying or not applying to a reaction, practically it is applied to a system including not only the color derived from the test substance but also the reagents, solvents and the normal impurities associated with the sample. An exception is the method by measurement of transmittance when a blank of solvent and reagents without test substance and without development of color has been used.

A spectroscopic analysis of the light transmitted through a copper sulfate solution would show less absorption in the blue than in the other colors. The eye reports this solution as blue because of the relative

---

[1] A. Beer, *Ann. der Physik. Chemie* (Poggendorff), (3), **26**, 78-88 (1852).

absence of other waves. Depending on the composition of the solution, yellow waves may or may not be greatly reduced. If there is lessened absorption in the yellow range the hue is changed from pure blue toward green.

**Symbols.** To permit interpretation of the mathematical derivations the following symbols are assembled for convenience in approximately the order in which they are introduced. A few not used in this chapter have been added.

$I_1$ (often designated as $I_0$) = initial intensity.

$I_R$ = loss of $I_1$ due to reflection.

$I_A$ = loss of $I_1$ or of $I_1 - I_R$, due to absorption.

$I_2$ (often designated as $I$) = emergent intensity.

$I$ when used without subscript = intensity not otherwise defined.

$T$ = transmittance = $I_2/I_1$.

$l$ (sometimes designated $d$) = length of column or thickness of absorbing medium.

$e$ = base of natural or Naperian logarithms = 2.71828.

$k'$ = absorption index, the reciprocal of the thickness of the absorbing medium which reduces $I_2$ to $I_1/e$.

$C$ = concentration of absorbing substance.

$k$ = absorption index of unit concentration = $k'/C$.

$K'$ = extinction coefficient, the reciprocal of the thickness of the absorbing medium which reduces $I_2$ to $I_1/10$.

$K$ = extinction coefficient at unit concentration = $K'/C$.

$T_s$ = specific transmittance, the fraction of incident light transmitted through unit thickness of the absorbing medium.

$D$ = optical density = $K'l$.

$\Sigma$ = molecular extinction coefficient = $K$ when concentration is expressed in moles per liter.

**Derivation of Beer's Law and Lambert's Law.** In passing a beam of radiant energy, whether or not essentially monochromatic, through a homogeneous medium, a part will be lost by reflection which is usually about 4 per cent for visible light at an air-glass interface, another part will be absorbed by the medium, and a third part will be transmitted. The proportions are independent of the intensity of the incident light. Thus,

$$(1) \qquad\qquad I_1 = I_R + I_A + I_2$$

With a correction for the reflection it is not difficult to measure either of the remaining factors, the loss of intensity due to absorption or the emergent intensity. Expressed as fractions of the incident intensity, these are designated "absorbance" and "transmittance," respectively. For a given absorbing medium they may vary with the wave length, the plot of the variation being the transmittance curve. Thus, by definition, the transmittance of the absorbing medium is

$$(2) \qquad\qquad T = I_2/I_1$$

Applying this with monochromatic light, Beer's law and Lambert's law follow. While passing through a unit layer of the solution, the energy of a given wave length is reduced by a fraction of its intensity. In the next unit layer a similar fraction of the remaining intensity is absorbed. The decrease of intensity per increment of depth of solution is therefore proportional to the intensity of energy passing through that layer according to the expression,

$$(3) \qquad\qquad \frac{-dI}{dl} = k'I.$$

Integration of this between the initial intensity $I_1$ and the emergent intensity $I_2$ gives

$$(4) \qquad\qquad -\log_e \frac{I_2}{I_1} = k'l.$$

In the final analysis the decline of intensity in a unit layer is directly proportional to the number of absorbing molecules encountered which will be proportional to the concentration of test substance present.

From (3) this gives

$$(5) \qquad\qquad \frac{-dI}{dl} = kCI$$

which between the limits $I_1$ and $I_2$ gives

$$(6) \qquad\qquad -\log_e \frac{I_2}{I_1} = kCl.$$

Changing the logarithms of base $e$ in (6) to those of base 10, and substituting the transmittance from (2) gives

$$(7) \qquad\qquad -\log T_\lambda = lCK_\lambda.$$

In this the subscript $\lambda$ indicates that the values for the terms are only for a given wave length of the radiant energy to which the transmittance $T_\lambda$ applies.

This is Beer's law and is often expressed without the limitation as to wave length in practical application, particularly in comparative colorimetry. Similarly (4) gives Lambert's law,

$$(8) \qquad -\log T_\lambda = lK'_\lambda.$$

It is a fine point of differentiation[2] to state that Beer's law cannot apply rigidly in an instrument using white light and that empirical correction curves are always necessary.

**Application of Beer's Law to the Colorimeter.** Assume that two solutions receive the same intensity of light at a wave length $\lambda$. Each contains a test subtance to which the absorption constant $K_\lambda$ applies. The concentration of test substance in the two solutions is different. If we adjust the depth of one solution until the intensity of light at wave length $\lambda$ is the same as from the other solution, their transmittances have then been made equal.

The values from (7) are then

$$(9) \qquad -\log T_\lambda = l_1 C_1 K_\lambda$$

$$(10) \qquad -\log T_\lambda = l_2 C_2 K_\lambda$$

from which it follows that

$$(11) \qquad l_1 C_1 = l_2 C_2 \text{ and } C_1 : C_2 = l_2 : l_1$$

The balancing colorimeter is a device specifically arranged for adjustment of the intensities of the light transmitted by two solutions until their transmittances are equal. Knowing $C_1$ and measuring $l_1$ and $l_2$ (11) can be readily solved for $C_2$.

This must of necessity be derived on the assumption that light of only a single wave length is used. To visualize the entire range a similar application must be assumed to each wave length. Since, in the absence of dichromatism, the ratio of the different wave lengths remain constant, all of the forms of (9), (10) and (11) would be the same and it follows that in practice (7) is simplified to

$$(12) \qquad -\log T = lCK$$

in which $T$ now represents the transmittance for the solution and $K$ a constant for the absorbing substance in the solution. Since their relation to each other is constant at all wave lengths they can be determined at any wave length.

[2] A. P. Mussakin, *Z. anal. Chem.*, **105**, 351-61 (1936).

When the statement is made that Beer's law holds for a system it means that the tint of the solution is dependent only on the mass of dissolved solute, independent of dilution. It could be expected to hold exactly only for nonionizable substances in true solution. On that basis it would seldom hold exactly. As a matter of practice it is observed to hold within the usual limits of observation for the majority of colorimetric methods of analysis.

As soon as white light is replaced by a variable bundle of bands as selected by a filter, the original conditions of derivation of Beer's law, or of Lambert's law, are approached more closely. A further step is attained when a spectrophotometer is used because the transmitted bands are more accurately defined.

Going back to (2) let this be taken in specific terms for clarification. Assume that 50 per cent of the incident light is absorbed in passing through a unit thickness, then 50 per cent of the remaining light will be absorbed in passing through the next unit thickness, and so on. Now, defining specific transmittance as

$$(13) \qquad\qquad T_s = \frac{I_2}{I_1}$$

for unit thickness, we have

$$(14) \qquad\qquad I_2 = T_s I_1 = 0.5 I_1$$

for the first unit thickness.

In a second unit thickness

$$(15) \qquad\qquad I_3 = 0.5 I_2 = 0.25 I_1 = I_1 T_s^2$$

and in a third unit thickness, similarly

$$(16) \qquad\qquad I_4 = 0.5 I_3 = 0.25 I_2 = 0.125 I_1 = I_1 T_s^3$$

This is clearly indicative of the logarithmic nature of numerical values of the light transmitted. Plotted against thickness it follows that a logarithmic curve will be given; or plotted as logarithms the result will be a straight line.

The general case for any thickness, $l$, is

$$(17) \qquad\qquad I_2 = I_1 T_s^l.$$

For this it is immaterial what the unit thickness is, whether 1 mm., 1 cm., or 5 cm. It need only be standardized, and the numerical value of $T_s$ be determined in terms of that thickness unit.

The more familiar form of (17) is

$$(18) \qquad \log \frac{I_2}{I_1} = l \log T_s.$$

Then, from (2), (8) and (18), we have

$$(19) \qquad l \log T_s = \log T = -lK'.$$

A more common expression of this value is the optical density, conventionally $D$,

$$(20) \qquad D = K'l = -\log I_2/I_1 = \log 1/T.$$

Just as Beer's law in (7) leads simply to Lambert's law in (8), so this is an expression of the relation between transmittance and thickness which has the same form as the relation between transmittance and concentration. That is to say, that double the thickness at half concentration is a full equivalent of unit thickness at unit concentration. Since from (7) and (8), $K'l = KCl$, when concentration is in moles per liter, the molecular extinction coefficient, $\Sigma$, is given by,

$$(21) \qquad D = K'l = \Sigma lC.$$

**Representation of Beer's Law.** The value of $C$ must be in moles per liter, at a standardized cell thickness, to apply $\Sigma$ as the molecular extinction coefficient. This will change every time the unit of thickness is changed, and often whenever the other contents of the test solution are changed. Thus, although a blank is always run to measure the effect of other dissolved ingredients on the light beam, those ingredients also affect the color developed—in all cases to a minor extent and in a few cases to a major extent. As an example, increase of the thiocyanate ion in a determination of iron will markedly increase the intensity of red color, although not materially affecting the absorption of the blank.

The absorption by the solvent is generally assumed to be independent of the effect of the test substance. Although subject to error if the amount of reagent used is near to stoichiometric, this is usually correct. The measured transmittance is a function of absorptive capacity of the system, cell length, and concentration.

Plotting the value of $T$ versus concentration on linear-linear paper gives a smooth logarithmic curve. By use of log-linear paper, readings plotted on the logarithmic scale and concentrations plotted on the linear scale, give a straight line whose slope is $K$, or $\Sigma$ when concentration is in moles per liter. Thus, if Beer's law applies, there is a constant molecular extinction coefficient, $\Sigma$, for all dilutions and thicknesses at a given wave length (see Figure 2). It is desirable to use the wave length of maximum absorption by the system, since at that wave length there is the greatest change in the transmittance for a given change in concentration (Figure 2).

If light outside the region of the absorption band of the solution is also present, the log-linear line will be smoothly curved. An extraneous colored substance will also cause deviation from linearity, the curve being a composite of absorption by both substances. In an equilibrium reaction, unless the reagent is in large excess, a linear relationship is not obtained.

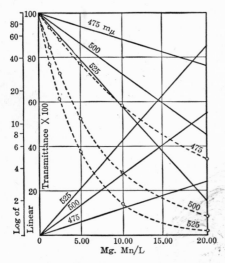

FIG. 2. Curves for solutions of potassium permanganate at three wave lengths

Change in molecular aggregation with change in concentration may occur. The larger aggregates may have a different absorption from the smaller, or may be large enough to be colloidal and have reflecting surfaces. Nearly all lines will deviate from linearity if a sufficient range of concentration is covered. By selection of conditions, a linear relation can be approached for most solutions.

Photoelectric methods tend toward determination of larger amounts, as by the use of thin cells for stronger solutions. Beer's law need not hold in order that a 0.1 cm. cell be equal to one-tenth of the absorption in a 1 cm. cell; although it may not necessarily be equal to the sample diluted to one-tenth concentration in a 1 cm. cell. This assumes that the effect of solvent is corrected in both cases.

**Multiple Colors.** In the absence of chemical interaction between two types of colored molecules, the absorbances are additive. Therefore, it is possible to determine the concentrations of several components in a mixture by measuring the transmittance of the mixture at various wave lengths. Carrying this to its logical conclusion, titanium, vanadium and molybdenum have been determined simultaneously.[4]

Considering a single color first, a molecule of a colored substance

---

4 Alfred Weissler, *Ind. Eng. Chem., Anal. Ed.*, **17**, 695-8 (1945).

in solution acts as if it contained a damped, simple, harmonic oscillator —for example, an electron—which has a natural frequency corresponding to that of the peak absorption.

The oscillator is impelled toward the equilibrium position by an elastic restoring force, and is also subject to a frictional damping resistance proportional to the velocity. An external light wave exerts a sinusoidal force, $F_o \cos \omega t$—alternatively, the real part of $F_o e^{i\omega t}$—which causes the oscillator to undergo forced vibration. Let $x$ be the displacement of the particle of mass $m$, $mk$ the frictional damping constant, $\omega_o$ the natural angular frequency, and $\omega$ the impressed angular frequency; then the differential equation of motion derived is

$$(22) \qquad m\frac{d^2x}{dt^2} + mk\frac{dx}{dt} + m\omega_o^2 x = F_o e^{i\omega t}.$$

Neglecting transients, this has a solution of the form $x = Ae^{i\omega t}$. The amplitude, $A$, may be a complex quantity consisting of a real part, $A_r$, and an imaginary part, $A_i$. The real part of the solution is

$$(23) \qquad x = A_r \cos \omega t + iA_i \sin \omega t.$$

It can be shown that the oscillator continually absorbs energy from the light wave, and that the absorbed energy goes into the frictional resistance. The rate of absorption is proportional to the component of amplitude out of phase with the impressed force. This component is the negative of the imaginary part of the amplitude, found, from the solution of the differential equation, to be

$$(24) \qquad A_i = -\frac{F_o}{m}\frac{2k\omega}{(\omega_o^2 - \omega^2)^2 + 4k^2\omega^2}.$$

Plotting this absorption component against the impressed frequency or wave length gives the characteristic spectral absorption curve. The shape of the experimental curves is partly due also to the distribution of vibrational and rotational frequencies and the varying solvation of the absorbing molecules.

Having the effect of a single type of molecules, the combined effect of many colored molecules in solution may be considered. It can be shown [5] that the intensity of monochromatic light transmitted by an absorbing solution decreases with the concentration, $C$, and the length of optical path, $l_1$, as $I_2 = I_1 e^{-kCl}$. Using Briggs logarithms, this is more

[5] T. R. P. Gibb, *Optical Methods of Chemical Analysis*, Chapter II, McGraw-Hill Book Co., New York (1942).

conveniently expressed as $-\log I_2/I_1 = KCl = D$ where $I_2/I_1$ is the transmittance, the negative log of which equals the extinction or optical density, $D$. The extinction cofficient, $K$, is characteristic of the nature of the colored molecule and it becomes numerically equal to the density when $l$ is 1 cm. and $C$ is also unity.

If the length of optical path is kept constant,

$$(25) \qquad \frac{D_1}{D_2} = \frac{C_1}{C_2} \quad \text{or} \quad C_1 = \frac{C_2}{D_2} D_1.$$

# CHAPTER III

## COMPARISON WITH A SERIES OF LIQUID STANDARDS

THIS is fundamentally the simplest colorimetric method and is widely used. The standards may be stable natural standards, unstable natural standards prepared at frequent intervals, or artificial standards designed to match the color developed from the test substance.

Because the identification of differences follows Weber's law (p. 143) it is theoretically preferable that such a series of standards be planned as a geometric rather than an arithmetic series.[1] Practically, because they usually cover only a limited range, the intervals are more often uniform. Adjacent standards should differ by no more than 20 per cent if accuracy better than 5 per cent is desired.

Many methods using a series of standards have official standing. Thus, the original color standards of the Fat Analysis Committee of the American Chemical Society and the American Oil Chemists Society are 23 solutions of inorganic salts whose colors have been recorded in wave-length distribution.[2] A special colorimeter, the Facolorimeter, has been designed for use with this series[3] Similarly varnish colors are usually read with a series of standards.[4]

Each set of standards required special consideration as to the factors concerned. Thus when chromate is used as a permanent color standard the wave-length distribution is affected by pH as well as concentration. Small changes in pH at intermediate levels make a large change in the color; therefore, the buffer under those conditions must have a high capacity to maintain uniform pH with variable amounts of chromate. At low or high pH this is not so important.[5]

**Test Tubes.** For the production of nonpermanent standards plain test tubes are often used. The solution may be quickly and conveniently emptied from these, and the breakage loss is not so great as from the

---

[1] V. G. Gurevich, *J. Gen. Chem.* (U.S.S.R.) **6**, 1433-43 (1936).

[2] W. M. Urbain and H. L. Roschen, *Oil and Soap*, **16**, 124 (1939).

[3] Lawrence H. Whyte, *Oil and Soap*, **19**, 199 (1942).

[4] G. G. Sward, *Am. Paint J.*, **21**, 16 (Aug. 30, 1937).

[5] R. E. Kitson and M. G. Mellon, *Ind. Eng. Chem., Anal. Ed.*, **16**, 42-4 (1944).

use of graduated Nessler tubes or bottles. Even with such simple tubes, proper lighting such as that shown in Figure 1 greatly facilitates comparison.

**Walpole Technic.** If a sample has a natural color it may still be examined by colorimetric methods provided the intensity of the natural color is not excessive. The technic provides for correction of the color of the standard by observing it through a tube of undeveloped sample.

Assume that oxygen is to be estimated by the pyrogallol method in a tube of a naturally colored sample. The standard does not contain a similar color but the same effect is obtained by looking through a tube

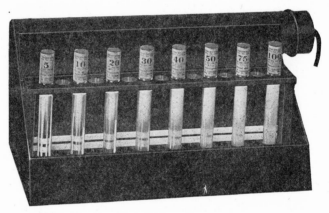

FIG. 3. Turbidimeter and nephelometer for comparison of series of standards. (*R. P. Cargille, New York, N. Y.*)

of untreated sample and the standard at the same time. To have the thickness of liquid observed with the sample the same, one looks through the developed sample and through a tube of water. If $A$ is the developed sample, $B$ the undeveloped sample, $C$ a tube of water, and $D$ one of the series of standards, one observes $A$ and $C$ against $B$ and $D$. Various standards are used as $D$ until the color of the pair $BD$ matches the pair $AC$.

**Gillespie Comparator.** As a form of the Walpole technic, originated for application to pH determination, a block colorimetric comparator is used for comparison of a sample tube with two additive standards. The details of the apparatus are shown in Figure 4. On the left side is the developed sample with one or two tubes of distilled water. On the right side are two standards with a third tube of undeveloped sample if the latter is colored. The principle is generally applicable for tubes of colorimetric standards. Use of quadrangular receptacles is preferable to round tubes.

**Bottles and Tubes.** Where a series of permanent standards is prepared, these are placed in stoppered tubes or in round or square glass bottles. Such a series of standards should be placed in a row, with sufficient space between each pair for a similar unit. The sample should be treated in a similar container after di-

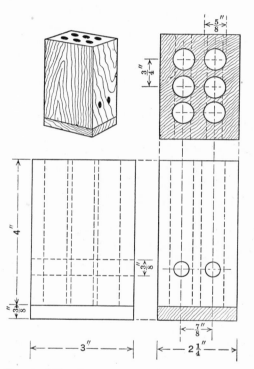

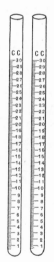

Fig. 4. Gillespie comparator: interior painted black

Fig. 5. Eggertz tubes

lution to the same volume as that of the standards, then placed in the various gaps between the standards until a place is found where one standard is higher than the sample and the one on the other side lower, as estimated from the intensities of their colors. The position of the sample relative to these two known quantities can then be estimated.

**Standard Tubes and Jars.** The following are the specifications for the only standard color comparison tubes recommended as stock sizes by the Committee on Guaranteed Reagents and Standard Apparatus of the American Chemical Society: [6]

FIG. 6. Typical block comparator for a series of liquid standards.
(*La Motte Chemical Products Co.*)

Eggertz tubes without stoppers, Figure 5, in sets of 2 or 4; capacity 30 ml. or 50 ml., calibrated to 0.1 ml.

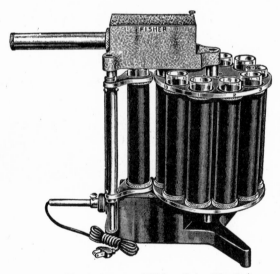

FIG. 7. Nesslerimeter. (*Fisher Scientific Co.*)

Nessler tubes in sets of 6 or 12, American Public Health Association Standard: tall form, clear glass, polished bottoms, calibrated at 50 ml., 100 ml., or 50 and 100 ml. Calibration marks on 50 ml. tubes are from 200 to 250 mm. from the bottom and on the 100 ml. tubes from 275 to 325 mm. from the bottom. In sets, the highest and lowest marks shall not be more than 1.5 mm. apart for the 50 ml. size and 2.0 mm. for the 100 ml. size.

Nessler jars or low-form Nessler tubes in sets of 2 or more: colorless glass, polished bottom, calibrated at 50 ml., 100 ml., or 50 and 100 ml. The calibrations of the

[6] W. D. Collins, *J. Ind. Eng. Chem.*, **14**, 655 (1922).

50 ml. tubes fall in the range of 125 to 145 mm., the 100 ml. of 145 to 170 mm. Standards for sets of low-form tubes are the same as for the tall form.

Bottoms may be fused on or, by more recent practice, are formed integrally without strains. The amount of color in the glass itself can introduce a rather serious error at times.

FIG. 8. Roulette comparator for a series of liquid standards. (*La Motte Chemical Products Co.*)

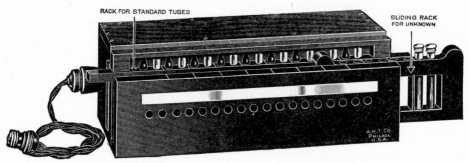

FIG. 9. Sliding comparator designed for sugar work. (*A. H. Thomas Co.*)

Figure 7 shows an instrument by which any of ten standards in Nessler tubes can be compared with the developed sample.[7]

**Sealed Tubes.** For specialized purposes, permanent standards in sealed tubes are convenient. For hydrogen-ion work these have been

[7] Cf. John C. Russell, *Eng. Mining J.*, **142**, 53-4 (Sept. 1941).

developed to a high degree of refinement. The equipment consists of kits of prepared standards. For rapid comparison of tubes of standards, rotary apparatus such as that shown in Figure 8 and sliding racks such as those shown in Figure 9 have been designed. Specialized sets are used for many purposes such as chlorine, available phosphorus, nitrate, potassium, alkali reserve of the blood, renal function, etc., and are used not only by chemists but also by doctors, agronomists and other professions. A microcolorimeter for comparison of 0.06 ml. with a series of standards was devised primarily for bromosulfonphthalein liver-function tests.[8]

Rechecking of solutions, even in sealed tubes, is often necessary at intervals, since all color standards may change due to solution of glass, fading by exposure to light, and other factors.

---

[8] T. W. Pratt and A. L. Tatum, *Science,* **82,** 305-6 (1935).

# CHAPTER IV

## COMPARISON WITH SOLID STANDARDS

**Lovibond Tintometer.** One of the best-known methods of estimating the color of a solution in terms of glasses is by the Lovibond tintometer. This has been calibrated for many quantitative determinations [1] as well as for recording the colors of numerous liquids. The apparatus consists

Fɪɢ. 10. Lovibond tintometer for pH determination. (*Tintometer, Ltd.*)

essentially of a cell or tube to contain the sample, the color of which is compared with standard red, blue, and yellow glasses. Those glasses vary in intensity from 0.1 to over 100 units of each. A complete set of glasses comprises 470 units, but no one type of work requires the complete set. Lovibond glasses are of greater importance than the instrument for which they were designed because they are used in other instruments.

---

[1] J. R. H. Coutts, *Soil Research,* **5,** 295-307 (1937); B. Bagshawe, *J. Soc. Chem. Ind.,* **57,** 260-5 (1938); I. Volk, *Myasnaya Ind.* (U.S.S.R.), **9,** No. 9, 27-30 (1938); *Chimie & Industrie,* **42,** 328 (1938).

Two methods of observing colors are used with the Lovibond tintometer. Ordinarily, no optical system is included, and the eye compares two parallel colors. For the other method, a set of prisms and an eyepiece is provided, similar to those of the Duboscq colorimeter (p. 69).[3]

The instrument has been used for recording and comparing a multitude of colored materials. The standard glasses come in sets for dyes, for fabrics and solids, for malt, sugar, wine, caramel, and spirit, for ammonia by the Nessler method, for carbon in steel, for oils, waxes, lards, fats, gelatin, varnish, etc., for cottonseed oil, for petroleum oil, for flour, for tannin, and for general purposes.

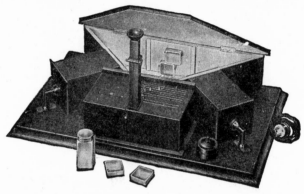

FIG. 11. Vertical form of Lovibond tintometer for use with artificial light.
(*Tintometer, Ltd.*)

In the use of color glasses the optical effect of two glasses is not identical with that of one darker glass equal to their sum. The difference is a gray tint introduced by the multiple glasses. Therefore, no more than an absolute minimum number of color glasses is permissible in taking any specific reading. The glasses are available mounted in discs for protection and ease of substitution. Mounting in protective frames is advisable where used routinely.[2]

The Wesson Colorimeter shown in Figure 12 is one of the best known of several colorimeters adapted to take Lovibond glasses.

The readings of the yellow to brown glasses of the American Institute of Cereal Chemists have been correlated with Lovibond glasses by the Coleman Spectrophotometer (p. 44).[3]    The transmittance of the glasses and of yellow and brown solutions were read at 430 m$\mu$ with a 30 m$\mu$

[2] Egbert Freyer, *Oil and Soap,* **16,** 234-5 (1936).
[3] G. F. Beyer, *J. Assoc. Official Agr. Chem,* **26,** 164-71 (1943).

FIG. 12. Two types of Wesson Colorimeter used in examination of vegetable oils. (*A. H. Thomas Co.*)

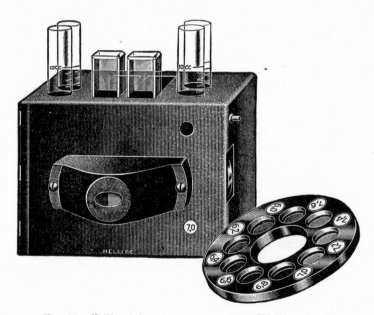

FIG. 13. Hellige laboratory comparator. (*Hellige, Inc.*)

slit and doubly monochromated light. The negative logarithm of the result multiplied by 10 corresponds to the Lovibond number.

**Hellige Colorimeter.** This instrument[4] compares the sample in a square or rectangular cell with a series of colored glasses mounted in a rotating disc (see Figure 13). It is designed for determination of hydrogen-ion but has been expanded by providing suitable color discs for

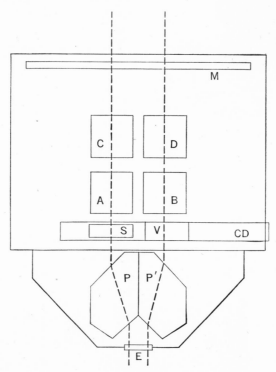

Fig. 14. Schematic diagram of Hellige comparator

ammonia, chlorine, nitrite, nitrate, hydrogen sulfide, copper, iron, lead, manganese, titanium, nickel, phosphorus, oil, varnish, malt and beer, hemoglobin, creatinine, blood, bromides, sugar, uric acid, cholesterol and bilirubin determinations, each by a specific method. Simplified industrial sets are relatively inexpensive.

A schematic diagram of the instrument is shown in Figure 14. For ordinary use, *A* contains water or untreated sample and *B* the test

---

[4] Paul A. E. Hellige, U. S. Patent 1,870,624 (1932).

solution with color developed. The water in $A$ serves to make the path of liquid through which the light must travel the same in each case. The color disc $CD$ is revolved to bring various glass standards into position at $S$ so that one superimposed on $A$ matches the color of $B$. Tubes $C$ and $D$ provide for the Walpole technic (p. 22) with a colored or turbid solution without the color disc. In that case, tube $A$ contains a standard, $C$ contains the untreated sample, $B$ contains the treated sample and $D$ contains water. Tubes $C$ and $D$ may also be used to superimpose filter colors on $A$ and $B$. $M$ is ground glass available in either white or blue.

FIG. 15. Simple Hellige comparator. (*Helige, Inc.*)

The dotted lines show the path of the light rays. Passing through $A$ and $B$ with or without $C$ and $D$ they are refracted by the Helmholtz double plate, $PP'$, and joined in an

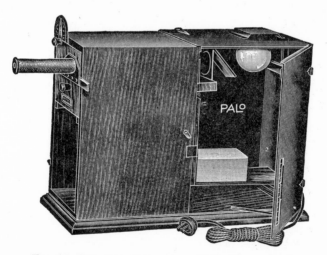

FIG. 16. Ives tint photometer. (*Palo-Myers, Inc.*)

eyepiece at $E$. The color disc is mounted with a large hollow center $V$ through which the light passes from $B$. Both pocket and laboratory types are available.

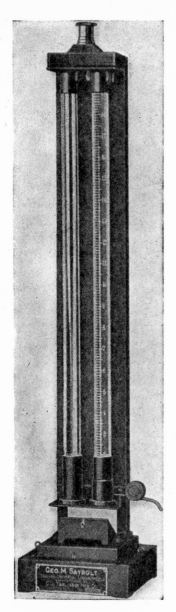

Fig. 17. Saybolt universal chromometer. (*C. J. Tagliabue Mfg. Co.*)

**Ives Tint Photometer.** Although designed originally to measure reflectance from solids, this instrument, shown in Figure 16, may also be used to record the transmission of color through solutions in terms of three glass standards. It is more useful for comparison of samples to ascertain a match than for recording complex analyses in terms of the color filters as artificial solid standards.

**Petroleum Colorimeters.** An instrument has been evolved by combination of the Lovibond tintometer and the Stammer colorimeter (p. 52) known as the Saybolt chromometer [5] (see Figure 17). This is intended solely for evaluating the colors of refined petroleum oils. It is similar to the Stammer instrument in that two tubes are provided, but the left-hand tube, *A*, is modified to an empty tube in which the color is obtained by the addition of 1 or 2 glass discs. In some designs these are on swivels and merely swing into place. The sample in *B* is drawn off until an amount is left which will duplicate the color of the disc or discs used. From the graduations the oil may then be graded in terms of the standards for petroleum oils. Lovibond readings are converted into Stammer readings by a curve reproduced as Figure 18.[6]

The Tag-Robinson colorimeter, Figure 19, for reading the colors of lubricating oils, operates by raising and lowering the tube containing the sample, thus varying the depth of color observed through a glass plunger. It is, therefore, a modified Duboscq colorimeter. Comparison with three glass

[5] ASTM D156-38.
[6] R. M. Wilhelm, *Tag Manual for Inspectors of Petroleum*, 26th Ed., p. 56, C. J. Tagliabue Mfg. Co., Brooklyn, N. Y. (1942).

standards is claimed to duplicate all oil colors, and to measure the "true color" of oils.[7]

In another type of instrument, the Union oil colorimeter,[8] Figure 20, a 4-ounce oil-sample bottle of the oil or a special glass jar of sample is compared with 15 slides of graded color. If the sample is too dark it

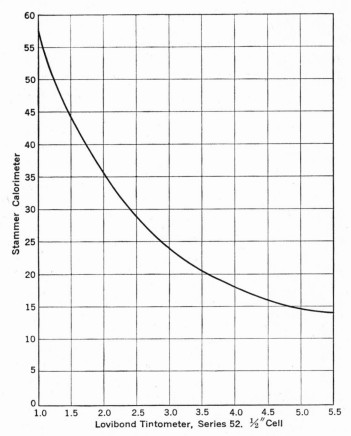

FIG. 18. Conversion of Lovibond to Stammer readings

may be diluted for reading. The effect of the depth of oil sample is matched by a tube of water on the other side. In some designs the glasses are mounted in a revolving disc. The instrument may be illuminated with artificial light corrected with a daylight glass.

---

[7] Harry Vinock, *Refiner Natural Gasoline Mfr.*, **16**, 601 (1937).
[8] ASTM D155-39.

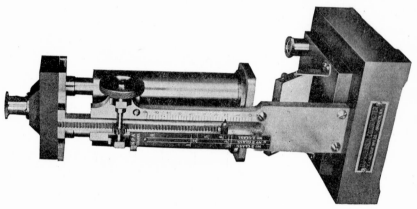

FIG. 19.  Tag-Robinson colorimeter.
(C. J. Tagliabue Mfg. Co.)

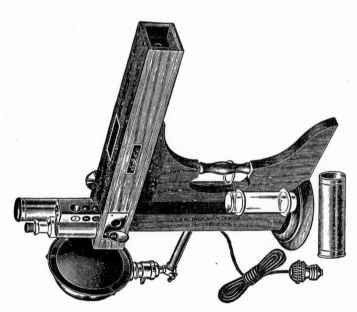

FIG. 20.  Union oil colorimeter.  (Emil Greiner Co.)

**Color Glasses.** One important consideration in using this type of equipment is the accuracy with which the glasses can be duplicated, not only as to intensity but as to transmittance, a subject of major importance for glass color filters to be discussed later. The most satisfactory standardization is by the spectrophotometer. The glasses can be mechanically polished to regrade to even units.[9]

The expression of Lovibond glass readings in terms of spectrophotometric results is difficult, and involves an empirical formula applicable

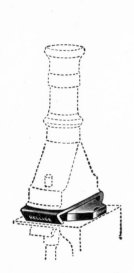

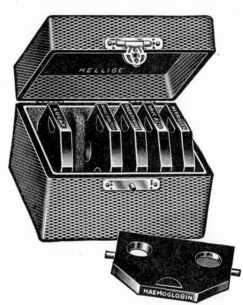

FIG. 21. Glass standard in place on Duboscq colorimeter. (*Hellige, Inc.*)

FIG. 22. Glass standards for use with Duboscq colorimeter. (*Hellige, Inc.*)

if only red and yellow glasses are used.[10] Readings in terms of glass color standards could be applied, simply requiring calibration curves, to nearly all colorimetric methods. A case in point is the use of the Newcomer disc in blood chemistry with the Duboscq colorimeter.

The use of glass color standards in various instruments such as the Lovibond, Hellige and other comparators represents a great convenience. In the case of such determinations as the Carr-Price method for vitamin A it is almost essential because of the transitory nature of the color.

[9] Roger S. Estey, Oil and Soap, **12**, 135-8 (1935).

[10] E. R. Bolton and K. A. Williams, *J. Intern. Soc. Leather Trades' Chem.*, **20**, 504-12 (1936).

Good correlation is obtained between Lovibond, Saybolt, and I. P. colors.[11]

Some natural standards require a long preparation, and the use of glass standards is a saving of time. The fundamentals for all the use of glass color slides as permanent standards are that they must remain unchanged in color and that they must be duplicable. Permanence of color is to be expected if the glass is properly selected.

---

[11] Color Panel of Standardization Sub-Committee 3—Liquified petroleum gases, gasoline, kerosene and light distillates, *J. Inst. Petroleum,* **29,** 357-60 (1943).

# CHAPTER V

## DILUTION AND DUPLICATION METHODS

**Dilution Method.** The dilution method consists simply of adding diluted reagent to the darker solution, whether sample or standard, until it matches the other in color intensity. The apparatus for comparison by the dilution method consists essentially of a pair of graduated tubes, viewed crosswise, and protected from side light. A convenient device

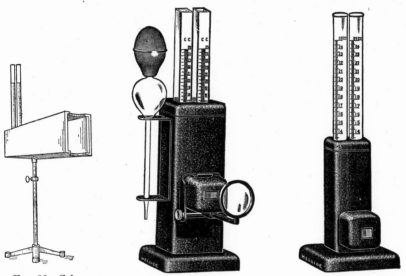

FIG. 23. Color camera.

FIG. 24. Dilution colorimeters. (*Hellige, Inc.*)

for use with this method is a light-proof box, painted black inside, with holders for two tubes near one end. The end near the tubes is fitted with a ground glass screen. The other end of this color camera, Figure 23, is fitted to the face of the observer so that no side light may enter. By the use of this a more accurate judgment as to the colors of the two tubes may be made than if they are compared in the open. This apparatus does not tire the eyes of the operator as quickly as some of the colorimeters used for the balancing method. More modern equipment, but less restful to use, is shown in Figure 24. Such equipment brings the images of the two tubes into juxtaposition and is relatively inexpensive. In all cases possible, a colorimeter should allow the use of both eyes for making the comparison so as to lessen fatigue. Comparison of the two tubes is often made simply by holding them in the hand against a sheet of white paper.

Whether or not apparatus more complex than two calibrated tubes is used, the operation of the dilution method is the same. Place standard and sample in two graduated tubes. The colors of the two solutions should be nearly alike. The experienced operator soon learns to choose his standard so that the resultant color will be nearly the same as that of the sample with which he is working. Add the same menstruum, solvent plus the same concentration of all reagents, as is present in sample and standard, to the darker, carefully mixing after each addition, until the colors of the two solutions, observed horizontally through the tubes, appear to be identical.

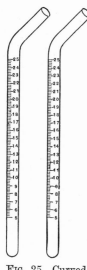

FIG. 25. Curved Julian tubes

When this point is reached the concentration of the test substance in each solution must be the same and their contents are then related to each other as the volumes. It is advisable to interchange the tubes and again check that there is no observable difference. Since the amount of test substance in the amount of standard used is definitely known, it is easy to calculate the test substance in the sample by a direct proportion. Care should be taken that the tubes used are clear and free from flaws and that the thicknesses of glass, internal diameters and graduations are identical. Matched pairs of Nessler tubes are sold for this purpose.

The curved Julian tube, Figure 25, is applicable to the dilution method. This has a bend about 2 inches from the top so that the tube may be lightly shaken, mixing the water added without danger of the contents being spilled. One dilution-type colorimeter [1] consists essentially of a syringe with a liquid chamber superimposed. Menstruum is added and mixed until solid artificial standards are matched. The syringe serves to mix the added solution and, when a' match is obtained, the solution is withdrawn into the calibrated syringe barrel for measurement.

**Duplication Method.** This method is closely related to titrimetry in that concentrated standard is added to the diluted reagent until the

[1] Louis Gross, U. S. Patent 2,090,041 (1937).

color of the sample is matched. When applicable this is by far the simplest method to use for a single sample, or even for a few samples. The method is usually applied in Nessler tubes. First, dilute the sample to some convenient, definite volume. Then add the same reagents as were added to the sample to a volume of water amounting to nearly the volume of the sample. The amount of water used for the blank varies according to the concentration of the standard to be used. To this blank, containing the same reagents as those used for the sample, add a standard solution, carefully mixing after each addition, until the color of the sample is duplicated by' that produced in the blank. The color of the blank having been made to duplicate that of the sample, they may still differ in volume. It is simple enough to calculate the amount of standard that would be necessary if the volumes were equal.

To eliminate error and to correct for the variation in salt and reagent concentration which would thereby result between sample and standard, duplicate the volume as well as the color of the standard. This is accomplished by addition of water and standard alternately until the two solutions are identical in both color and volume. Check this by interchanging the positions of the two tubes. Addition of an extra drop or two of standard after comparison is a wise precaution. The tube to which it is added should then be appreciably darker. The same precautions apply to this method as to the dilution method so far as apparatus is concerned. The tubes used must be of the same size, thickness of glass and internal diameter and the graduations on the outside must correspond in height. Beer's law need not hold but the color must be developed almost instantaneously.

A modification occasionally used, to apply this method to reactions where the color does not develop rapidly, is to add to the menstruum in the standard tube a predeveloped concentrated solution of the test substance. The applicability of this technic is limited.

# CHAPTER VI

## BALANCING METHOD

THE balancing method is one based strictly on the proportionality predicted by Beer's law. The depth of sample or standard, whichever is the darker, is varied until a color match is obtained. Except for photoelectric instruments (Chapter XI) the comparators used for the balancing method include the most elaborate of the colorimeters and their use is the simplest. The various instruments used include Hehner cylinders, Nessler tubes and various types of colorimeters. The apparatus for this method may be subdivided into types in which the actual depth of standard liquid used is varied, and those in which it appears to be varied. The second type is further subdivided into cylinder types and wedge types. The following discussion starts with the simpler forms of apparatus.

**Nessler Tubes.** In its most elementary form, the apparatus for the balancing method consists of two similarly graduated cylinders. Place the sample in one tube and hold the two tubes over a reflecting surface such as a sheet of white paper. Pour standard solution into the standard tube until the color observed through the lengths of the cylinders is identical. The amount of standard used and its content of the test substance per unit volume are known. The test substance in the sample is then inversely proportional to the volume, if the content per unit volume is desired, or the total amount of test substance in the two solutions is identical. If the diameters of the two cylinders are not identical, the strengths of the solutions are inversely proportional to their depths. For accuracy, the concentrations of sample and standard should be similar when Beer's law holds. If Beer's law is only approximated, the concentrations must be very nearly the same. This can be attained by controlled dilution of the standard to approximately the color of the sample. A great number of devices have been developed for increasing the accuracy with which the color of the two tubes can be matched and for simplifying the operation.

**Hehner Cylinders.** Hehner cylinders, Figure 26, consist of two glass tubes with flat bottoms. Each has a side tube with a stopcock near the bottom. Thus, they are essentially Nessler tubes provided with stopcocks. For a determination, place the solution of sample in one tube. Partially fill the other tube with the standard so that the depth of color seen by looking downward through the length of the column of liquid is deeper than that seen by similarly looking down through the sample. Draw off standard until the colors of the two tubes observed in this way are the same. Read the depths of solution in the two tubes, or, if their diameters are identical, the reading may be taken by volume.

An enclosing case for the Hehner cylinders converts them into a balancing type of colorimeter.[1] The next stage of refinement is to pro-

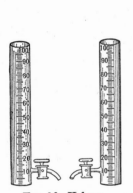

FIG. 26. Hehner cylinders

FIG. 27. Campbell-Hurley colorimeter. (*Eimer & Amend*)

vide one or both of the Hehner cylinders with a reservoir for the solution, connected by rubber tubing so that the level of solution in the cylinder may be varied by raising or lowering the reservoirs. A modified form raises or lowers the solution by pressing a rubber bulb.[2]

**Campbell-Hurley Colorimeter.** As the next stage of development, the column of liquid in one cylinder is fixed at a definite level and that in another varied by a mechanical method of addition or removal. Such an instrument may be relatively inexpensive. The Campbell-Hurley type of colorimeter illustrated, Figure 27, is the common form of such

[1] Cf. J. D. Hird, U. S. Patent 2,007,087 (1935).
[2] Rudolf Seifert, *Süddent. Apoth. Ztg.*, **76**, 376-7 (1936).

an instrument.[3] This is a modification of the Kennicott-Sargent type of apparatus and is sometimes known as the Kennicott colorimeter. The unknown solution is placed in tube A, Figure 28, and, since the volume can be readily governed so as to come to some even graduation, markings are placed only at 5 mm. intervals. The standard solution is placed in the right-hand tube B, which is graduated to single millimeters. Tube B is permanently connected by a glass tube with the reservoir C, in which the glass plunger D works. The level of the liquid in B may be readily

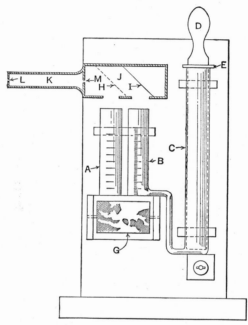

Fig. 28. Schematic representation of the Campbell-Hurley colorimeter

controlled by raising or lowering the plunger. Since the tube B and the reservoir C are made in one piece, the standard comes in contact only with glass. The plunger D is provided with a rubber collar E to prevent it from coming into contact with the bottom of the reservoir. Tubes A and B and reservoir C rest on wooden supports with holes under A and B for the passage of light. All glass parts are held in place by spring clips which allow easy removal for cleaning.

For operation, turn the colorimeter with the back toward a window, preferably a north one, and adjust the mirror G to reflect skylight

[3] E. D. Campbell and W. B. Hurley, *J. Am. Chem. Soc.*, **33**, 1112-15 (1911).

upward through A and B. By this arrangement the back of the colorimeter serves as a screen to cut off light, except that reflected from G.
The light passing through tubes A and B impinges on the two mirrors,
H and I, cemented to brass plates which slide in grooves cut at an
angle of 45° in the sides of the wooden box J. This box has a loosely
fitted cover so that it may be removed for cleaning the mirrors. The
mirror H is cut vertically and cemented in such a position as to reflect
one-half of the circular field of light coming through tube A. The light,
passing upward through B, is reflected horizontally
by the mirror I through a hole in the brass plate
supporting the mirror H. One-half of the circular
field of light from the tube B is cut off by the
mirror H, the vertical edge of which acts as a
dividing line between the two halves of the circular
field. The image of one-half of the tube B is then
observed in juxtaposition to the opposite half of
that from the tube A.

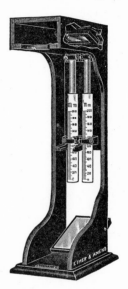

The images are observed through tube K, 2.5 cm.
in diameter and 16 cm. long, lined with black felt
and provided with an eyepiece having a hole 1.5
mm. in diameter. At point M in tube K is placed a
diaphragm, having an aperture 8 mm. in diameter.
All parts inside the box J, except the mirrors,
are painted black so that no light, except that coming through the tubes A and B, passes through K.
By having the apertures in the eyepiece and the
diaphragm properly proportioned only the images

Fig. 29. Schreiner
colorimeter
(*Eimer & Amend*)

of the bottoms of tubes A and B can be seen, pre-
venting the interference of side light.

A person looking through the eyepiece observes a single, circular field
divided vertically by an almost imperceptible line when the two solutions
are of the same intensity of color. By manipulating plunger D the level
of the liquid in B can be raised or lowered, thus causing the right half
to assume a darker or lighter shade at will. In matching colors with an
ascending column in B, that is, gradually deepening the color of the
right half of the field, the usual tendency is to stop a little below the
true reading, whereas in comparison with a descending column the
opposite is the case. The operator should take readings in each direction until after a little practice this tendency to error has been overcome. Modifications permit work with ether solutions and work in the
absence of oxygen.

**Schreiner Colorimeter.**[4] The Schreiner colorimeter, Figure 29, has two tubes similar to Nessler tubes but graduated in millimeters of depth instead of by volume. These are held by brass clips and move up or down on two smaller, hollow-glass plungers.

The principle is intermediate between the simple use of Nessler tubes and the Duboscq colorimeter. The latter is much easier to use both

FIG. 30. Standard Duboscq colorimeter. (*Bausch & Lomb*)

mechanically and optically. This instrument was devised primarily for examination of soil extracts. The optical system is readily modified to join the two images in the usual split circle. Comparison may also be made with the color of standard glass slides using this instrument.

**Duboscq Colorimeter.** In the Duboscq type of instrument, Figures 30 and 31, the same result as in the Campbell-Hurley type is obtained

---

[4] Oswald Schreiner, *J. Am. Chem. Soc.*, **27**, 1192 (1905).

by a different method. The two independent tubes, A and B, are of the
same size and hold the solutions of the unknown and the standard. Each
is mounted in holders M and N, which slide up and down in slits cut in
the backboard of the instrument and are operated by a rack and pinion.
Light is reflected upward through the tubes by mirror G. Directly

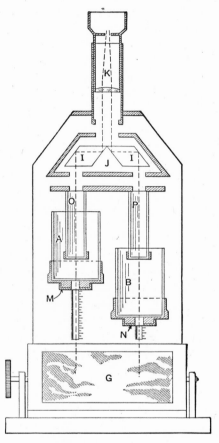

over tubes A and B, which contain
the solutions to be compared, are
two glass plungers, O, P, of a diameter less than that of A and B.
The bottoms of these plungers are
finely ground and in the best instruments are either fused on or
else the plungers are of solid glass.
In the less expensive instruments
the bottoms are fastened with an
adhesive.

The telescope K, for observation
of the colors, is perpendicular to
the base so that the operator looks
downward into the instrument. The
light reflected upward through the
solutions in A and B is so reflected
by the prisms I, I in the box J
that two fields appear side by side,
one from A and one from B. The
arrangement of the prisms is such
that the images observed in the
field of the telescope are those of
the bottoms of the plungers O, P
rather than of the entire depth
of liquid in A and B. By suitable
reduction of the aperture by
screens, reflection from the sides
of the tubes is cut off.

FIG. 31. Schematic diagram of Duboscq
colorimeter

For use, place the instrument to face a source of light and adjust
mirror G at the proper angle to reflect skylight upward through A and B.
Fill both cups about half full of clear water and bring the plungers into
contact with the water. On observing this through the eyepiece a circle
with a rather indistinct line through the middle will be seen. There

should be no detectable difference between the intensity of the two halves of the field. If there is a difference, adjust the location of the instrument so that they are equally bright.

Place the cups in position and turn up until they just touch the bottom of the plungers. Set the scale so that the zero mark corresponds with this setting of the cups, or adjust the cup carriers so that the scales are at the zero marks when the cups just touch the bottoms of the plungers. Be sure that the cups are not interchanged after setting the zero point as the bottoms may not be of equal thickness.

Place in one cup a solution of standard and in the other the developed sample. Move the cup having the lighter color upward until the plunger just touches the surface of the liquid, or to a definite reading standardized for the method. Then move the other cup upward, observing its movement through the eyepiece, until the image of the base of the plunger in that liquid appears to be of the same intensity as that observed from the other field. The instrument is then balanced and the depths of liquid underneath the plungers have the same relation to each other as the total depths of liquid in A and B when the Campbell-Hurley instrument is balanced. The slits in which the holders of A and B move are calibrated so that the depths of liquid may be read directly and errors in reading depths of liquid in glass are eliminated.

As a further method of elimination of side light it is desirable to surround the cups with a suitable shield, furnished with many of the instruments, or to use cups with opaque sides.

With this type of instrument, the nature of the color is not important—provided it is apparently the same in sample and standard— since only the intensities are compared. By simple modification the same instrument is suitable for colorimetry, nephelometry and bichromatic pH work.

The usual cups for the Duboscq instrument are 40 mm. deep for biological work or 50 mm. deep for chemical work. Micro instruments, Figure 32, are apt to be 20 mm. deep, in which the volume can be supplied by 10 cubic mm. of solution.[5] Instruments designed for examination of dilute solutions are available, Figure 33, and usually have an effective depth of 100 mm.

A modern, molded plastic design of a Duboscq colorimeter [6] shown in Figure 34 is read at an angle of about 50° from the vertical and has

---

[5] J. Ch. Somagyi, *Nature*, **138**, 763-4 (1936); *Z. Biol.*, **98**, 60-9 (1937).

[6] Hellige, Inc., 3718 Northern Blvd., Long Island City 1, N. Y.; Paul A. E. Hellige, U. S. Patent 2,244,839 (1941).

drums actuating the vertical movement of the cups, readily readable
to 0.1 mm. on illuminated scales from the normal position of the observer.
Artificial illumination is provided in the base with a Corning Daylite

Fig. 32. Micro Duboscq colorimeter. (*Bausch & Lomb*)

filter. Liquid depths to 100 mm. can be used. Small cups permit micro
determinations on small samples with the same instrument. Glass
standards can replace the usual developed liquids. Figure 35 shows
another design.

Yet another direct-reading Duboscq colorimeter[7] has the eyepiece at an angle to the plungers and tubes and reads the depths on a drum without vernier, which is fixed as to height rather than moving with the cups, and is observable from the position for adjustment of the instru-

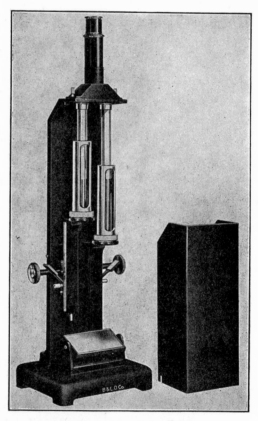

FIG. 33. Duboscq colorimeter with armored cups, for dilute solutions.
(*Bausch & Lomb*)

ment. Plungers enter the liquid at a slight angle to avoid bubbles. The cups have separable bottoms and are on the front of the instrument.

[7] Spencer Lens Co., Buffalo 11, N. Y.; Alva H. Bennett and Roger S. Estey (Spencer Lens Co.), U. S. Patent 2,310,608 (1943); Roger S. Estey and Kennard W. Harper (Spencer Lens Co.), U. S. Patent 2,310,624 (1943); Roger S. Estey (Spencer Lens Co.), U. S. Patent 2,328,631 (1943); Roger S. Estey, William F. Peck and Kennard W. Harper (Spencer Lens Co.), U. S. Patent 2,353,716 (1944).

**Modifications of Duboscq Colorimeter.** One design has a magnifier for reading the scales immediately in front of the eyepiece. In another [8] images of the scales of the Duboscq are projected into the

FIG. 34. Hellige-Duboscq colorimeter

eyepiece, Figure 36. The plunger of a Duboscq may have the plate at the end attached by fusible metal.[9]

In the Vim-Scheftel type, Figure 37, for blood chemistry, the depth

[8] Arno Schmidt, U. S. Patent 2,084,538 (1937).

[9] Walter W. Graeper (Bausch & Lomb Optical Co.), U. S. Patent 2,074,086 (1937).

of the unknown is adjusted with a calibrated glass plunger [10] from which results are read directly by reference to a set of charts. This design has been further modified for determination of phosphorus, creatinine and

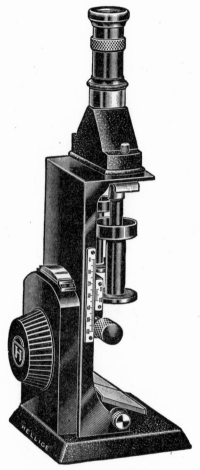

FIG. 35.  Direct-reading Duboscq colorimeter

FIG. 36.  Duboscq colorimeter with magnifier scale which can be read from observing position. (*Bausch & Lomb*)

bilirubin.[11]  In another, shown in Figure 38, the scale reads directly as the ratio between sample and standard. This avoids the necessity of

[10] Abraham G. Sheftel, U. S. Patent 1,916,589 (1933).
[11] John A. Schindler, *J. Lab. Clin. Med.*, **20**, 975 (1935).

setting the standard at a definite depth since the depth of either is immaterial provided the ratio between them is shown.[12]

In the Bock-Benedict colorimeter the prisms of the Duboscq colorimeter are replaced by mirrors, resembling in that feature the Campbell-Hurley instrument.[13]

For comparison with bichromatic solutions, it may be necessary to vary two colors. Such equipment is represented in Figure 39 [14] and diagrammatically in Figure 40. A and B represent the conventional

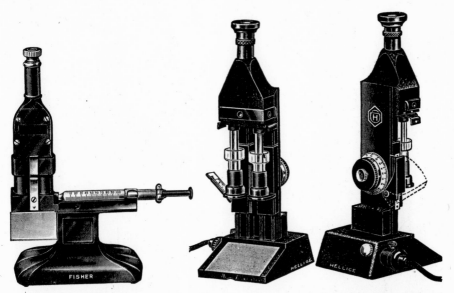

FIG. 37. Vim-Sheftel colorimeter. (*Fisher Scientific Co.*)

FIG. 38. Colorimeter reading directly as ratio of sample and standard. (*Hellige, Inc.*)

fixed plungers; C and D represent containers for sample and standard. Both are fixed. E is a movable container for another form of standard. An important application is for pH determination with bichromatic indicators. The hydrogen-ion type of Duboscq colorimeter has two cells for the standard, one of which fits inside the other. The acid form of

[12] Cf. Paul Szekely and Pierre Schwartz, French Patent 804,984 (1936); John P. Tully and Neal M. Carter, *J. conseil intern. exploration mer*, **13**, 58-66 (1938); H. Voigt, *Deut. Apoth. Ztg.*, **56**, 309-10 (1941).

[13] James Campbell Todd and Arthur Hawley Sanford, *Clinical Diagnosis by Laboratory Methods*, 10th Ed., p. 349, W. B. Saunders Co., Philadelphia, Pa. (1943).

[14] Cf. Wilfred F. Langelier, U. S. Patent 2,216,976 (1940).

the indicator is used in either E or C and the alkaline form in the other. D is filled with the sample solution. By variation of E the effective depth in C is also varied and the total depth in C and E is equal to the depth in D. As another example, a known amount of blood in urine in the outer cup and urine without blood in the inner cup are matched against a sample of urine for estimation of the blood content.

The Duboscq colorimeter has been modified by interposing barrier-layer photoelectric cells below the prisms without altering the instrument.[15] The sensitivity of this cell is very similar to that of the human eye. It can be used as a comparison spectrophotometer.[16] Photoelectric colorimeters are described in Chapters X and XI.

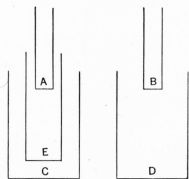

FIG. 39. Duboscq-type hydrogen-ion colorimeter. (*Bausch & Lomb*)

FIG. 40. Diagrammatic arrangements of Duboscq type of hydrogen-ion colorimeter

**Stammer Colorimeter.** The Stammer colorimeter, Figures 41 and 42, is also a modified form of Duboscq and is particularly used for determination of the color of sugar solutions, sugar-beet juice [17] and oils. The colors of the fields are transmitted to the telescope K by

---

[15] G. Bernheim and G. Revillon, *Ann. fals.*, **29**, 5-10 (1936).

[16] Marjorie R. Mattice, Catherine F. Gannon and Carl H. Greene, *J. Lab. Clin. Med.*, **25**, 629-33 (1940).

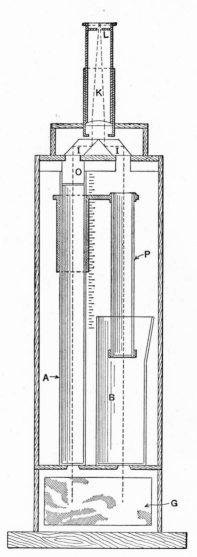

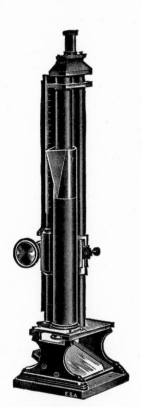

FIG. 41. Stammer
colorimeter
(*Eimer & Amend*)

FIG. 42. Schematic diagram of
Stammer colorimeter

prisms I, I, as in the Duboscq type. The alteration is in the character
of the fields. Instead of two movable containers and two fixed pistons
as in the other instrument the containers are fixed and one movable
piston, P, is provided for the variation of the column in B. A false
piston, O, is provided so that the light through A will have to pass
through a similar thickness of glass. The column in A remains permanent.
Light is reflected upward by a mirror at G as in previous instruments.

**Wedge-Type Colorimeters.** Another method of varying the depth
of solution through which light is transmitted is to use a hollow wedge
which can be moved vertically by a rack and pinion and give a direct
scale reading. In principle this might be compared with the unknown
in a cell of fixed thickness or in a similar wedge. Numerous models of
this type of instrument have been devised but none of the simple models
seems to have become as popular as the Campbell-Hurley or Duboscq
instruments. There is one popular design of wedge-type filter
instrument.

---

[17] Hermann Eichler, *Deut. Zuckerind,* **65**, 118 (1940).

# CHAPTER VII

## ARTIFICIAL LIQUID STANDARDS

In many cases, the color produced by a reaction fades in a short time in the light. In such an event, either a standard must be prepared at the same time as the sample and the comparison made quickly or permanent artificial standards must be used, and then only the series-of-standards method is applicable. Such standards are usually made with solutions of inorganic salts, combining colors if necessary. A simple example is the use of potassium bichromate for determination of sugar by the picric acid method.

The idea is very old, the color of London water having been read in terms of artificial standards in 1881; a platinum color standard proposed in 1892 is still included in the Methods of the American Public Health Association. The most complete series of artificial standards was originally worked out for caramel and tincture of cudbar but later it was adapted to general use [1] and accepted in the *Pharmacopoeia*.[2] Three separate series were required. To furnish more basic data for preparation and evaluation of artificial standards, the spectral transmissions of the salts used have been included in a study of vanadium, chromium, manganese, iron, cobalt, nickel and copper compounds, including the effect of variation in acidity.[3]

Half-normal acidified solutions of the nitrates and chlorides of cobalt, iron and copper may be combined in such a way as to form any color desired except the deep blues and reds. Solutions of ferric chloride, 0.02-0.5 $M$ containing 0.05-5.0 $M$ hydrochloric acid, are stable. It has been found that some of the missing colors can be obtained by using ammoniacal solutions with dichromate in place of iron. The remaining colors are obtained by combinations of potassium dichromate and potas-

---

[1] H. V. Arny, *Amer. Druggist*, **59**, 35 (1912); *Proc. 8th Int. Cong. App. Chem.*, **26**, 319 (1912); *J. Am. Pharm. Assoc.*, **2**, 76-80 (1913); *Deutsch-Amerikanische Apotheker Zeitung*, **33**, 165 (1913); H. V. Arny and E. G. Pickhardt, *Druggists Circ.*, **57**, 131 (1914); H. V. Arny and C. H. Ring, *J. Am. Pharm. Assoc.*, **4**, 1294-9 (1915); *J. Franklin Inst.*, **180**, 199-213 (1915); H. V. Arny and Abraham Taub, *J. Am. Pharm. Assoc.*, **12**, 839-49 (1923); *J. Franklin Inst.*, **196**, 858 (1923).

[2] *Pharmacopoeia of the United States*, **12**, 743 (1942).

[3] M. G. Mellon and C. T. Kasline, *Ind. Eng. Chem., Anal. Ed.*, **7**, 187-9 (1935); C. T. Kasline and M. G. Mellon, *Ibid.*, **8**, 463-5 (1936).

sium permanganate. Thus, a mixture of the acid series—cobalt three parts to iron nine parts, diluted with water—corresponds to the color given by Nessler's reagent in reaction with ammonia. Varied dilutions of this may be used for a series of standards, making each standard correspond to the colors obtained by the use of a known amount of ammonia treated with the reagent. In a similar manner, permanent standards may be prepared for any determination, keeping in mind the fact that every standard must be checked against a known amount of the test substance to make sure of its accuracy. Later work[4] has made some corrections which are incorporated in the directions which follow.

**Cobalt-Iron-Copper Series.** In this series all solutions are half normal and contain 1 per cent of hydrochloric acid. The composition of the solutions follows:

*Cobalt.* 59.59 grams of cobalt chloride ($CoCl_2 \cdot 6H_2O$), per liter in 1 per cent hydrochloric acid.

*Iron.* 45.05 grams of ferric chloride ($FeCl_3 \cdot 6H_2O$), per liter in 1 per cent hydrochloric acid.

*Copper.* 62.43 grams of copper sulfate ($CuSO_4 \cdot 5H_2O$), per liter in 1 per cent hydrochloric acid.

These solutions are stable for at least two years.

**Cobalt-Chromate-Copper Series.** For this 0.02 $N$ solutions in 2.8 per cent ammonium hydroxide are used.

*Purpureo Cobalt Chloride.* Dissolve 12 grams of cobalt chloride ($CoCl_2 \cdot 6H_2O$) in about 100 ml. of water. Filter if necessary, and add 100 ml. of concentrated ammonium hydroxide. Shake well, and keep at 50-70° for 8 hours with occasional shaking. Let stand overnight at room temperature. Warm again to 50-70° and gradually dilute to 1 liter with water, not permitting the temperature to fall below 50° until dilution is complete. The resulting solution is red with a yellow tinge. Add excess of concentrated hydrochloric acid, and boil for a few minutes. Purpureo-cobaltic chloride, $[Co(NH_3)_5Cl]Cl_3$, is precipitated. The solution may be cooled in running water to hasten precipitation. Filter, wash on the filter with 1:40 hydrochloric acid, and dry in an oven at 100°. For use, dissolve 2.7 grams in 500 ml. of 1:4 ammonium hydroxide, and dilute to 1 liter with water.

---

[4] M. G. Mellon and F. D. Martin, *J. Phys. Chem.*, **31**, 161-77 (1927); O. T. Kasline and M. G. Mellon, *J. Am. Pharm. Assoc.*, **26**, 227-30 (1937).

*Chromate.* Dissolve 0.420 gram of ammonium bichromate in about 500 ml. of water. Add 100 ml. of concentrated ammonium hydroxide and dilute to 1 liter.

*Copper sulfate.* Dissolve 2.49 grams in 500 ml. of water, add 100 ml. of concentrated ammonium hydroxide, and dilute to 1 liter.

The cobalt and chromium solutions are stable for at least 1 year. The copper solution precipitates in a few weeks unless it is hermatically sealed.

The 88 possible blends obtainable with various mixtures totaling 12 ml. of this series consist of 36 spectrum colors in which only 2 solutions have been used, 27 hues in which only 1 ml. of a third solution is used, 18 blends in which 2 ml. of a third solution is uses, 9 blends which are nearly gray, and a gray containing 4 ml. of each solution.

**Permanganate-Chromate Series.** For this series neutral solutions of 0.001 *N* potassium permanganate and 0.01 *N* potassium bichromate are used. They match purples unobtainable from the previous two standards. They are not stable if exposed to organic contamination, and in any care not over two hours.

**Standard Mixtures.** Some typical mixtures, expressed in parts by volume, are shown in Table 2.

**Comparison of Standards.** The transmission curves of the stock solutions are shown in Figure 43. Mixtures of 4 parts of the three colors, of either the acid or ammoniacal series, give a neutral gray, showing that apparently these metals give equivalent intensities of different colors at the same ionic concentration. That this does not hold for all metals is well known.

The use of ordinary C.P. chemicals gives results indistinguishable from those with exceptionally pure chemicals. Neutral standards precipitate within a few days but acid standards are stable for five years.

For yellows, solutions of picric acid or potassium chromate are often used. Boiled mashes are matched against bichromate and ferricyanide.[5] Stable dye solutions have found some application. The iron-cobalt-copper series of acid standards is preferable to caramel standards for carbon in steel but the method itself is now rarely used.

Some of the conventional pH indicators have been matched. Mixtures of 2 ml. of 20 per cent cobalt nitrate and 98 ml. of 0.03 per cent potassium bichromate, and of 5 ml. of 20 per cent cobalt nitrate and 95 ml.

---

[5] V. Shmelev, *Spirto-Vodochnaya Prom.*, **15**, No. 10, 30-1 (1938).

of 10 per cent copper sulfate correspond to pH 6.0 and pH 7.6 respectively with bromothymol blue. Graded mixtures give the intermediate values. By use of 4 ml. of 10 per cent cobalt chloride and 96 ml. of 0.03 per cent potassium bichromate, and of 26 ml. of 10 per cent cobalt chloride and 74 ml. of glacial acetic acid, in differing proportions, methyl red and phenol red respectively were duplicated. Much other

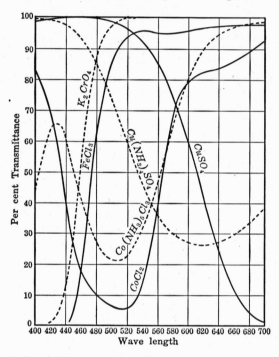

Fig. 43. Spectral transmission curves for Arny's stock solutions

work has been done on artificial standards for pH. The only artificial standard optically satisfactory for matching monochromatic indicators such as *m*- or *p*-nitrophenol and α- or γ-dinitrophenol was potassium chromate or bichromate.

Various other artificial standards include: methyl red in acid solution as standard for measurement of potassium permanganate;[6] standards for oil;[7] inorganic standards for biochemical analysis;[8] tincture

[6] M. V. Alekseeva, *Zavodskaya Lab.*, **5**, 872-3 (1936).

[7] Kokiti Osima and Taturo Sugawara, *J. Agr. Chem. Soc. Japan*, **15**, 653-8; *Bull. Agr. Chem. Soc. Japan*, **15**, 110-11 (1939).

[8] Morand, *Arch. méd. pharm. navales*, **129**, 96-111 (1939).

of cudbar [9] for urea; nonprotein nitrogen; proteins;[10] and calibration
of the Stammer colorimeter with inorganic salts.[11]

TABLE 2. TYPICAL COMBINATIONS OF COLOR STANDARDS

SAMPLE SOLUTION
TO BE MATCHED                                ARTIFICIAL STANDARD

*Cobalt-Iron-Copper Series*

|  | Cobalt | Iron | Copper | Water |
|---|---|---|---|---|
| Standard caramel .............. | 4 | 7 | 1 | 0 |
| Nessler nitrogen 1 : 500,000 ....... | 3 | 9 | 0 | 12 |
| Nitrate by phenolsulfonic acid method 1 : 500,000 .......... | 0 | 12 | 0 | 6 |

*Cobalt-Chromate-Copper Series*

|  | Cobalt | Chromate | Copper | Water |
|---|---|---|---|---|
| Phosphoric acid by the molybdate method 1 : 20,000 ........... | 0 | 12 | 0 | 68 |
| Vanillin by Folin's method 1 : 100,000 ................. | 3 | 3 | 10 | 0 |
| Uric acid by Riegler's method 1 : 40,000 .................. | 2 | 2 | 8 | 0 |
| Salicylic acid by the ferric chloride method 1 : 50,000 ........... | 7 | 1 | 5 | 6 |

*Chromate Permanganate Series*

|  | Chromate | Permanganate | Water |
|---|---|---|---|
| Nitrite 1 : 10,000,000 ............. | 15 | 1 | 13 |

**Errors.** Artificial standards are open to the following objections:

1. If an unstable substance is being determined, a natural standard
will decompose at approximately the same rate, whereas an artificial
standard does not decompose. The result is a longer period during which
correct results can be obtained with the natural standard than with the
artificial.

2. The artificial standard must be calibrated in terms of the natural
standard. The sample must then be read in terms of the artificial
standard. A double error of observation is introduced.

---

[9] Karl B. Rosen, *Bull. Natl. Formulary Comm.,* **9,** 59-61 (1940).

[10] Earl J. King, *Brit. Med. J.,* **1940,** II, 445-7.

[11] A. Mirčev, *Z. Zuckerind, Böhnen Mähren,* **66,** 19-22 (1942).

3. The artificial standard, although apparently the same in color, is not actually the same in wave-length distribution. This is illustrated in Figure 44 by three pairs of visually matching solutions, only one pair of which match spectrophotometrically. Individuals vary in their response to different colors. If the components of the two colors are different, as

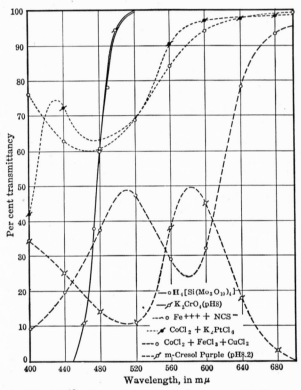

FIG. 44 [12]. Spectral transmittance curves for visually matched solutions

will always occur with artificial standards, irregular results will be obtained since the operators differ in sensitivity to the colors present.

Regardless of these weaknesses there are many determinations in which artificial standards may be used. For creatinine, potassium bichromate was used for many years because the natural standard was not available. This practice has been rendered unnecessary by the commercial production of creatinine at a reasonable price.

---

[12] M. G. Mellon, *Colorimetry for Chemists*, p. 25, G. Frederick Smith Chemical Co., Columbus, Ohio (1945).

**Turbidity.** Preparation of standard artificial turbidities for nephelometry or turbidimetry is best accomplished by use of Pyrex glass suspensions.[13] Such standards have replaced barium sulfate because they are stable in storage and require only infrequent shaking.

*Preparation.*[14] Break clean discarded Pyrex glassware into 20 mm. or smaller chips. Put in a clean Pyrex bottle about 150-175 mm. in diameter to a depth of about 65 mm. and just cover with distilled water. Seat the Pyrex stopper and shake violently by machine. One with 130 cycles per minute and a 2-inch stroke is recommended. After 6 hours pour off the aqueous layer, replace with fresh water and again shake. Repeat until the suspension approximates the opacity of skim milk, using a fresh lot of water each time. The time required varies from 24-120 hours, depending on whether the chips were freshly broken.

Let the suspension stand in covered liter cylinders for 48 hours to settle particles of 2 microns or larger. Decant, let stand for 24 hours, and again decant. Determine the turbidity of the second decantate in test tubes by one of the standard instruments. The reading should be about 40 in a Luximeter, 590 in a Klett-Summerson instrument. If above that value, dilute with distilled water. If too diluted, return to the original bottle, shake for a sufficient time and repeat the subsequent procedure.

TABLE 3.   ARTIFICIAL TURBIDITY STANDARDS

| Turbidity Standard | Per Cent Stock Suspension | Turbidity by Luximeter | Turbidity by Klett-Summerson Instrument |
|---|---|---|---|
| 0.5 | 3.32 | 95 | 40 |
| 1 | 8.34 | 89 | 100 |
| 2 | 18.8 | 78 | 210 |
| 3 | 30.0 | 70 | 290 |
| 4 | 39.6 | 63 | 360 |
| 5 | 52.2 | 57 | 420 |
| 6 | 60.5 | 53 | 460 |
| 7 | 66.7 | 50 | 490 |

When the turbidity standard is attained, determine the amount of solids on evaporation. If below 0.20 per cent, shake in the cylinder used

[13] J. H. Brewer and E. B. M. Cook, *Am. J. Pub. Health*, **29**, 1147-8 (1939); F. W. Gilcreas and Francis J. Hallinan, *Proc. N. Y. State Assn. Pub. Health Labs.*, **21**, 32-3 (1941); Francis J. Hallinan, *Ibid.*, **33**, 137-40 (1943).
[14] Francis J. Hallinan, *Am. J. Pub. Health*, **33**, 137-40 (1943).

for the second decantation and let settle for a shorter time. If above 0.25 per cent reshake and let settle for a longer time. Either of the last two steps will involve a redetermination and adjustment of turbidity followed by solids determination.

Table 3 shows the approximate turbidity of standards diluted from the turbidity and solids contents just mentioned. When standards have not been adequately protected against evaporation they can be brought back to volume with distilled water without loss of validity.

# CHAPTER VIII

## SPECTROPHOTOMETRY

THE spectrophotometer is an instrument in which the wave band measured is selected from white light, suitably dispersed. The reading may be either visual or by photoelectric means. Spectrophotometry is measurement of relative radiant energy, whether emitted, transmitted, or reflected, as a function of wave length.[1]

The human eye can detect about 10,000 different gradations of color. At a maximum a spectrophotometer can detect more than 2 million gradations. If two samples have identical spectrophotometric curves they will always match under any lighting conditions to any eye.

Methods of adjustment of light intensity listed in order of decreasing relative importance are (1) aperture types, (2) wedge types, (3) polarization types, and (4) distance types. The first three are represented among the well-known instruments, either true spectrophotometers or filter photometers.

Although the instrument may determine the light transmitted at various wave lengths and thus give a specrophotometric disribution curve, it may also be used to measure the light transmitted in a restricted and controlled wave band and when so used is a form of colorimeter. Over its wave-length range there are no restrictions on the wave-length selections to be used with the spectrophotometer. An important application of the true spectrophotometer is in routine determinations which only semi-skilled employees make. With proper supervision to insure that the instrument is maintained in proper operating condition, a highly developed standardization of technic becomes possible. For such routine work the unskilled technician can then, usually, do more accurate routine work day after day than the skilled technologist.

Any spectrophotometer consists of the following elements: (1) a source of light, (2) a device for obtaining relatively monochromatic light, (3) an absorption cell for the sample and one for the blank, and (4) a means of measuring the difference of absorption between the sample and the blank. In the case of the photoelectric spectrophotometer

---

[1] H. E. Parker, *Symposium on Color*, pp. 47-59, American Society for Testing Materials and Inter-Society Color Council (1941); A. E. Ruehle, *Proc. Am. Soc. Testing Materials*, **44**, 118-19 (1944).

this means of measurement consists of a photocell or photocells for translation of the transmitted light into electric current and a suitable current-measuring device. Sensitive thermopiles have also been used.

With the photoelectric spectrophotometer the slit can be so adjusted as to be independent of the spectral distribution of the light source, spectral response of the photocell and spectral selectivity of the sample solution.

When a photoelectric spectrophotometric method is applied, the method is changed from subjective to objective, the opinion of the circuit is substituted for the opinion of the eye. Development of such spectrophotometric devices has occurred at a greatly accelerated pace in the last decade.[2] Transmittancy is customarily read between 5 per cent and 90 per cent, with maximum accuracy around 37 per cent. The error increases rapidly as soon as the $\log_{10}$ transmittancy is below 0.1 or above 0.8, which are the corresponding log values.

**Monochromator.** The accurate source of approximately monochromatic light is a monochromator. This may be a prism, which varies in dispersion with wave length but offers but little problem in elimination of stray light. It may be a diffraction grating which is equally accurate at differing wave lengths. Stray light from reflection by elements of the instrument and nonspecular scattering can be reduced by a second monochromator, with reduction in the intensity of available light. This involves a more sensitive system for translation of the transmitted light. The band taken from a true monochromator usually varies from 10-30 m$\mu$.

An alternative is monochromatic light from a metal vapor lamp. A sodium lamp gives yellow lines at 589.6 m$\mu$ and 589 m$\mu$, with less than 1 per cent of the intensity at red and green lines 616.1 m$\mu$ and 568.8 m$\mu$. A cadmium lamp emits the red line 643.9 m$\mu$, the green line 508.6 m$\mu$ and the blue line 480 m$\mu$. A mercury lamp emits yellow lines at 577 and 579 m$\mu$, a green line at 546 m$\mu$ and a violet line at 435-436 m$\mu$.

In filter photometry a less expensive and much less accurate monochromator is a glass filter, or combination of filters. This gives relatively broad bands in many cases.

**Definitions.** There are several terms which are used only in spectrophotometry in its various forms, including abridged spectrophotometry and filter photometry.

---

2 John L. Hague, *Proc. Am. Soc. Testing Materials*, **44**, 712-19 (1944).

*Transmission* is the over-all proportion of energy transmitted through the solution, whereas *transmittance* is this value corrected for reflection at the surface. The latter is the significant property in colorimetry. The terms for the converse properties are also important.

*Absorption* is the loss in transmission and *absorbency* bears the same relation to the transmittancy.

**Visual Instruments.** The simplest method of evaluation is by visual methods but that is not the most accurate. Further, visual methods are time-consuming and fatiguing if distribution curves are to be recorded. This is simplified only if a colorimetric reading at a single wave length is desired.

The early instruments depended on prisms to break up the light into a series of wave lengths of which a band could be selected. Such instruments have been marketed by Gaertner, and by Bausch and Lomb. The latter has indicated that their instrument will not again be placed on the market.[3] Corresponding foreign instruments are those of Hilger-Nutting, and of Koenig-Martens as made by Schmidt and Haensch. Keuffel and Esser have offered a rotating sector spectrophotometer.

The visual instrument is limited in its application to the visible spectrum with the further specification that its greatest sensitivity is near the middle of the visible spectrum. Visual spectrophotometers depend on the relationship expressed as follows:[4]

$$\text{Transmittance} = \frac{I_1}{I_2} = \frac{\tan^2 a}{\tan^2 a_0}$$

where

$I_1$, often designated as $I_0$ = Initial intensity.

$I_2$, often designated as $I$ = Emergent intensity.

$a$ = angle of match when solution and solvent are placed in appropriate beams.

$a_0$ = angle of match when both beams are blank or contain similar cells with the same solvent.

The Bausch and Lomb visual spectrophotometer and the corresponding instrument of the Gaertner Scientific Corporation are both direct reading in wave length, in transmittance and in $\log_{10}$ transmittance.

---

[3] Private communication.
[4] Kasson S. Gibson, *Proc. Am. Soc. Testing Materials,* **44**, 725-32 (1944).

**Calculation of Values.** Analytical values can be calculated from the spectrophotometric results by a method not always applicable to the filter photometer.[5]

$$(1) \qquad\qquad I_2 = I_1 \times 10^{-kbc}$$

$$(2) \qquad\qquad C = \frac{\log_{10} I_1/I_2}{\Sigma_l}$$

This concentration in moles per liter is used to calculate $\Sigma$ for a desired wave length. Then, as applied

$$(3) \qquad\qquad C = \frac{\log T_l}{\Sigma_l}$$

For maximum accuracy the value of $\Sigma$ should be large. As so applied to analysis of copper matte, the accuracy is as good as by titration. Practically it is easier to use a calibration curve, even when $l$ is standardized so that $C = Ef$ in which $f$ is $1/\Sigma_l$. Tentatively recommended practice of the ASTM indicates a preference for calculation with $\Sigma$ determined with at least 3 concentrations and averaged, and $l = 1$ cm.

**General Electric Spectrophotometer.** The aristocrat of photoelectric instruments is the G. E. recording spectrophotometer.[6] The instrument is shown in Figure 45 and the details in Figure 46. This is made according to designs of Arthur C. Hardy of the Massachusetts Institute of Technology. The instrument covers the range of 400-750 m$\mu$ and can be extended to 1000 m$\mu$. It reads directly, as a multiple of 5, as log, or as log-log. The usual slit width is 10 m$\mu$ but 8, 6, and 4 m$\mu$ slits are available. Dispersion is by two prisms, the second effectively dispersing stray energy. The scale is based on the same tan$^2\alpha$ scale as visual instruments. Therefore, linearity of response of the photocell is not essential.

It is so complex and expensive that only a relatively small number have been built, about 100 at the end of 1946. Such an instrument has unquestionable advantages in initial research on the specific colorimetric method, thereby determining and recording the absorption curve instrumentally over the entire range. The unit is sufficiently

---

[5] The terms are defined on p. 13.

[6] General Electric Co., Schenectady 5, N. Y.; A. C. Hardy, *J. Optical Soc. Am.*, **25**, 305-11 (1935); J. L. Michaelson, *J. Optical Soc. Am.*, **28**, 365 (1938); J. L. Michaelson and H. A. Liebhafsky, *Gen. Elec. Rev.*, **39**, 445-50 (1936).

complicated, and the sources of difficulties so varied, that a skilled operator should be in charge, although data may be obtained by a technician.

FIG. 45. General Electric recording spectrophotometer

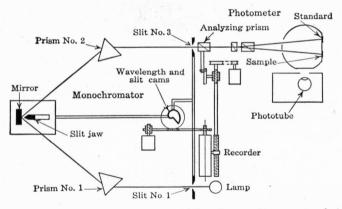

FIG. 46. Schematic diagram of the General Electric recording spectrophotometer

**Beckman Instruments.** The Beckman photoelectric quartz spectro-photometer shown in Figure 47 is designed to cover the range 200-2000m$\mu$,[7] but available photocells at present permit only the use of the range to about 1000 m$\mu$. Two tubes, interchangeable by a switch.

---

[7] National Technical Laboratories, South Pasadena, Cal.; H. H. Cary and Arnold O. Beckman, *J. Optical Soc. Am.*, **31**, 682-9 (1941).

are provided for maximum sensitivity in the red-infrared and blue-ultraviolet ranges. The lower range is provided by a hydrogen arc, the upper by a tungsten-filament light source. For some purposes a mercury arc is used. It is a single dispersion instrument, using a crystal quartz prism, and is relatively free from stray rays. This is accomplished by use of a small number of optical surfaces between the entry and exit slits, and inclosure of the optics of the instrument in a dust-

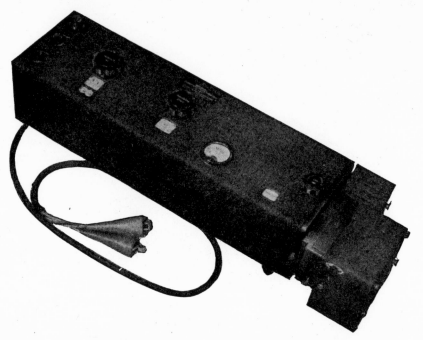

FIG. 47. Beckman photoelectric quartz spectrophotometer.
(*National Technical Laboratories*)

excluding chamber. A stray light filter is used below 400 m$\mu$ when necessary. The prism dispersion is a source of nonuniformity across the spectrum so that for constant width of spectral band the slit width must be adjusted for each wave length. This is not necessary with a grating spectrophotometer.

Full sensitivity is attained in the range of 220-1000 m$\mu$ by use of an electronic amplifier. High sensitivity permits the use of extremely narrow slits, and the spectral purity of the energy used is high. Wave lengths are reproducible to 0.05 m$\mu$ in the ultraviolet and 0.5 m$\mu$ in the infrared. For readings of less than 10 per cent transmittance the scale can be expanded 10 times. The absorption path can be varied from 10 mm. to 1 meter.

The photoelectric current from the irradiated photocell produces a voltage drop across the phototube load resistor. This is balanced by a potentiometer. While making this null setting, the degree of lack of balance is amplified electronically and indicated by the instrument galvanometer. Linearity of the irradiation-current relationship is necessary and should hold closely. Numerous extinction coefficients determined with this instrument have been reported.[8]

The Beckman recording ultraviolet spectrophotometer will automatically record on a 5-minute cycle the spectral absorbency of either

FIG. 48. Coleman universal spectrophotometer. (*Coleman Electric Co.*)

gases or liquids over the range of 220-320 m$\mu$ with an accuracy of ±1 per cent. The essential elements are an ultraviolet lamp, a monochromator, a sealed absorption cell to accommodate a sample of liquid or gas, a photocell and associated amplifier, and a recorder with chart calibrated in per cent transmittancy. A corresponding infrared spectrophotometer is available.[9]

**Coleman Instruments.** The Coleman Universal spectrophotometer,[10] Model 11, Figure 48, is a relatively inexpensive instrument for its

[8] J. M. Vanderbilt, Jean Forsyth and Ann Garrett, *Ind. Eng. Chem., Anal. Ed.,* **17**, 235-7 (1945).

[9] Another infrared spectrophotometer is available from the Perkin-Elmer Corporation, Glenbrook, Conn.

[10] Coleman Electric Co., 318 Madison St., Maywood, Ill.; Wilkens-Anderson Co., 111 N. Canal St., Chicago, Ill.

type. By use of a single grating monochromator any 35 m$\mu$ band in the range 300-800 m$\mu$ can be selected. As compared with a filter photometer this means approximately double the instrumental cost to cut the observed band from those of filters shown with various other instruments to 35 mm. A single barrier-layer cell serves as detector, with interchange of cuvettes between readings. Filters are used to reduce stray energy. Either direct transmittance readings can be taken from the reflection galvanometer with some degree of inaccuracy, or it can be used as a null instrument. The scale reads by the ratio-of-deflections method and therefore linearity of response is essential.

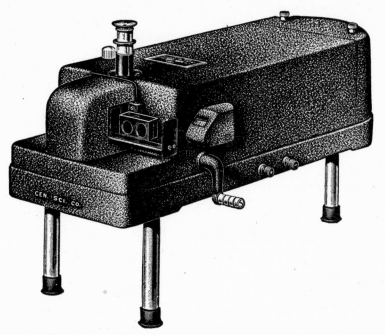

Fig. 49. Spectrophotelometer. (*Central Scientific Co.*)

The scale reads in both transmittance and optical density. Sample depths range from 0.5 to 50 mm. The instrument operates on 110-volt line current or, preferably, from an 8-volt storage battery. It takes various forms of cells. Accuracy to be expected is to 0.1 per cent. The same instrument can be used in the ultraviolet to 300 m$\mu$, in the infrared to 800 m$\mu$, or for turbidity.

Models 10 and 10S are double monochromator spectrophotometers, thus eliminating stray energy by the second dispersion. Model 10 operates with a 30 m$\mu$ slit, the Model 10S with 5, 7.5, 15 and 30 m$\mu$. The range is 350-1000 m$\mu$. The detector is an electron-emission phototube, which must have a linear response to be accurate. The voltage drop produced by the current from the phototube across the phototube load resistor is balanced by a potentiometer. An auxiliary meter indicates the electronically amplified lack of balance during adjustment. The Coleman Junior clinical spectrophotometer is a single-grating type, a simplified form of the Universal Model 11 spectrophotometer. It covers the range 400-700 m$\mu$ but has only a direct reading galvanometer scale and takes only test tubes as cells.

**The Spectrophotelometer.** This relatively inexpensive grating-type spectrophotometer[11] is shown in Figure 49. Light from the entrance slit is directed to a concave reflecting diffraction grating which may be rotated. The detector is a barrier-layer cell. The range is 325-750 m$\mu$, and the lower limit depends on the characteristic of the light source used. Filters are used to eliminate stray light below 390 m$\mu$ and above 650 m$\mu$. The transmittance is shown by the ratio-of-deflections method on a box-type galvanometer. Slit widths are 2.5, 5, 10 and 20 m$\mu$. Linearity of response of the cell is essential to accuracy.

---

11 Central Scientific Co., Chicago 13, Ill.; Charles Sheard and Marshall N. States, *J. Optical Soc. Am.*, **31**, 64 (1941); Herbert J. Dutton and Glen F. Bailey, *Ind. Eng. Chem., Anal. Ed.*, **15**, 275-7 (1943).

# CHAPTER IX

## VISUAL FILTER PHOTOMETRY

ONE would need only to apply a filter in the eyepiece of the conventional colorimeter or to inspect a pair of Nessler tubes through a filter in order to make the method one of filter photometry. Practically, that is not what is meant. Rather the term as applied refers to measurement of the light transmittance or absorbency of the developed sample in some absolute terms and correlation with a predetermined curve or formula which in turn was obtained with standards at the same light distribution.

Thus, the visual filter photometer is the visual spectrophotometer, much simplified, principally because the monochromator, which is expensive, has been replaced by a filter. The sensitivity has been thus radically decreased. All filter photometry is often called, appropriately, "abridged spectrophotometry."

**Light Used.** The band of wave lengths selected by the spectrophotometer often is referred to as monochromatic light. Actually, it is only a single wave length in the instruments too expensive to use for routine chemical colorimetry. The reference to monochromatic light is even less significant when a filter is used. For convenience all discussion of filters and their transmissions will be made in Chapter XII.

**Designation of Methods.** When a light beam has been standardized, the extent of absorption of a restricted wave band by a solution can be measured and is a colorimetric determination. This value or its logarithm has been designated not only as absorbency but also as optical density and extinction. The method has been termed absolute colorimetry, abridged photometry, filter photometry and absorptiometry.

If the comparison was to be made between two solutions, the method would be one of comparative colorimetry. In contradistinction, when a single solution is read in terms of absorbency or transmittance and then compared with a standardization curve the method is one of absolute colorimetry. Only a true monochromatic light source is needed to make the method one of spectrophotometry,[1] although not necessarily good spectrophotometry.

---

[1] R. Havemann, *Z. physik. Chem.*, **188A**, 182-90 (1941).

Since the comparison is with a calibration curve based on natural standards it follows that it is a modified method of comparison with liquid standards. Of relatively minor importance when limited to visual reading, it has increased greatly in importance as photoelectric methods were more widely used. When read by eye it can be less accurate than comparison methods using equipment of an equal degree of development because the errors of two readings are added in the final result. In photoelectric methods, properly conducted, this cumulative error is more than offset by the greater accuracy of reading.

**Conditions.** The necessary conditions for maximum sensitivity of photometric methods, whether visual or photoelectric, are (1) absence of colloidal material in the solution examined, (2) a thickness of solution suitable for maximum accuracy, and (3) monochromatic light.[2] These are ideals to be approximated rather than realized.

Although photoelectric filter photometry is the more important, except for the use of the photoelectric cell, the principles are much the same. As was the case with the spectrophotometer, the visual instrument is subjective, whereas the photoelectric instrument is objective. Again, as in the case of spectrophotometers, the visual instruments are most sensitive in the middle of the visual range and fall off in sensitivity toward the red and violet where the response of the eye is limited. The same inherent flaw is present as in the usual colorimeter, the final result depending on matching two adjacent fields with the eye.

That the filter photometer is inadequate for fundamental measurements has been well illustrated by data of Mellon shown in Figure 50. The 35 m$\mu$ band of the spectrophotometer does not show the peaks and valleys in the transmittance, but the line joining the points recorded by 8 filters shows almost nothing. The true photometer by contrast has an almost unlimited number of points.[3]

The band transmitted is often narrowed in filter photometry by use of a combination of filters. Aside from still not approaching the sharp cut-off of a spectrophotometer, this radically decreases the intensity at the dominant wave length.

The maximum transmittance of the color developed from the test substance and of the filter should be at the same wave length. If they are not, the selection of wave band may be the source of deviation from Beer's law. A rule of thumb for use of the filter photometer is: Select

[2] C. Mahr, *Agnew. Chem.*, **53**, 257-8 (1944).
[3] M. G. Mellon, *Ind. Eng. Chem., Anal. Ed.*, **11**, 80-5 (1939).

that filter which shows the greatest difference in reading between two concentrations of the unknown.

**Preliminary Adjustments.** An essential feature of filter photometry is the setting of the instrument at what would be called the "zero point" or "blank." Actually, those phrases usually mean that a cuvette is filled with water and inserted in place, and the instrument adjusted

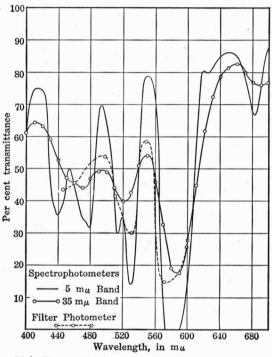

Fɪɢ. 50 [4]. Transmittance curves for didymium glass using different spectral bands

to read 100 per cent transmittance. This corrects for the thickness of liquid which is to be used for transmission and, more important, for reflection of light at the entrance and exit planes of glass of the cell. Whereas each case is a law unto itself, usually all reagents should be present but none of the test substance. Naturally, this cannot be applied if the reagent gives an absorption and is applied in stoichiometric proportions as occurs in determination of lead by dithizone using the single-color method. A safe procedure is to set the instrument at 100 with

[4] M. G. Mellon, *Colorimetry for Chemists,* p. 76. G. Frederick Smith Chemical Co., Columbus , Ohio (1945).

solvent, usually water, in the cuvette. Replace with solvent containing all reagents which are to be in the sample, including the color-producing reagent. If the reading is the same, it is proper to adjust the original setting of the instrument with solvent alone. If not the same, there is color absorption by the reagents, perhaps due to an impurity reacting in the same way as the test substance. In that case, in all future runs, the specific grades and amounts of all reagents should be present in making the original setting, or the original setting should be made with water, and a blank then obtained and subtracted in terms of the test substance from the amount determined. Technics differ as to the desirable choice between these. The first is easier.

When possible, it is even better to obtain a blank from a developed sample from which the color due to the test substance has been bleached [5] or a solution of the sample to which all reagents have been added except those producing the color.

In speaking of the value measured, absorbency or transmittance are merely expressions for the same property—in one case the units absorbed, in the other, those not absorbed. The term "absorbency" is sometimes incorrectly replaced by absorption, and "transmittance" by the incorrect use of transmission. For definitions see p. 65.

An exception to the use of calibration curves occurs when two substances reacting with the same reagent are determined by measuring at the peak absorbency of each. Practically, the curve form is such that usually they overlap and solution by simultaneous equations is necessary. An example is the reaction of titanium and vanadium with hydrogen peroxide. The color due to molybdenum may also be present and all three determined. Similarly, manganese and chromium are determined at different wave lengths and corrections applied in calculation.

**Calibration Curves.** A log-linear plot of concentration vs. transmittance or absorbency should give a straight line if Beer's law is followed (Figure 2, page 18). By a proper blank this line will pass through the origin. When water is used as the reference liquid, correction for the use of another solvent may be included in the calibration curve. Knowing the slope of the line, a value $k$ obtained expresses this slope. From this value, results may be calculated but readings are obtained more quickly from a calibration curve.

Such a curve should always be obtained for the specific instrument to be used, not taken from a reference. Among other significant factors

---

[5] George P. Rowand, Jr., *Ind. Eng. Chem., Anal. Ed.*, **11**, 442-5 (1939).

in it are the properties of the photoelectric cell used. Again, it is sometimes suggested or recommended that a single point be determined and a straight line drawn from it through the origin. But a little more time will be required to obtain readings at half and double the concentration at that point and to ascertain whether the three define a straight line passing through the origin. If not, the blank may be wrong which will cause the line to be straight but not to pass through the origin. The line may be curved showing that the system with that filter and instrument does not fully conform to Beer's law.

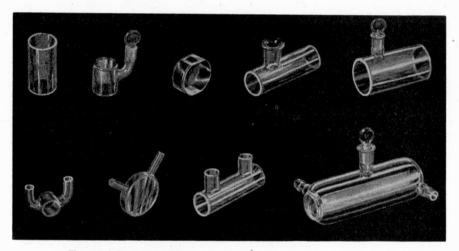

Fig. 51. Representative types of cuvettes or absorption cells.
(*American Instrument Company*)

**Cells or Cuvettes.** Generally, the cell used is of a decimal thickness, 1 cm. or 10 cm. Of all values obtained, probably 90 per cent are 1 cm. thickness. The term "cuvette" is applied to these cells by many manufacturers. Preferably, it is of optical glass with the parallel faces fused on. Cemented cells may vary in thickness, due to variable thicknesses of the cement layer, and the faces may not be parallel. But for clinical work with filter photometers to be discussed later the cells are often plain test tubes. Occasionally, they are of quartz for work in the near-ultraviolet and ultraviolet. Some instruments are limited to a single size of cell, others permit a choice. Figure 51 shows an assortment of cells representative of the many types in use. A noncommercial modification such as a pipet cell is shown in Figure 52.[6] The cell A is 1 cm.

[6] S. T. Bowden, *J. Soc. Chem. Ind.*, **55**, 180T (1936).

thick and 1.8-2.0 cm. in diameter. The usual pipet tubes, B, C, are fused to it, and a pinch clamp completes the assembly.

**Importance.** One type of German instrument has been used widely for the purpose, and a book has been written solely on its applications.[7] The best known is the Pulfrich photometer of Zeiss, although the competitive Leifo instrument of E. Leitz does not differ in any essential

Fig. 52.
Colorimeter
pipet cell

Fig. 53. Zeiss-Pulfrich photometer. (*Carl Zeiss, Inc.*)

principle. It does not appear probable that visual filter photometers have any really significant place in the future development of the art. Rather, in an electronic age, even the colorimeters have gone electronic and results indicate that the trend is a desirable one.

**Pulfrich Photometer.**[8] This visual instrument, often called the "step photometer," is a diaphragm type of abridged spectrophotometer

---

[7] A. Thiel, *Absolutkolorimetrie*, Walter De Gruyter and Co., Berlin (1939).

[8] Carl Zeiss, Inc., 485 Fifth Ave., New York, N. Y.; Pulfrich, *Z. Instrumentenk.*, **45**, 35, 61, 109, 521 (1925).

depending on a controlled width of slit. The instrument is shown in Figure 53 and the schematic diagram in Figure 54. A common light source diverges into two parallel paths of light. Each path passes through condensing lenses, glass cells of equal dimensions containing menstrum and the test solution, variable calibrated apertures, and, after passage through lenses and suitable prisms, a biprism and appropriate filter, finally to fall on the ocular and the eye of the observer.

A pair of slits—facing, 90°, V-notches are varied to give the readings. One is used to set the instrument at 100 initially. The test reading is obtained by adjusting the calibrated aperture pertaining to the water cell until the two fields are matched. Thus, on a calibrated measuring drum, the transmittance of the developed sample is compared with that of the menstrum. If the latter was originally set at 100, the former

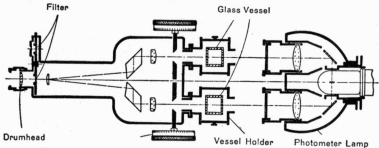

FIG. 54. Schematic diagram of Zeiss-Pulfrich photometer

will read in direct values. Since calibration is either linear or logarithmic the instrument can be read directly in transmittance or absorbency, and their logarithms. Alternatively, a calibration curve or a factor may be used.

The instrument can be modified for measurement of reflected color, glass, nephelometry, turbidity or fluorescence. Light is taken through filters. Mercury or quartz-mercury lamps are also available. Glass neutral filters with a thin film of atomized platinum are sometimes used. Light may be diffused by frosted or opal glass plates. The cells permit 1 to 50 cm. columns. Accuracy to 1 per cent at best can be expected. Several modifications of this instrument have been developed.[9]

The filters offered for this instrument are of particular importance because of the frequent expression in German literature of the desired

[9] A. Thiel, *Sitzber. Ges. Beforder. ges. Naturw. Marburg*, **71**, 17-27, 86-93 (1936); H. Thiel, *Agnew. Chem.*, **53**, 192-3 (1940); J. E. R. Winkler, *Schweiz. Arch. Angew. Wiss Tech.*, **6**, 194-201 (1940); Erik Asmus, *Z. anal. Chem.*, **126**, 161-72 (1943).

wave band for absorption in terms of these filter numbers, rather than as dominant wave length. Table 5, page 108, shows their values.

An instrument similar in purpose is called the "Leifo" colorimeter

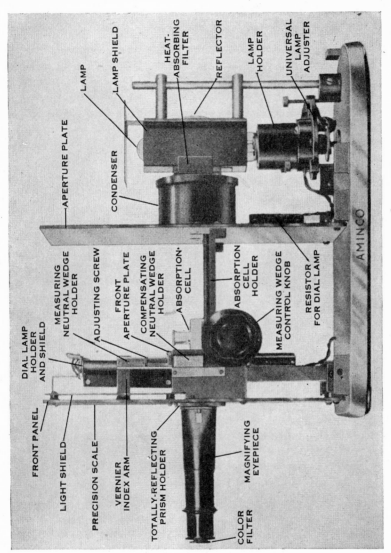

FIG. 55. Aminco neutral wedge photometer

but differs in that it varies the beams by the rotation of polarizing prisms. It too reads directly in absorbency or transmittance, or their logarithms.

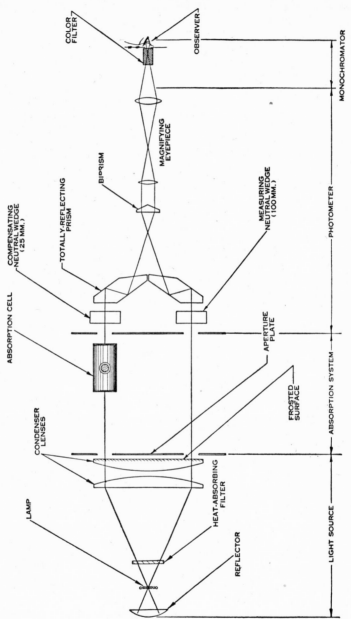

FIG. 56. Schematic diagram of Aminco wedge photometer

**Aminco Neutral Wedge Photometer.** The light can be reduced in a visual comparison instrument by a neutral wedge. Figure 55 shows an instrument of this type [10] and Figure 56 the schematic diagram, with all parts labeled in both cases. The lightly frosted surface of the second condenser lens furnishes duplicate patches of light in the aperture plate. Illumination is by a 100-watt projection lamp, or an 85-watt mercury vapor lamp. Cells are available in lengths of 1, 2 and 5 mm. and outside diameters of 10 and 16 mm., using 0.05-15 ml. of solution. Transmission by the wedges varies from 37 to 46 per cent over the range 405 to 700 m$\mu$. Readings of the wedge over the range 1-100 per cent transmittance is by a vernier against an illuminated Lucite scale. The small compensating wedge gives both fields the same appearance. Values for the filters available are shown in Table 6, page 109.

An alternative used in other instruments is a neutral gray solution of variable thickness to reduce the intensity of the direct beam.

**Polarization Type.**[11] The type of instrument is not of importance but the principle should be presented. Entering light passes two totally reflecting prisms, then through an adjustable absorption cell, through a photometer cube, and finally is reflected through a color filter and eyepiece. Another portion of the original beam is reflected from adjustable mirrors and enters the polarizing head. By rotation of one Nicol prism with respect to another the intensity of light is cut down to match that traversing the first path. A scale reads directly in terms of the angle of rotation.

---

[10] American Instrument Co., Silver Spring, Md.

[11] Ralph H. Müller, *Ind. Eng. Chem., Anal. Ed.*, **13**, 707 (1941).

# CHAPTER X

# PHOTOELECTRIC FILTER PHOTOMETRY [1]

PROBABLY the first person who attempted to measure the concentration of a test substance by impingement of the colored light beam on a photoelectric cell quickly realized that a dozen new sources of error had replaced that inherent in the use of the human eye. These sources of error have been minimized sufficiently so that this method now can be used reliably. The statement has been made that the light available at the eyepiece is in general most efficiently utilized by substitution of a photocell for the eye.[2] This cannot be taken at its face value as applying to chemical colorimetry.

Any general assumption that *per se* the photoelectric cell is more sensitive or more accurate than the human eye is unwarranted; much more than replacing the eye with a photocell is required. However, under proper conditions the increase of sensitivity over that of the eye is important. Moreover, the proper photoelectric filter colorimeter with the right combination of units is sensitive in the ultraviolet and infrared, both invisible to the eye, as well as in the range 400-700 m$\mu$ where the sensitivity of the eye is applicable. The experience of the past two decades with photometers of varying degrees of development has placed them firmly in the chemical laboratory. Of those in use the majority are filter photometers, mainly for reasons of cost.

The filter photometer is limited to the wave-length restrictions resulting from the combination of filter, photocell, and source of light. Without proper equipment and proper operation inaccurate results are more likely to be obtained photoelectrically than visually.[3] However, properly designed and used with a series of special cells, the photoelectric colorimeter can be made more accurate than the eye.[4] Photoelectric tristimulus colorimetry [5] is outside the field of colorimetric analysis. Standard methods are usually readily modified for photoelectric colorimetry.

---

[1] The fundamentals of filter photometry are included under preceding chapters and should be studied before taking up this variation.

[2] A. C. Hardy and F. H. Perrin, *Principles of Optics*, p. 422, McGraw-Hill Book Co., New York (1932).

[3] Paul F. Shuey and L. K. Darbaker, *J. Am. Pharm. Assoc.*, **27**, 1216-17 (1938).

[4] Herbert E. Ives, *Science Supplement*, **84**, 8-9 (1936).

[5] For more details see Richard S. Hunter, Circular C429, National Bureau of Standards (1942).

**Method of Reading.** In visual filter photometry the use of color filters was introduced. In photoelectric filter photometry there is an additional series of problems. The first is the translation of a light ray into a minute electric current by the photoelectric cell. Second, there is often multiplication of that minute electric current into one more easily measured. And, finally, there is the measurement of that current. It follows that there may be some doubt as to whether analytical colorimetry is more a field for the physicist or the chemist. The obvious answer is an expansion in the curriculum for the analyst.[6]

**Cautions.** Monochromacity of the light can be approached with a spectrophotometer but not approximated with a filter photometer. Therefore, the validity of the calibration curve for the latter assumes a stable combination of illuminant, filter, spectral sensitivity, and illumination-current relationship of the photoelectric cell.

Uniformity of light is a very important factor in determining the necessity of a new standardization curve. Stabilization of the voltage supplied to the instrument does not fix the wave-length distribution as a function of filament temperature. Rather, with use, the filament material evaporates and the filament temperature therefore decreases.[7] When infrared radiation interferes with the determination, filtration through a 1 per cent copper sulfate solution will eliminate it.[8] Glass heat-absorbing filters also serve this purpose.

**Applicability.** In general, where many determinations of the same type have to be made, a filter photometer will give the desired decreased time per determination. It is seldom necessary for a few determinations where usual accuracy will be adequate and the same type is not to be repeated. Occasionally, where a single determination is of such importance as to justify the time, it is desirable to do it photoelectrically for the sake of increased accuracy.

Provided close screening is not necessary to separate an interfering wave band, a filter photometer can be fully as satisfactory as a true spectrophotometer and is, of course, much less expensive. For some types of work a true spectrophotometer is necessary for accurate work when an interfering band is close, as for example titanium in the presence

[6] Beverly L. Clarke, *Proc. Am. Soc. Testing Materials,* **44,** 710-11 (1944).

[7] R. Havemann, *Angew. Chem.,* **54,** 105-8 (1941).

[8] E. R. Bolton and K. A. Williams, *J. Intern. Soc. Leather Trades Chem.,* **20,** 504-12 (1936).

of vanadium when developed with hydrogen peroxide.[9]  Generalizations about filter photometers are dangerous. Some are relatively simple and use only 3 color glasses. Others provide a comprehensive series of glasses with close ranges of filtration. Recent improvements in the production of filters have done much for the filter photometer. Still, the filter photometer must always suffer from imperfect selection of wave lengths. Offsetting this, it transmits more light from a given source in the desired band, particularly more than a double monochromator. Sensitivity will be lost if the filter does not transmit its peak at the peak of the color developed from the test substance. Light at other wave lengths is stray light, just as truly as internal reflection in an instrument.

**Light Source.** For work in the visible range the source of light is almost universally a tungsten-filament lamp. When working near the lower limit of visible light, below 400 m$\mu$, the filament temperature must be high. If heat is not removed from the photometer by adequate ventilation, error is introduced. As the lamp ages, tungsten vaporizes from the filament to the wall of the bulb and alters the energy distribution curve of the lamp. This is controlled by frequent standardization. Ordinarily, current is drawn from the usual electric lines through a constant voltage transformer. Batteries under continuous charge give closer control and avoid fluctuations in line voltage. The latter are important with a single-cell instrument, of lesser importance with a 2-cell photometer.

**Photoelectric Cells.** The cells used are usually (1) a photovoltaic or barrier-layer cell, or (2) a photocell of the emissive type.

Barrier-layer cells have a response curve extending from 300-700 m$\mu$ but otherwise it is much like that of the eye. They operate well at high levels of illumination, but with feeble light there may be pronounced nonlinearity of response. Also they show reversible fatigue, particularly at low luminosities. At a high light intensity, such a cell may give 0.1 milliampere response to light filtered through a slightly colored solution. It follows that often they need no amplification.

The spectral response of a photoemissive cell depends on the alkali metal used and the treatment during manufacture. Often it is low in the blue region. Ordinarily, after a few minutes' exposure, the response is constant. Such a photocell is apt to give a current of the order of $10^{-3}$ milliamperes, which must be amplified.

---

[9] A. E. Ruehle, *Proc. Am. Soc. Testing Materials*, **44**, 718-19 (1944).

**Single-cell Type.** The general diagram is shown in Figure 57. With this type, interpose the solution to be measured between the cell and the source of light and measure the transmittance directly with a microammeter or galvanometer in terms of current output of the photoelectric cell, compared to the value obtained with the pure solvent or menstruum.[10]

It is of paramount importance in instruments of this type to use a light source of constant intensity during the period in which a pair of readings is being taken. This may be accomplished by use of a storage battery, incorporating a current-regulating lamp in a circuit buffered by an accumulator,[11] or by use of a constant temperature transformer. The light required is such that a wave band of about 25 m$\mu$ is a minimum band. If the cell is of a type showing a fatigue effect it is necessary to allow it to attain its equilibrium current after each change of light intensity.

One may detect the response of the cell with a sensitive galvanometer or microammeter. The output may be measured in milliamperes, in arbitrary readings of the scale marking the position of a diaphragm or shutter, or by the electrical resistance necessary to maintain the output of the cell at a definite value.

Although single-cell methods have been criticized by proponents of double-cell circuits, results of undoubted reliability have been reported.[12] The requirements are rather that the entire circuit be adapted to the specific use contemplated. Thus, by use of a single, photoelectric vacuum tube with an electronic amplifier the sensitivity is increased and a milliammeter employed. In any case, batteries are required for sufficient constancy, and individual photoelectric cells must be calibrated and constantly checked.[13] Other instruments of this type use a sensitive galvanometer to measure directly the current output from a single, self-generating, photovoltaic or barrier-layer cell under the variable conditions of light transmission. Variations between individual photoelectric cells are sufficient to require new calibration curves, and

---

[10]R. A. Osborn, *J. Assoc. Official Agr. Chem.*, **17**, 135 (1934); John H. Yoe and Thomas B. Crumpler, *Ind. Eng. Chem. Anal. Ed.*, **7**, 281-4 (1935); R. S. W. Thorne and L. B. Bishop, *J. Inst. Brew.*, **42**, 15-26 (1936); L. E. Howlett, *Canadian J. Res.*, **14A**, 38-42 (1936).

[11]Ralph H. Müller, *Ind. Eng. Chem., Anal. Ed.*, **13**, 708-9 (1941).

[12]Ralph H. Müller, *Mikrochemie*, **11**, 353-68 (1932); *Ind. Eng. Chem., Anal. Ed.*, **7**, 223-6 (1935); A. H. Sanford, Charles Sheard and A. E. Osterberg, *Am. J. Clin. Path.*, **3**, 405-20 (1933); T. R. Hogness, F. P. Zscheile, Jr., and A. E. Sidwell, Jr., *J. Phys. Chem.*, **41**, 379-415 (1937).

[13]Joseph G. Baier, Jr., *Ind. Eng. Chem., Anal. Ed.*, **15**, 144-48 (1943).

deterioration of the cells requires frequent rechecking of the curves. Some instruments use directly a single, photoelectric vacuum tube and a direct-reading galvanometer.

**Two-cell Type.** Two photoelectric cells may be illuminated by the same source of light, as shown in Figure 57, and balanced against each other through a galvanometer. The solution of test substance is placed before one cell, the solvent or menstruum without test substance before the other, and the current-output difference mesaured [14] by cutting down the more intense until it matches that from the test substance. Small fluctuations in the light source, even while comparing, are cancelled. Therefore, lighting with ordinary alternating current is suitable.

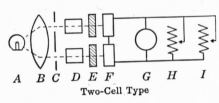

A   B C   D E F      G    H     I

Two-Cell Type

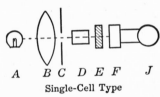

A     B C   D E F    J

Single-Cell Type

FIG. 57. Filter photometers of single-cell and two-cell types. (*A. E. Ruehle*)

The characteristic response curves of different photo-emission cells differ, and permit selection of one having the maximum response to the wave band being measured. Barrier-layer cells may be used, or phototubes, with or without amplification. Although the desired band is usually obtained by color filters, light nearer to monochromatic is obtained by filtering the light from such metal-vapor discharge lamps as mercury or sodium lights.

A low-resistance circuit of this type is advantageous in that the current output varies linearly with the difference in light intensity falling on the two cells, a small difference in illumination can be read in a high sensitivity range of the meter, and fluctuations of the light source are to a large extent compensated.[15] The amount of absorption in the sample cell is compensated by adjustment of a diaphragm until it matches the standard cell. The drum control for the diaphragm is calibrated in units of extinction.

[14] B. Lange, *Chem. Fabrik*, **1932**, 457-9; *Ibid.*, **1935**, 31-5; Ch. Zinzadze, *Ind. Eng. Chem., Anal. Ed.*, **7**, 280-1 (1935); R. B. Withrow, C. L. Shrewsbury and H. R. Kraybill, *Ibid.*, **8**, 214-19 (1936).

[15] Morris Rosenfeld, *J. Biol. Chem.*, **129**, 179-87 (1939).

# PHOTOELECTRIC FILTER PHOTOMETRY

Changes in the intensity of the light are unimportant when a sin_
source is used and the light passes through essentially identical optical
paths to two photoelectric cells.[16] This results in stability, sensitivity
and simplicity. Thus, null-point balancing of the two cells against each
other as indicated by a sensitive galvanometer largely eliminates errors
due to temperature change and cell fatigue. The latter assumes that
the effect is the same on each half of the circuit. The cells used should
nearly match in spectral response.

**Method of Use.** Whatever the type of instrument, the method is
substantially the same. In measuring the absorbency of the colored
solution, one selects the wave length or wave band for which the solution
shows a maximum absorption. The
advantages are maximum sensitivity
and a logarithmic calibration curve
when the system conforms to Beer's
law. By measurement at two suitable
wave lengths it is often possible to
determine two or more substances in
admixture (pp. 18, 208, 220). Use
of the quartz spectrograph permits
extension of measurements into the
ultraviolet, as of vitamin A at 328mμ.

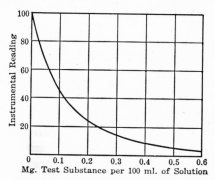

FIG. 58. Typical calibration curve

The reading usually requires interpretation from a calibration curve
prepared for that specific instrument and solutions containing the same
concentrations and kinds of reagents, other than the test substance.
Literature giving calibration curves cannot generally be accepted as
an alternative.

**Calibration Curves.** By having the intensity of the incident light
as 100, the reading of transmitted light on a proper scale will be directly
in per cent transmittance. With a few instruments the reading is on
an arbitrary scale and the ratio is calculated. Having two or more,
preferably more, of such transmittance or absorbency values for a
particular instrument and test substance, the question of what to do
with them arises. They may be plotted linear-linear but rarely are.
This will always give a curved line of greater or less complexity, which

---

[16] Arnoldus Goudsmit, Jr., and William H. Summerson, *J. Biol. Chem.*, **111**, 421-33
(1935).

is simplified to a standard logarithmic curve if the system conforms to Beer's law. The curves which are commonly plotted all take into account the logarithmic response inherent in the laws of Bouguer, Beer, and Lambert.

Thus, such data giving a curved calibration, plotted on log-linear paper, will give a straight line, provided that Beer's law holds for the system. An alternative to plotting linear values on log-linear paper is the direct calibration of the instrument logarithmically. The great majority of instruments now provide for the direct reading of transmittance in logarithmic terms. It is simply provided—merely a logarithmic calibration alongside the linear one.

Thus, Figure 58 shows a typical calibration curve in terms of the values read.[17] A point or two on the calibration curve must be checked at fairly frequent intervals to insure that the instrument is in proper condition. Calibration of a filter photometer for a given determination is only established as proper if a smooth curve can be drawn through several determined points.[18]

A calibration curve can be constructed for all types of photometers. It is necessary to construct one for those of the types reading in terms of an arbitrary scale, now relatively limited in number.

A blank is not essential and rather it is preferable to correct to zero by calculation. For this, two or more points are taken on the logarithmic curve, preferably more than two, and the straight line drawn through them. This is then extrapolated to zero concentration and the correction for log transmittance is obtained for corresponding subtraction or addition.

---

[17] Figures 92 and 93 show logarithmic calibration curves.

[18] M. N. States and J. C. Anderson, *J. Optical Soc. Am.*, **32**, 659-66 (1942).

# CHAPTER XI

## PHOTOELECTRIC FILTER PHOTOMETERS

To show every instrument which has been manufactured would unduly complicate the presentation. Therefore, those discussed in this chapter are the leading instruments on the American market followed by brief mention of others. Several are imported types of which the German ones may not again become available. They are included

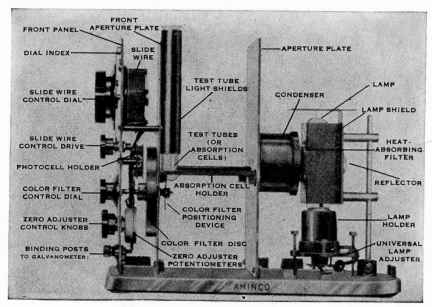

FIG. 59. Aminco type F photometer

because many are in laboratories and they ordinarily have a long life.

The corresponding sets of filters designed for use with these instruments are collected in the next chapter, together with some filters not designed for a specific instrument.

**Aminco Type F Photometer.**[1] This is a filter photometer, using two barrier-layer photocells. The instrument is shown in Figure 59 and

[1] American Instrument Co., Silver Spring, Md.; Brooks A. Brice (Henry A. Wallace), U. S. Patent 2,064,517; J. C. Keane and Brooks A. Brice, *Ind. Eng. Chem. Anal. Ed.*, **9**, 258-63 (1937).

diagrammatically in Figure 60. Filters of broader transmission than for the corresponding neutral wedge instrument (p. 81) are required in order to provide adequate light for the photocells. The range of those available is shown in Table 7 (p. 109). Solutions are usually contained in test tubes or 16 mm. absorption cells but cells giving a 1 mm. layer with 0.15 ml. can be used. With a blank in one cell and developed sample in the other a resistance is adjusted until the galvanometer is no longer deflected. There is no appreciable error introduced by 3 per cent in voltage, the normal tolerance of public utilities.

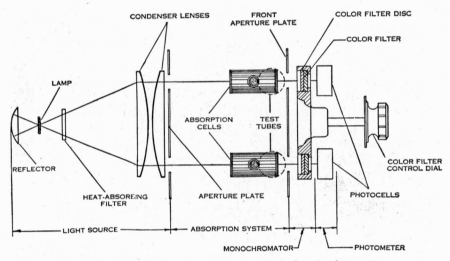

FIG. 60. Schematic drawing of Aminco photoelectric photometer

**Hellige-Diller Photoelectric Colorimeter.** This instrument[2] is shown in Figure 61. The light source is a 15 candle-power automobile headlight bulb illuminated by 110-volt line current through a transformer regulator. Fluctuation of 15 volts is not serious. The bulb is adjustable as to location. The light passes through a heat-absorbing filter, a convex-parabolic lens to produce a broad beam, then through a glass color-filter. A biconvex lens focuses the beam at substantially the location of the specimen. The beam emanating from the specimen falls on the barrier-layer photoelectric cell. Provision is made for another filter between the specimen and the photocell. The resulting current is read by a D'Arsonval galvanometer with both linear and

2 Hellige, Inc., 3718 Northern Blvd., Long Island City, N. Y.; Isaac M. Diller, U. S. Patent 2,232,169 (1941); *J. Biol. Chem.*, **115**, 315-22 (1936).

logarithmic scales. If Beer's law holds the latter is a direct reading of concentration. Specimens are contained in tubes of 7.5, 12.5, 20 and 25 mm. diameter, accurate to 0.1 per cent transmission. The volume of solution needed in these varies from 0.6 to 8 ml. A micro-cell permits measurement of 0.05 ml. in a 0.25 mm. layer if sufficiently highly colored. Both broad and narrow band filters are available, and a revolving disc

FIG. 61. Hellige-Diller photoelectric colorimeter

carries 7 such filters in the instrument so that any filter or none can be readily interposed. The range of these filters is shown in Table 8 (p. 110).

**Photelometer.** This filter photometer [3] consists of a constant 6-volt incandescent light source, absorption-cell, filter, barrier-layer photocell,

[3] Central Scientific Co., Chicago 13, Ill.; Charles Sheard, Arthur H. Sanford and Dana A. Rogers, U. S. Patent 2,051,317 (1936); Marshall N. States (Central Scientific Co.), U. S. Patent 2,051,320 (1936); Charles Sheard and Arthur H. Sanford, *J. Am. Med. Assoc.*, **93**, 1951-6 (1929); Arthur H. Sanford, Charles Sheard and A. E. Osterberg, *Am. J. Clin. Path., Tech. Sup.*, **3**, 405-20 (1933); A. S. Giordano, Marshall N. States and Charles Sheard, *Ibid.*, **4**, 122-9 (1940); Marshall N. States and J. C. Anderson, *J. Optical Soc. Am.*, **32**, 659-66 (1942).

and a low-resistance microammeter. The schematic diagram is shown in Figure 62, the exterior view in Figure 63, the filters in Table 9 (p. 110). The intensity of light is controlled by an iris diaphragm which precedes the glass filter and solution. Checks after many months indicate retention of constancy of calibration. Changes of the order of 0.1 per cent can be estimated. Variation over the range 105-120 volts causes a change of no more than 0.5 scale division. One type operates from line current, the other from a storage battery. Different models permit use of 1 cm. and 5 cm. cells. This instrument has been successfully applied to the Carr-Price method for vitamin A.[4] The same manufacturers also produce a simple clinical model shown in Figure 64, and a true spectrophotometer (p. 71).

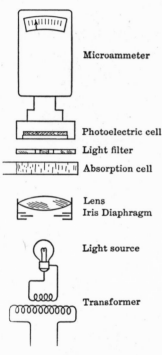

Microammeter

Photoelectric cell

Light filter

Absorption cell

Lens
Iris Diaphragm

Light source

Transformer

FIG. 62. Schematic diagram of photelometer

**Fisher Electrophotometer.** The Fisher filter photometer,[5] known as an Electrophotometer, is shown in Figure 65. Normally, a 23 ml. volume is used in a round cell but this can be reduced to 3 ml. in a round micro cell and altered to give a path of 50 mm. in a rectangular cell. Line current is used. The illumination is variable at 4 levels. Two cells are used by the null method with a potentiometer to indicate the endpoint. The filters described in Table 10 (p. 110) are furnished in plastic holders. Both linear and logarithmic scales are provided. Readings are duplicable to 0.5 per cent. The Fisher Electro-Hemometer is a simple, single photocell instrument for reading hemoglobin content either in grams per 100 ml. or per cent of normal. It operates on 2 dry cells.

**Spekker Photoelectric Absorptiometer.** Adam Hilger, Ltd.,[6] calls its form of filter photometer an absorptiometer. Figure 66 shows the

---

[4] R. B. French, *Ind. Eng. Chem., Anal. Ed.*, **12**, 351-2 (1940).

[5] Fisher Scientific Co., 711 Forbes St., Pittsburgh, Pa., St. Louis, Mo.; Eimer and Amend, New York, N.Y.; G. M. Laboratories, Inc., 1737 Belmont Ave., Chicago, Ill.

[6] Jarrell-Ash Co., 165 Newbury St., Boston, Mass.; Spekker, *J. Sci. Instruments*, **13**, 268 (1936).

FIG. 63. Photelometer. Analytical model

FIG. 64. Photelometer. Clinical model

instrument and Figure 67 the schematic diagram. The null-point circuit operated by line current balances the two rectifier photocells against each other by use of a galvanometer. The calibrated aperture reading is the numerical measurement. Cells are usually 1 cm. or 4 cm. long, but 20 cm. can be used in a modified instrument. Filters must be in matched pairs on either half of the circuit.

Fig. 65. Fisher Electrophotometer

The standard model is used with broad-band glasses of the H455 series, shown in Table 11 (p. 111). A sensitive model uses broad-band glasses of the H455 series, narrow-band glasses of the H558 series (Table 11, p. 111), a mercury vapor lamp with adapter, and microcells. A sodium lamp may also be used. A micro model uses small capacity cells with a path of 0.25-4 cm. Another model uses long cells, and this is also made in a sensitive type.

FIG. 66. Spekker photoelectric Absorptiometer. (*Adam Hilger, Ltd., London*)

These data are not a substitute for complete transmission curves; they merely serve to identify the filters approximately. The H455 set of Hilger ranges from less than 30 per cent maximum transmission for OB 1 to over 90 per cent for OR 2 at the maximum; the H558 series ranges from 6 per cent for 605 to 28 per cent for 601. Naturally, the H558 series requires much more powerful lighting. The H455 series are glass, the H558 series gelatin. Special filters are also obtainable. Heat-absorbing filters are used with the H558 series. The accuracy is to 1 per cent in the region of maximum sensitivity.

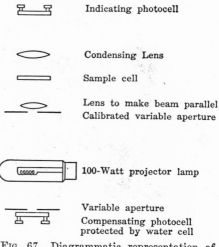

Indicating photocell

Condensing Lens

Sample cell

Lens to make beam parallel
Calibrated variable aperture

100-Watt projector lamp

Variable aperture
Compensating photocell
protected by water cell

FIG. 67. Diagrammatic representation of the Spekker Absorptiometer

**Klett-Summerson Colorimeter.** This instrument [7] shown in Figure 68 is a relatively simple and inexpensive design. The sample

[7] Klett Manufacturing Co., 179 E. 87th St., New York, N. Y.; Arnoldus Goudsmit, Jr., and William H. Summerson, *J. Biol. Chem.*, **111**, 421-33 (1935); William H. Summerson, *Ibid.*, **130**, 149-66 (1939); U. S. Patent 2,193,437 (1940).

illuminated by filtered white light is read in either a test tube or a glass cell as a quantitative measurement, with the menstruum as zero, which can then be compared directly with a standard reading on the same instrument or interpreted from a calibration curve. The range of filters is shown in Table 12 (p. 111). By substitution of a special tube, reading

FIG. 68. Klett-Summerson photoelectric colorimeter

FIG. 69. Lumetron colorimeter Model 402-E

of 1 ml. is possible. All readings with ordinary tubes are through a depth of 12.5 mm. The use of cells permits 2.5, 10, 20 and 40 mm. as well as the test tubes of the simpler instrument. Readings are on a logarithmic scale. It is primarily an instrument for clinical analysis.

The same instrument is applicable as a turbidimeter. Either test tubes or cells up to 150 mm. are applicable in the standard instrument, while other models take only test tubes of variable diameter. Filters are of 2-4 glass layers designed to give a 30-m$\mu$ band. A set of 4 broadband filters is also used for less selective work.

**Lumetron.**[8] This is another filter photometer operating directly on line voltage. The light source is a 100-candle-power projection lamp. One design of instrument is shown in Figure 69, the optical system in Figure 70, the filters in Table 13 (p. 112).

Light from lamp A is brought into parallel beams by L, passes the filter J, and then is split into two parts. One part of the beam passes through the sample C to strike the photocell D. The other part, reflected

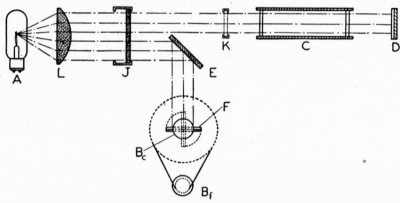

FIG. 70. Optical system of Lumetron

from the mirror E, strikes the balance photocell F. By turning F through an angle of 90°, the light striking it is varied between 0 per cent and 100 per cent. Movement of the cell F by coarse and fine adjustments determines the absorption in C. The holder K is to provide a gray filter for C if necessary.

**KWSZ Colorimeter.** This filter photometer,[9] shown in Figure 71, used a pair of cesium oxide vacuum cells, a dial decade bridge, and a galvanometer to read directly in transmittance with an accuracy of about 1 per cent and reproducibility of about 0.1 per cent. Changes in line voltage or lamp brightness have no significant effect. The filters,

[8] Photovolt Corporation, 95 Madison Ave., New York, N. Y.; F. Loewenberg, *Am. Dyestuff Reptr.*, **28**, 706 (1939).

[9] Wilkens-Anderson Co., 111 N. Canal St., Chicago, Ill.; R. B. Withrow, C. L. Shrewsbury and K. R. Kraybill, *Ind. Eng. Chem., Anal. Ed.*, **8**, 214-19 (1936).

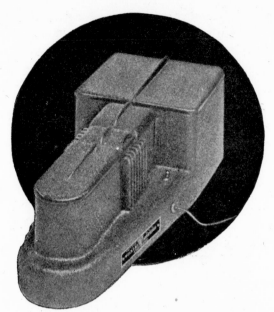

FIG. 71. KWSZ colorimeter. (*Wilkens Anderson Co.*)

FIG. 72. Lange photoelectric colorimeter

shown in Table 14 (p. 113), are built up of Corning Glass filters, selected from the full list rather than the abridged series of Table 4. For heat absorption, use 9780 with filters 1 to 4, and 3965 with 5 to 8. Although no longer manufactured, there are considerable numbers in use in industry.[10]

**Lange Photoelectric Colorimeter.** Another two-photocell instrument [11] with a compensating circuit is shown in Figures 72 and 73. The filament bulb at 1 delivers light to lenses 2 and 3. This must pass through solutions in cuvettes 11 and 12 to reach the photocells 4 and 5. Adjustment of iris diaphragms 6 and 7 correspondingly adjusts the

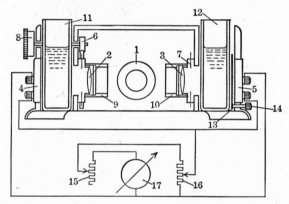

Fig. 73. Diagrammatic circuit of Lange photoelectric colorimeter

light transmitted. A measuring drum, 8, reads the setting of iris 6. Sleeves 9 and 10 exclude outside light. A shutter at 13 operated by a knob 14 gives a reading of the extent to which light has to be shut off from photocell 5. The sensitivity of the galvanometer, 17, is regulated by variable rheostats, 15 and 16. Both linear and logarithmic scales provide data for plotting or give direct readings. Color filters, of which transmission bands are not available, are used. The Lange colorimeter has been described as sufficiently accurate for technical work but not for scientific laboratories.[12]

[10] Private communication.

[11] Pfaltz and Bauer, Inc., 350 Fifth Ave., New York, N. Y.; B. Lange, *Chem. Fabrik*, **1934**, 45-7.

[12] M. Werkenthin, *Gaz. Cukrownicza*, **75**, 235-45 (1934); A. Zelazny, *Ibid.*, **76**, 337-42 (1935); Cf. Anders Ringbom and Folke Sundman, *Z. anal. Chem.*, **115**, 402-12 (1939).

**Evelyn Photoelectric Colorimeter.** This instrument,[13] Figure 74, is a single barrier-cell instrument. Light is furnished by a flashlight bulb from a battery, the cells are test tubes and emphasis is placed on close control of the wave band which reaches the photocell. For this purpose, the color filters are built up of glass discs. The range available is indicated in Table 15 (p. 114). A separate galvanometer is used.

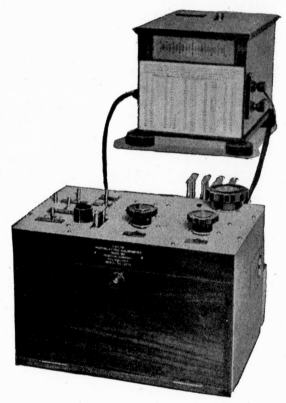

FIG. 74. Evelyn photoelectric colorimeter.  (*The Rubicon Co.*)

The standard model can use a 6-ml. sample with accuracy to 2 per cent. About one determination per minute is feasible.[14]

As further developed as a micromodel it uses 0.1-2 ml. of faintly colored solutions to give 0.1-1.0 mm. layers of deeply colored media.[15]

[13] The Rubicon Co., 29 North Sixth St., Philadelphia, Pa.; Kenneth A. Evelyn, *J. Biol. Chem.*, **115**, 63-75 (1936).

[14] Isaac M. Diller, *J. Biol. Chem.*, **115**, 315-22 (1936).

[15] Kenneth A. Evelyn and A. J. Cipriani, *J. Biol. Chem*, **117**, 365-9 (1937).

With some further modifications accuracy to 0.5 per cent was reported.[16]

**The Leitz Clinical Colorimeter.**[17] This is a clinical instrument supplied with calibration charts. The unit consists of a constant light source maintained by a voltage regulator, a set of four interchangeable glass light filters, a barrier-layer cell, and a microammeter. Cells of square cross section, or tubes, are used as the sample containers.

**Instruments and Uses.** The photoelectric filter photometer may be simple, inexpensive and portable. [18] But it must not be overlooked that true spectrophotometers are available at costs under $1000 and that they permit more accurate work.

For work on water and sewage, vertical-beam types of photoelectric instruments have been designed.[19] One is of an unbalanced type,[20] the others are of balanced type.[21] A special design of photoelectric photometer has been accepted as the standard in evaluation of either white sugars or their solutions.[22]

The photoelectric filter photometer has been applied to the old and troublesome problem of measurement of color of petroleum products.[23] A gray wedge and monochromatic light have been used for this purpose.[24] Ultraviolet instruments are used for vitamin A.[25] Aside from those

---

[16] Kenneth A. Evelyn and John G. Gibson, 2nd, *J. Biol. Chem.*, **122**, 391-4 (1938).

[17] E. Leitz, Inc., 730 Fifth Ave., New York, N. Y.

[18] Russell H. Morgan and Sidney Wienhouse, *Am. J. Clin. Path., Tech. Suppl.*, **4**, 114-22 (1940).

[19] W. D. Hatfield and George E. Phillips, *Ind. Eng. Chem., Anal. Ed.*, **13**, 430-5 (1941).

[20] G. Hurwitz, *Sewage Works J.*, **11**, 134-5 (1939).

[21] R. B. Winthrop, C. L. Shrewsbury and H. R. Kraybill, *Ind. Eng. Chem., Anal. Ed.*, **8**, 214-19 (1936); B. A. Brice, *Rev. Sci. Instruments*, **8**, 279-83 (1937).

[22] J. C. Keane and B. A. Brice, *Ind. Eng. Chem., Anal. Ed.*, **9**, 258-63 (1937); H. Hirshmüller, *Intern. Sugar J.*, **39**, 399 (1937); E. Landt and H. Hirschmüller, *Z. Wirtschaftsgruppe Zuckerind.*, **87**, Tech. Tl. 449-60 (1937); A. R. Nees, *Ind. Eng. Chem., Anal. Ed.*, **11**, 142-5 (1939).

[23] I. M. Diller, R. J. DeGray and J. W. Wilson, Jr., *Ind. Eng. Chem., Anal. Ed.*, **14**, 607-14 (1942); I. M. Diller, J. C. Dean, R. J. DeGray and J. W. Wilson, Jr., *Ind. Eng. Chem., Anal. Ed.*, **15**, 367-73 (1943).

[24] Hans Siebeneck, *Oel, Kohle, Erdoel, Teer*, **12**, 793-5 (1936); *Allgem. Oel- u. Fett-Ztg.*, **34**, 109-13 (1937).

[25] Joseph R. Edisury, Albert E. Gillam, Isidor M. Heilbron and Richard A. Morton, *Biochem. J.*, **26**, 1164-73 (1932); R. L. McFarlan, J. W. Reddie and E. C. Merrill, *Ind. Eng. Chem., Anal. Ed.*, **9**, 324 (1937); D. T. Ewing, J. M. Vandenbelt, D. Emmett and O. D. Bird, *Ibid.*, **12**, 639-44 (1940); Allen F. Parker and Bernard L. Oser, *Ibid.*, **13**, 260-2 (1941); Beaumont Demarest, *Ibid.*, **13**, 374-6 (1941).

described, there are numerous other designs.[26] One design uses a transparent rectangular tube and a solid glass wedge curved logarithmically.[27] Another, depending on changing the planes of polarization by adjustment of an analyzer, records the color obtained in matching a sample,

[26] William G. Exton, U. S. Patent 1,954,925 (1934); *Ibid.*, 1,971,443 (1934); *Am. J. Clin. Path.*, 7, 42-68 (1937); Virgil A. Schoenberg, British Patent 429,347 (1935); Hubert C. S. de Whalley and James D. Atkinson (Tate and Lyle, Ltd.), British Patent 440,365 (1935); Ralph H. Müller, *Ind. Eng. Chem., Anal. Eng.*, 7, 223-6 (1935); Ch. Zinzadse, *Ibid.*, 7, 280-1 (1935); F. M. Turrell and Louis Waldbauer, *Proc. Iowa Acad. Sci.*, 42, 63-6 (1935); Th. W. Schmidt, *Z. Instrumentenk.*, 55, 336-46, 357-67 (1935); Alfred E. Traver (Socony-Vacuum Co., Inc.), U. S. Patent 2,042,281 (1936); Ralph H. Müller, U. S. Patent 2,043,589 (1936); Bertrand W. Story (Socony-Vacuum Co., Inc.), U. S. Patent 2,043,816 (1936); M. L. Kudor, U. S. Patent 2,048,554 (1936); Friedrich Rappaport, Austrian Patent 144,341 (1936); K. K. Tomson and A. A. Vishnevskif, Russian Patent 47,833 (1936); Joseph F. Brewster, *J. Res. Natl. Bur. Standards*, 16, 349-58 (1936); Instrument-Photometric, Chemical Department of the South Metropolitan Gas Co., *J. Soc. Chem. Ind.*, 56, 387-390T (1936); G. Bernheim and G. Revillon, *Ann. fals.*, 29, 5-10 (1936); Paul Meunier, *Bull. soc. chim. biol.*, 19, 113-18 (1937); Gustave Fassin and John R. Miles (Bausch and Lomb Optical Co.), U. S. Patent 2,101,933 (1937); Joseph Lebowich, Richard J. Lebowich and M. Dinburg, *J. Lab. Clin. Med.*, 23, 284-92 (1937); H. Dreyer, *Ann. physik*, 30, 650-64 (1937); B. N. Singh and N. K. Anantho Rao, *Current Sci.*, 5, 416-18 (1937); E. Landt and H. Hirschmüller, *Z. Wirtschaftsgruppe Zuckerind.*, 87, Tech. Tl. 449-60 (1937); *Ibid.*, 88, 247-79 (1938); J. C. Somagyi, *Z. Biol.*, 98, 60-9 (1937); *Plant Physiol.*, 13, 419 (1938); H. I. James and E. A. Birge, *Trans. Wis. Acad. Sci.*, 31, 1-154 (1938); C. Reichert Optische Werke, German Patent 655,127 (1938); K. Hare and R. E. Phipps, *Science*, 88, 153-4 (1938); V. A. Sukhikh, *Zavodskaya Lab.*, 7, 348-50 (1938); Friedrich Assmus (F. Hellige and Co.), U. S. Patent 2,167,060 (1939); Robert K. Schofield and Edward J. Russell, British Patent 506,282 (1939); Franz Schmidt and Haensch, German Patent 682,289 (1939); Morris Rosenfeld, *J. Biol. Chem.*, 129, 179-87 (1939); Jerome E. Andes and David W. Northrup, *J. Lab. Clin. Med.*, 24, 197-206, 529-37 (1939); R. Havemann, *Biochem. Z.*, 301, 105-15 (1939); *Ibid.*, 306, 224-35 (1940); Igranic Electric Co., Ltd., British Patent 527,333 (1940); Charles J. Barton and John H. Yoe, *Ind. Eng. Chem. Anal. Ed.*, 12, 166-8 (1940); Paul A. Clifford and Brooks A. Brice, *Ibid.*, 12, 218-22 (1940), based on A. H. Pfund, *J. Optical Soc. Am.*, 18, 167 (1928); *Ibid.* 19, 387 (1929); Arthur Weil, *Am. Clin. Path., Tech. Suppl.*, 5, 31-4 (1941); O. H. Weber, *Angew. Chem.*, 54, 56-7 (1941); Robert H. Osborne, *Ind. Eng. Chem., Anal. Ed.*, 14, 572-5 (1942); Earl J. King, *Lancet*, 1942, I, 511-12; R. J. Taylor, *Analyst*, 67, 248-54 (1942); M. C. Schwartz and L. W. Morris, *Ind. Eng. Chem., Anal. Ed.*, 15, 20-23 (1943); G. Forsyth and T. I. Pound, *J. Intern. Soc. Leather Trades Chem.*, 28, 103-16 (1944); G. Berraz and E. Virasoro, *Anales. inst. investigaciones cient. technol.* 12/13, 147-63 (1943); H. L. Andrews and B. L. Horecker, *Rev. Sci. Instruments*, 16, No. 6, 148-52 (1945).

[27] Paul A. E. Hellige, U. S. Patent 2,050,608 (1936).

and thus the value by comparison with a table.[28]  A special device provides for the uniform positioning of the cell.[29]

This type of instrument has been adapted to clinical work,[30] food analysis,[31] microestimation of the copper-ammonia complex,[32] textiles,[33] fertilizer analysis,[34] hemoglobin,[35] analysis of rayon spin-bath,[36] blood serum,[37] and plasma,[38] high speed reactions,[39] color of water,[40] metals,[41] soil constituents,[42] distilled spirits[43] biological determination of pH, sodium, and phosphates,[44] hydrogen sulfide by formation of methylene blue,[45] the color of paprika,[46] phosphatase,[47] and cereal work.[48] Using an absorption spectrophotometer, after oxidation, manganese and chromium can be determined at 575 m$\mu$ and 450 m$\mu$ in 15 minutes with 1 per cent accuracy.[49] Where colors developed by aluminum and iron with hemotoxylin cannot be separated by the photoelectric

[28] Wilhelm Nagel, U. S. Patent 2,068,301 (1937) ; British Patent 439,276 (1935).

[29] Daniel S. Stevens, U. S. Patent 2,391,076 (1945).

[30] F. Wurstlin, *Münch. med. Wochschr.*, **82**, 1656-7 (1935) ; T. W. Pratt and A. L. Tatum, *Science*, **82**, 305-6 (1935).

[31] Fortunato Carranza, *Bol. soc. gruin. Peru*, **1**, No. 5, 7-27 (1935) ; E. B. Hatz, *Mikrochemie*, **21**, 38-46 (1936) ; Karl Woidich, *Oesterr. Chem.-Ztg.*, **39**, No. 11, 88-9 (1936).

[32] Ken-ichi Yamamoto and Mochiyuki Abe, *Bull. Waseda Applied Chem. Soc.*, **21**, 1-16 (1933) ; *Ibid.*, **25**, 1-10 (1935).

[33] N. H. Chamberlain, *J. Textile Inst.*, **35**, T61-76 (1944).

[34] B. V. Mikhal'Chuk and E. B. Brutskus, *Zavodskaya Lab.*, **6**, 161-71 (1937).

[35] A. Dognon, *Compt. rend. soc. biol.*, **129**, 467-8 (1938).

[36] K. Kruger, *Jentgen's Kunstzeide u. Zellwolle*, **24**, 587-93 (1942).

[37] P. Bonet-Maury, *Compt. rend. soc. biol.*, **135**, 197-201 (1941) ; A. Dognon and Y. Simonet, *Ibid.*, **135**, 146-8 (1941).

[38] A. Dognon, *Ibid.*, **135**, 113-15 (1941).

[39] Kurt G. Stern and Delafield DuBois, *J. Biol. Chem.*, **116**, 575-86 (1936); Britton Chance, *Rev. Sci. Instruments*, **13**, 158-61 (1942).

[40] Tetsuo Tomiyama and Minorn Watanabe, *J. Agr. Chem. Soc. Japan*, **14**, 187-97; *Bull.* **14**, 15 (1938) ; S. K. Chirkob and N. P. Evgrafova, *Vodosnabzhenie Sanit. Tekh.*, **16**, No. 1, 25-7 (1941) ; A. L. Davuidov and A. M. Avrunina, *Zavodskaya Lab.*, **5**, 927-31 (1936).

[41] H. Pinsl, *Metalwirtschaft*, **18**, 417-19, 437-41 (1939) ; K. Dietrich, *Mitt. Leitz-Werke*, 1941, No. 63, 19-22; *Physik. Ber.*, **22**, 1292 (1941).

[42] C. L. Wrenshall, *Sci. Agr.*, **19**, 236-40 (1938).

[43] G. F. Beyer, *J. Assoc. Official Agr. Chem.*, **22**, 156-8 (1939).

[44] A. Leclère, *Bull. biol. pharm.*, 1938, 530-41.

[45] M. T. Burton, *Gas*, **12**, No. 5, 41, 60, 62 (1936).

[46] Pal. Selenyi, *Kem. Lapja*, **2**, No. 9, 12-13 (1941).

[47] W. H. Boynton and P. E. Nelbach, *J. Milk Tech.*, **1**, No. 4, 8-9 (1938).

[48] E. Berliner and W. Kranz, *Muhlenlab.*, **7**, 89-94 (1937).

[49] R. W. Silverman and J. Alfred Curtis, *Metals and Alloys*, **15**, 245-8 (1942).

colorimeter, a mathematical method has been developed for separation of the overlapping effects.[51]    The methods have even been applied to light absorption effects in glass.[52]

The color of opaque objects has been photographed, and the color transparencies so obtained studied by spectrophotometric methods.[53] Suitably modified they should be applicable to either comparison with a series of glass or other standards or to reading by abridged spectrophotometry and become a true colorimetric method. Even oxygen saturation of blood hemoglobin is measured through the scapha membrane of the ear to an accuracy of 2 per cent, without sampling, by measuring the characteristics of a beam with a photocell.

---

[51] Harold W. Knudson, Villiers W. Meloche and Clancy Juday, *Ind. Eng. Chem., Anal. Ed.*, 12, 715-18 (1940).

[52] M. Demkina, *Tech. Phys.*, U.S.S.R. 4, 380-2 (1937).

[53] Maurice E. Stansky and John A. Dasson, *Ind. Eng. Chem., Anal. Ed.*, 14, 13-15 (1942).

# CHAPTER XII

## FILTERS

BECAUSE filters are not always used with the instrument for which they were designed, because directions for one instrument must often be applied to another, and because filters are often in use which were not designed for any specific instrument, there has been gathered in this chapter the significant data about filters for all the instruments, if such information is available. In the literature, occasional use of Å for expression of dominant wave band of the filter implies an accuracy not present in the types of instruments used in colorimetric analysis.

There are two standard makers of such filters for general use, and their product has been adapted to colorimetry. Filters are often prepared from dyed film[1] or gelatin.[2] Thus a 0.02 per cent picric acid solution in 5 per cent gelatin has been used for silica and mixed with a similar Congo red solution for iron and titanium. They involve difficulties in reproducibility to a greater degree than when commercial filters are used but the difficulty is of degree rather than kind. A calibration curve must have been prepared with the identical filter used.

**Glass Filters.**[3] The color of a glass is dependent on (1) the dissolved and often reacted metal oxide or, alternatively, the dispersed colloidal element, (2) the basic batch composition, and (3) the heat treatment given. All glasses deliver at the opposite surface less light than falls on them. The losses are due to light reflected from the two surfaces and that absorbed in the glass itself. The ratio of the two values is known as the transmission of the glass. As an example, a glass with a refraction of 1.5 cannot have a transmission of over 92 per cent due to reflection losses.

One way of getting a narrow band of light through a glass filter is to use a gaseous light source and a filter which will transmit only one of the wave bands. The bands so available are strictly limited.

The reproducibility of wave length varies. Blue, green and some yellow glasses consist of solutions of a colored silicate and can be matched very closely, first by composition, second by varying the thickness in

---

[1] W. P. Stowe, *Am. J. Clin. Path., Tech. Suppl.*, **2**, 249 (1938).

[2] F. Ya. Galakhov, *Zavodskaya Lab.*, **10**, 90-2 (1941).

[3] O. A. Gage, *Proc. Am. Soc. Testing Materials*, **44**, 720-4 (1944).

grinding. Where there is a sharp cut-off in the wave length the duplication is more difficult, variations falling on a sharply ascending curve. Also, sharp cut-off glasses such as are shown in Figure 75 in the red, orange and yellow are dependent for their color on heat treatment as well as composition. These are colloidal dispersions and the particle size may be varied. Standardization on both hue and thickness is not possible.

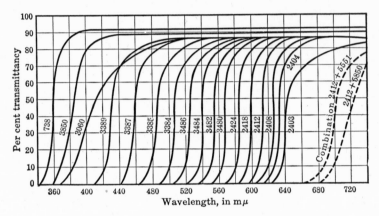

FIG. 75. Some sharp cut-off Corning glasses

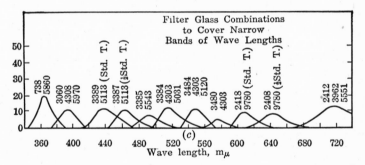

FIG. 76. Transmission of some combination filters of Corning glasses

When a combination of glass filters is used to give only a narrow band of wave lengths the maximum transmission will be low and for reading must depend on substantial amplification. This is illustrated in Figure 76 which refers to combinations of Corning glasses.

Ordinarily there is no change in color of glass with age. A very few glasses are attacked by atmospheric moisture to give an etched surface which is reclaimable by polishing. As the temperature of a glass filter rises, the absorption bands become wider. Correspondingly, the greater the absorption by the glass, not to include reflection, the greater the rise in temperature as the light rays absorbed are converted into heat.

**Corning Filter Glasses.** One of the most complete sets of duplicable glass filters are those of the Corning Glass Co. Many were originally developed for signal lens manufacture. They are sold in slightly rough form or polished to a standard, the thickness varying for different glasses and different batches. Some of the spectrophotometric absorption curves are so complicated that the details in Table 4 are not as complete as desirable. Reference to the original literature of the manufacturers[4] is preferable to use of the tabulation. Of the 61 color filters the table shows data on a selected group of 10.

TABLE 4. SELECTED LIST OF CORNING GLASS FILTERS.
(All but 2540 are heat resisting)

| Code | Name | Maximum $m\mu$ | Range Over 10% Transmittance $m\mu$ |
|------|------|---------|-----------------------------|
| 2412 | H. R. Lantern | 650 up | 610 up |
| 3421 | H. R. Umber Shade A | 660 up | 425 up |
| 3482 | H. R. Lantern Yellow | 600 up | 550 up |
| 4084 | H. R. Emerald Green | 510 | 450-570 |
| 4441 | H. R. Lantern Green | 490 | 590 down |
| 5543 | H. R. Lantern Blue | 425 | 490 down |
| 5330 | H. R. Furnace Door Blue | 400 | 525 down |
| 5874 | H. R. Red Purple Ultra | 365 | 325-395 |
| 3966 | Extra Light Shade AKLO | 500 | None |
| 2540 | Heat Transmitting | 1500 | 750-4250 |

**Wrattan Filters.** This type of filter was originally designed for use in photography. Due to availability and standardization they have been applied from time to time in colorimetric uses. The filter consists of dyed gelatin, ordinarily cemented between two square or circular sheets of optical glass. The B grade is satisfactory for most purposes; the A grade is between hand-surfaced optical flats. The list is extensive, going far beyond the uses of colorimetry. Complete transmission curves are available.[5]

---

[4] *Glass Color Filters*, Corning Glass Works, Corning, N. Y.

[5] *Wrattan Light Filters*, Eastman Kodak Co., Rochester, N. Y., 17th Edition (1944).

In cleaning mounted Wrattan filters, only the surface should be moistened; any water in contact with the gelatin at the edges will swell it and separate the glass plates. Storage at low humidity is desirable. Stability to light varies.

**Commercial Filters.** The information available about different commercial filters varies. Such as can be obtained is shown in a series of tables as follows:

Table  5.  Filters for Zeiss Pulfrich Photometer.
Table  6.  Filters for Aminco Neutral Wedge Photometer.
Table  7.  Filters for Aminco Type F Filter Photometer.
Table  8.  Filters for Hellige-Diller Colorimeter.
Table  9.  Filters for Photelometer.
Table 10.  Filters for Fisher Electrophotometer.
Table 11.  Hilger Filters for Spekker Instruments.
Table 12.  Filters for Klett-Summerson Colorimeter.
Table 13.  Filters for Lumetron Colorimeter.
Table 14.  Filters for KWSZ Colorimeter.
Table 15.  Filters for Evelyn Colorimeter.

TABLE 5. FILTERS FOR ZEISS-PULFRICH PHOTOMETER.

| Filter | Principal Spectrum Line mμ | Range Over 1/10 Transmission mμ |
|---|---|---|
| S43 | 434 | .. |
| S47 | 463 | 44 |
| S50 | 494 | 46 |
| S53 | 530 | 35 |
| S57 | 572 | 38 |
| S61 | 619 | 66 |
| S72 | 729 | .. |
| S75 | 750 | .. |
| K1 | 630 | 8 |
| K2 | 650 | 6.8 |
| K3 | 563 | 3.8 |
| K4 | 536 | 4.7 |
| K5 | 510 | 6.5 |
| K6 | 480 | .. |
| K7 | 460 | .. |
| L1 | 680 and above | above 615 |
| L2 | 530 | 510-557 (over 1%) |
| L3 | 445 | below 498 (over 1%) |

TABLE 6. FILTERS FOR AMINCO NEUTRAL WEDGE PHOTOMETER.

| Filter | Principal Spectrum Line mμ |
|---|---|
| 42 | 424 |
| 44 | 444 |
| 46 | 458 |
| 49 | 488 |
| 50 | 500 |
| Pb | 510 |
| 51 | 514 |
| 52 | 524 |
| 54 | 539 |
| 56 | 559 |
| 57 | 570 |
| 58 | 579 |
| 59 | 591 |
| 61 | 606 |
| 62 | 620 |
| 63 | 635 |
| 65 | 646 |
| 68 | 677 |
| 72 | 720 |
| 436 | 435.8 mercury arc |
| 546 | 546.1 mercury arc |
| 578 | 578.0 mercury arc |

TABLE 7. FILTERS FOR AMINCO TYPE F FILTER PHOTOMETER.
(Corrected for photocell response)

| Designation | Maximum Transmission % | Principal Spectrum Line mμ | Range of Transmission mμ |
|---|---|---|---|
| 42 | 34 | 424 | to 500 |
| 46 | 26 | 458 | 420-560 |
| 51 | 24 | 514 | 450-600 |
| 53 | 23 | 525 | 480-620 |
| 58 | 18 | 579 | 530-670 |
| 65 | 21 | 646 | 585 up |

TABLE 8.  FILTERS FOR HELLIGE-DILLER COLORIMETER.

| Filter Number | Principal Spectrum Line mμ |
|---|---|
| 70-30 | 660 |
| 80-30 | 620 |
| 700-1 | 610 |
| 730-1 | 585 |
| 730-2 | 560 |
| 740-1 | 530 |
| 469-40 | 520 |
| 550-50 | 440 |
| 760-2 | 390 |

TABLE 9.  FILTERS FOR PHOTELOMETER.

| Designation | Principal Spectrum Line mμ | Range of Transmission mμ |
|---|---|---|
| 335B | | below 410 |
| 390 | 390 | 60-80 |
| 435 | 435 | 60-80 |
| 465 | 465 | 60-80 |
| 490 | 490 | 60-80 |
| 515 | 515 | 60-80 |
| 550 | 550 | 60-80 |
| 610 | 610 | 60-80 |
| 610B | | below 610 |
| 410P | 410 | broad |
| 525P | 525 | broad |
| 610P | 610 | broad |
| 645P | 545 | broad |

TABLE 10.  FILTERS FOR FISHER ELECTROPHOTOMETER.

| Visible Color | Principal Spectrum Line mμ | Range of Transmission mμ |
|---|---|---|
| Blue | 422 | upper limit 508 |
| Green | 504 | 493-550 |
| Red | 630 | lower limit 597 |

TABLE 11. HILGER FILTERS FOR SPEKKER INSTRUMENTS.

| Filter | Principal Spectrum Line mμ | Range of Over 10% Transmission mμ |
|---|---|---|
| H 455 | | |
| OB1 | 440 | < 480 |
| OB2 | 480 | < 580 |
| OG1 | 580 | 480–580 |
| OY2 | > 600 | > 540 |
| OR2 | > 540 | > 590 |
| H 558 | | |
| 602 | 435 | 405–455 |
| 602 | 465 | 460–470 |
| 603 | 480 | 475–485 |
| 604 | 520 | none |
| 605 | 550 | none |
| 606 | 575 | none |
| 607 | 600 | 590–620 |
| 608 | > 675 | > 640 |

TABLE 12. FILTERS FOR KLETT-SUMMERSON COLORIMETERS.

| Designation | Principal Spectrum Line mμ | Range of Transmission mμ |
|---|---|---|
| 66 | 660 | 640–700 |
| 54 | 540 | 500–560 |
| 42 | 420 | 400–450 |
| KS40 | 400 | 300–430 |
| KS42 | 420 | 400–450 |
| KS44 | 440 | 410–480 |
| KS47 | 470 | 470–530 |
| KS50 | 500 | 470–530 |
| KS52 | 520 | 485–550 |
| KS54 | 540 | 520–580 |
| KS55 | 550 | 520–600 |
| KS56 | 560 | 540–590 |
| KS59 | 590 | 565–630 |
| KS60 | 600 | 580–640 |
| KS62 | 620 | 590–660 |
| KS64 | 640 | 620–680 |
| KS66 | 660 | 640–700 |
| KS69 | 690 | 660–740 |

TABLE 13. FILTERS FOR LUMETON COLORIMETER.

| Filter Designation | Principal Spectrum Line $m\mu$ | Range of Transmission $m\mu$ |
|---|---|---|
| B420 | 420 | broad |
| B530 | 530 | broad |
| B590 | 590 | broad |
| B660 | 660 | broad |
| M365 | 365 | 30 |
| M390 | 390 | 30 |
| M420 | 420 | 30 |
| M440 | 440 | 30 |
| M465 | 465 | 30 |
| M490 | 490 | 30 |
| M515 | 515 | 30 |
| M550 | 550 | 30 |
| M575 | 575 | 30 |
| M590 | 590 | 30 |
| M610 | 610 | 30 |
| M620 | 620 | 30 |
| M640 | 640 | 30 |
| M660 | 660 | 30 |
| M700 | 700 | 30 |
| M730 | 730 | 30 |

TABLE 14. FILTERS FOR KWSZ COLORIMETER.

| Filter Designation | Principal Spectrum Line mμ | Composite in 2″ × 2″ Corning Polished Filters [a] |
|---|---|---|
| 1A | 370 | 5970 3965 |
| 1 | 400 | 5113 |
| 2A | 440 | 3389 5543 |
| 3 | 490 | 3387 5031 |
| 4 | 520 | 4010 |
| 4A | 520 | 4010[b] 3385 |
| 5 | 575 | 3482 9780 (half)[c] |
| 6 | 625 | 2424 3962 |
| 7 | 650 | 2408 3962 |
| 8 | 690 | 2403 3962 (half) |
| 9 | 740 | 2412 5551 |

[a] Standard thickness unless indicated as half-standard.
[b] Use 4A for sharper left cut for lead dithizonate.
[c] Add 9,780 to sharpen on the right.
[d] 2,468 may be replaced by 241 at half thickness.

TABLE 15.  FILTERS FOR EVELYN COLORIMETER.

| Number and Principal Spectrum Line | Range of Transmission |
|---|---|
| 720 | 690–770 |
| 690 | 665–745 |
| 660 | 635–720 |
| 635 | 615–680 |
| 620 | 595–660 |
| 600 | 580–635 |
| 580 | 565–610 |
| 565 | 550–585 |
| 550 | 525–570 |
| 540 | 515–570 |
| 540M | 515–585 |
| 515 | 485–550 |
| 520M | 470–580 |
| 490 | 465–530 |
| 440 | 410–475 |
| 420 | 380–460 |
| 400 | 380–430 |

# CHAPTER XIII

## NEPHELOMETRY

A COLORED material in true solution is estimated by comparison of color with that of a standard—a colorimetric method. The transmission of light is measured, and reflection is zero. On the other hand, a colloidal dispersion of a colored precipitate colors the transmitted light and also reflects some light. On the assumption that its reflection is negligible, it may be estimated by colorimetric methods. If the reflection becomes very great, the error becomes serious and the reflection of light must be measured instead of the transmission. Photoelectric methods are applicable as well as visual ones,[1] and a portable unit[2] has been used. Thus there is no sharp division between colorimetry and nephelometry. Some organometallic derivatives, such as copper diethyl-dithiocarbamate in aqueous media, and sulfides such as lead sulfide, are in colloidal dispersion in colorimetric methods.

A rough dividing line is to use colorimetric methods if there is conformity to Beer's law so that the usual nephelometric corrections are not needed. Protective colloids are often useful in either maintaining the particle size fine enough for colorimetric measurement or stable enough for nephelometric.[3] Synthetic surface-active agents of like charge have been successfully used for this purpose.[4]

Introduction of photoelectric measurements has further complicated nephelometry since it has been observed that two colloidal lead sulfide dispersions which are apparently identical in shade to the eye may be appreciably different in photoelectric measurements.[5] For true nephelometric determinations such as of zinc as ferrocyanide, the photoelectric instrument is reported to be appreciably more accurate than the eye.[6]

---

[1] S. P. Reimann, *Proc. Soc. Exptl. Biol. Med.*, **23**, 520-3 (1926); Charles H. Greene, *J. Am. Chem. Soc.*, **56**, 1269-72 (1934); N. Howell Furman and George W. Low, Jr., *Ibid.*, **57**, 1588-91 (1935); V. A. Sukhikh, *Zavodskaya Lab.*, **7**, 348-50 (1938).

[2] T. R. Thomas and Leslie Silverman, *Ind. Med.*, **11**, *Ind. Hyg. Sect.*, **3**, 188-90 (1942).

[3] L. de Brouckere and S. Solowiejezyk, *Bull. Soc. Chim. Belg.*, **43**, 597 (1934); C. Zinzadze, *Ind. Eng. Chem., Anal. Ed.*, **7**, 227 (1935).

[4] Chester M. Alter and Deane S. Thomas, Jr., *Ind. Eng. Chem., Anal. Ed.*, **12**, 525 (1940).

[5] "Committee Report to Society of Public Analysts," *Analyst*, **60**, 541 (1935).

[6] N. Strafford, *Analyst*, **61**, 170 (1936).

The border-line cases justify inclusion of nephelometry in a collection of methods which are mainly colorimetric. The same instrument suitably modified may be used for both. Some nephelometric methods are not in any way border-line cases, since the reflection is from a white precipitate which could not be measured colorimetrically. The earlier development of the nephelometer was largely in connection with atomic weight determinations by comparison with silver.

**Nephelometric Equipment.** The simplest nephelometric equipment is, like that of colorimetry, a series of standard tubes. In general, nephelometric standards change with time due to growth of size of

FIG. 77. Duboscq colorimeter with nephelometer attachment.
(*Bausch & Lomb*)

particles, so that the standards and sample must usually be prepared at the same time. A protective colloid modifies this requirement to some extent.

The standard type of visual nephelometer is a modification of the Duboscq instrument, Figure 77. In the usual nephelometer the opaque tubes with clear glass bottoms used in colorimetry have been replaced with clear glass tubes with opaque bottoms, usually 50 mm. deep but often 100 mm. (Figure 78). An artificial source of light is essential for accurate work (Figure 79). This light shining through the side of standard and sample tubes is reflected upward through the tube and eyepiece. The amount of reflection is controlled as in colorimetry by variation of the depth of liquid underneath the plunger. Unlike colorimetric methods which in general follow Beer's law, the relationship is not strictly linear.

As an alternative to varying the depth of reflective solution, the amount of artificial light delivered to the tubes may be altered by a variable aperture.

The Mueller photoelectric nephelometer [7] is a single photocell instrument which measures the light reflected at either 45° or 90°. It is standardized by a Lucite plate. Other instruments are designed for micro work [8] and for both colorimetry and nephelometry.[9]

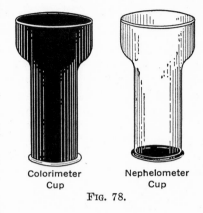

Colorimeter Cup     Nephelometer Cup

FIG. 78.

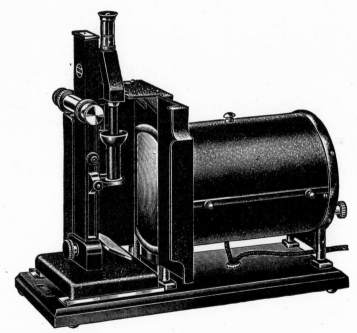

FIG. 79. Kober nephelometer. (*Eimer and Amend*)

[7] White Research Associates, 899 Boylston St., Boston, Mass.

[8] J. M. W. Milatz and P. B. Rattier, *Zentr. Bakt. Parasitenk.*, II Abt., **94,** 227-40 (1936).

[9] B. E. Semeikin, *J. Applied Chem.*, (U.S.S.R.), **9,** 2332-7 (1936).

**Correction Curve for the Nephelometer.** It is necessary to standardize the instrument with solutions of different concentrations and draw a correction curve or apply a suitable formula. The use of a curve is simpler, but not quite as accurate.

Prepare various dilutions of standard such as 0.9, 0.8, 0.7, 0.6 and 0.5 times standard. Match against the full-strength standard. From these comparisons the nephelometric constant can be calculated, the several determinations at different concentrations serving as checks. The formula is

$$y = \frac{s}{x} - \frac{(1-x)sk}{x^2}$$

in which $x$ = ratio of dilute standard to concentrated standard, $y$ = height of dilute standard, $s$ = height of concentrated standard and $k$ is the unknown nephelometric consent. A more convenient form is

$$k = \frac{x(xy - s)}{s(x - 1)}$$

It is even more convenient to plot the determined values with readings obtained as ordinates and the ratio of solutions as abscissae. This curve applies for a definite depth of a definite standard. By changing the depth of standard to correspond, when the concentration is varied, the same curve may be used.

**Range of Usefulness.** In sufficiently dilute solution almost any precipitate may be so modified by addition of a protective colloid or a surface-active agent as to be determinable with the nephelometer. For colored precipitates of colloidal dimensions, the colorimetric method is usually preferable.

# CHAPTER XIV

## TURBIDIMETRY

TURBIDIMETRY may be taken as a special case of nephelometry. Instead of measuring the reflection of light, the depth necessary to obscure a light source to a definite degree is determined.[1] Beer's law does not hold. The method is in standard use with the Jackson Turbidimeter for determination of sulfur in bomb washings or in water samples, or turbidity of water. It is occasionally called Tyndallometry.

The majority of standard turbidimetric determinations can be made by measurement of transmittance, that is, with an abridged spectrometer or a true spectrophotometer. If the suspending medium is colorless, there is no selective absorption of light in the visible spectrum and any wave band can be used. The particles must not settle rapidly. These conditions are met by most microorganisms and colloids. If the medium is colored, maximum sensitivity will be attained at the wave length of maximum transmittance of the medium.

The importance can be illustrated by the use of turbidimetric methods to speed up evaluation of penicillin.[2] Effective stabilization of turbidimetric suspensions has been obtained by addition of a surface-active agent of like charge.[3]

FIG. 80. Jackson turbidimeter (*Fisher Scientific Co.*)

**Jackson Turbidimeter.** The best-known form of apparatus is the Jackson Turbidimeter shown in Figure 80. This may be operated either with a candle or a 1 candle-power electric bulb. The solution is simply poured in until the image of the candle flame or the electric filament can no longer be observed. The depth of solution is then the measure of turbidity.

A somewhat more elaborate form of this instrument, shown in Figure 81, is totally enclosed and has an electric bulb as the source

---

[1] For a theoretical study see E. G. Richardson, *Proc. Phys. Soc.* (London), **55**, 46-63 (1943).

[2] J. R. McMahan, *J. Biol. Chem.*, **153**, 249-58 (1944).

[3] Chester M. Alter and Deane S. Thomas, Jr., *Ind. Eng. Chem., Anal. Ed.*, **12**, 525 (1940).

of light. To operate, pour the solution into the turbidimeter and insert the plunger tube. Put the eyepiece tube and eye shield in place. Adjust the rheostat on the base of the turbidimeter until 3 volts is shown on the voltmeter. Adjust the depth of the tube by the rack and gear mechanism until the filament either just disappears, or just appears. The former is more convenient. The scale will then give the reading of the depth directly. As a modification the stationary tube is replaced with a 13 mm. hard rubber tube having an optical glass bottom. Similarly

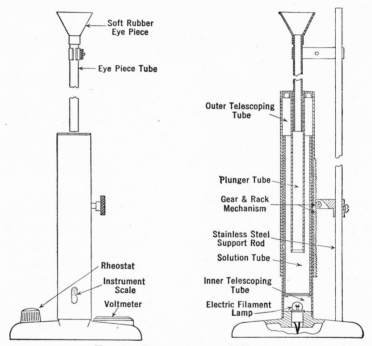

Fig. 81.  Burgess-Parr turbidimeter

the inner tube is replaced by an 8 mm. one of rubber. By this change only 25 ml. of sample containing 0.7 to 1.3 mg. of sulfur are required.

**Betz-Hellige Turbidimeter.** Another form of turbidimeter[4] is shown in Figures 82 and 83. Artificial light is reflected into the tube and the effect observed. Thus, the opal light B furnishes light to the contents of the tube T, either by reflection from R, or from the milk glass reflector MR. The adjustable slit S permits control of the light reflected from MR, until it balances that reflected from R. A glass

4 R. T. Sheen, H. K. Kahler and E. M. Ross, *Ind. Eng. Chem., Anal. Ed.,* 7, 262-5 (1935).

plunger, P, standardizes the depth examined. The turbidity can be read up to 150 ppm.

**General Electric Luximeter.** This instrument is shown in Figure 84. Originally developed for measurement of the blue color obtained in the phosphatase test for pasteurization of milk, it has been applied to measurement of light transmission through turbid suspensions. An

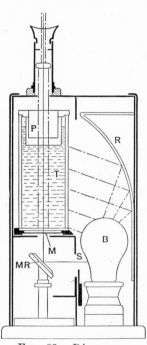

FIG. 82. Betz-Hellige turbidimeter

FIG. 83. Diagrammatic view of Betz-Hellige turbidimeter

example is the turbidity of sugar syrups. The usual range is 100-3500 ppm. on the silica scale.

The instrument is simple consisting of a 6-volt bulb lighted by dry cell, wet battery, or a constant voltage transformer operating on 110-volt, 60-cycle current. No filters are added. The light passing the sample tube impinges on a photocell and the current so produced is indicated on a microammeter. Transmission as read is a percentage of that passing a similar tube containing a control liquid, and is therefore percentage transmittance. In measurement of the transmittance of a colored solution the standard is the filtered sample, thus compensating in the blank for the effect of the color present.

**Miscellaneous Instruments and Uses.** Instruments,[5] which are substantial equivalents of a two-cell abridged photometer measure turbidity by two photovoltaic cells in a bridge circuit, determine the null-point with a galvanometer, and read density on a linear scale directly by a logarithmically calibrated potentiometer. The limitation

FIG. 84. General Electric Luximeter

on sensitivity is that of the circuit and the galvanometer. A stabilized amplifier system,[6] photoelectric vacuum tubes,[7] and an electronic amplifier system [8] have been applied to vary the sensitivity. A special null-point turbidimeter is for determination of hydrocyanic acid.[9] One depends on thermoelectric recording.[10]

---

[5] Shirleigh Silverman, *Rev. Sci. Instruments*, **12**, 77-8 (1941).

[6] Joseph G. Baier, Jr., *Ind. Eng. Chem., Anal. Ed.*, **15**, 144-8 (1943).

[7] T. J. B. Stier, W. Arnold and J. N. Stannard, *J. Gen. Physiol.*, **17**, 383-92 (1934); L. G. Longworth, *J. Bact.*, **32**, 307 (1936).

[8] Ronald L. McFarlan, J. Wallace Reddie and Edward C. Merrill, *Ind. Eng. Chem., Anal. Ed.*, **9**, 324-6 (1937); Cf. Charles J. Barton and John H. Yoe, *Ind. Eng. Chem., Anal. Ed.*, **12**, 166-8 (1940); William D. Hatfield and George E. Phillips, *Ibid.*, **13**, 430-5 (1941).

[9] E. T. Bartholomew and E. C. Ruby, *Ind. Eng. Chem., Anal. Ed.*, **7**, 68 (1935).

[10] Roger J. Williams, Edward D. McAlister and Richard R. Roehm, *J. Biol. Chem.*, **83**, 315-20 (1929).

The Lovibond Tintometer has been modified[11] for determination of turbidities to 1000 ppm. A white-light cabinet contains two standard light sources which illuminate a magnesium carbonate block and the sample. The beams of light are juxtaposed in a field with either corrected with such Lovibond glasses as are desired, and a control of the obstruction of the brighter to give equal intensity reads as visual density. As modified[12] a 5.25-inch cell is used below 100 ppm. and a U-tube from 100-1000 ppm. The latter is adaptable for all nephelometric work.

Evaluation of Portland cement by turbidity in kerosene has become important [13] and a special instrument [14] has been designed for the purpose. Similarly in application to white enamel frits,[15] 0.4 ml. of 270-325-mesh sample is suspended in 10 ml. of kerosene and the transmittance read against 100 for kerosene alone. Measurement of the concentration of suspended particles of substituted anthraquinones photoelectrically has been worked out.[16]

As a special case which may be considered to be turbidimetry, the opacity to transmitted light of glass slides carrying a film of heavy metal soaps deposited in washing is measured in a special type of photometer by the effect on a photocell.[17] A large beam is used with the photocell relatively far from the slides. To increase the effect the plates are set at an acute angle and to increase the effect further multiple plates are used. The result is additive.

In turbidimetric estimation of bacteria the standard is either a barium sulfate suspension, or, better, a suspension of particles of Pyrex glass.[18] A special comparator has been developed and satisfactorily applied in the study of the growth of yeasts and bacteria.[19]

---

[11] R. K. Schofield, *J. Sci. Inst.*, **16**, 74 (1939).

[12] C. S. Fawcett and J. Hewitt, *J. Soc. Chem. Ind.*, **58**, 342-4 (1939); British Patent 506,282.

[13] A.S.T.M. C115-42.

[14] T. W. Parker and R. W. Nurse, *J. Soc. Chem. Ind.*, **57**, 436-8 (1938).

[15] R. M. King, *J. Am. Ceram. Soc.*, **28**, 326-8 (1945).

[16] William Seaman, A. R. Norton and Charles Maresh, *Ind. Eng. Chem., Anal. Ed.*, **14**, 350-7 (1943).

[17] John L. Wilson and Elwyn E. Mendenhall, *Ind. Eng. Chem., Anal. Ed.*, **16**, 251-4 (1944).

[18] Francis J. Hallinan, *Am. J. Pub. Health*, **33**, 137-40 (1943).

[19] E. E. Snell and F. M. Strong, *Ind. Eng. Chem., Anal. Ed.*, **11**, 346-50 (1939); Derrol Pennington, Esmond E. Snell and Roger J. Williams, *J. Biol. Chem.*, **135**, 213-22 (1940); Richard P. Krebs, Patricia Perkins, Alfred Tytell and H. Kersten, *Rev. Sci. Instruments*, **13**, 229-32 (1942).

# CHAPTER XV

## FLUOROMETRY

THE methods of fluorometry differ from those of the usual chemical colorimetry in that a different wave length and source are used. The fluorescing substance is illuminated by ultraviolet light which it absorbs and re-emits at a longer wave length with a lesser amount of energy due to quenching effects. Thus, the factors which control the intensity of fluorescence are (1) concentration of the test substance, (2) wave length of excitation, (3) pH, (4) temperature, (5) presence of foreign ions, and (6) presence of fluorescing materials other than the test substance.[1] The fluorescense comparison may be against either artificial or natural standards. Beer's law does not hold over any substantial range. Readings may be made either visually or photoelectrically.

The methods differ from photometry in that (1) the source of radiant energy is usually a mercury arc lamp, (2) the filters pass only this ultraviolet radiant energy, (3) the photocell filters pass only radiant energy, and (4) the radiant energy measured emerges from the absorption cell at right angles to the incident ultraviolet beam.

Fluorometric determinations are usually applied for amounts of substance so small that colorimetric methods will not work. The substance must usually fluoresce with light in the range 300-450 m$\mu$. There are exceptions where ultraviolet emission has been read photoelectrically. The sensitivity decreases with increase of concentration according to Weber's law (p. 143). The fluorescence of the sample usually fades on continued exposure to ultraviolet. Therefore, the practice is to expose only momentarily, frequently by use of a shutter in the instrument for that purpose.

The usual application is to vitamin analysis but the concentration of mineral oil in blends with sulfurized oil and the concentration of the blend in emulsion in water have been determined fluorometrically by comparison with a series of standards.[2]

---

[1] Ralph H. Müller, *Ind. Eng. Chem., Anal. Ed.*, 12, 571-629 (1940); M. Haitinger, *Angew. Chem.*, 53, 181-3 (1940).

[2] Henry Benjamin, *Ind. Eng. Chem., Anal. Ed.*, 16, 331 (1944).

**Standards.** Although quinine sulfate, thiochrome, fluorescein, etc., are suitable standards for fluorometric analysis, they tend to fade with age. An alternative is uranium glass standardized against natural standards.[3] Two specific types have been produced equivalent to thiamine hydrochloride at 0.0005-0.001 mg. per ml. and to riboflavin at the same concentration. Whereas canary glass shows loss in fluorescence when exposed to continuous ultraviolet radiation[4] these standards are not so affected. The exact value varies from melt to melt and they must therefore be calibrated by the user.

**Instruments.** Many of the filter photometers described can be used when provided with suitable accessories. This may vary from a simple clinical type to the most complex. The step photometer (p. 77), a visual instrument, is so used.[5] Photoelectric methods are more sensitive.[6]

With an ultraviolet illuminator the Coleman spectrophotometer (p. 69) is adaptable to fluorometry of 0.1-50 mm. layers. A special instrument, the Coleman Electronic Photofluorometer shown in Figure 85, uses a mercury vapor lamp operated through an autotransformer from line voltage, a high vacuum phototube and automatic shutter, removable filters, and an electronic magnifier. Ordinary test tubes are used as cuvettes. This is a simple alternative to use of the spectrophotometer with ultraviolet illuminator.

Two models of Klett Fluorometers [7] are available, one for fluorometry only, the other adapted also to photometry. They use a 2-cell balanced circuit lighted by line current and a mercury lamp and have a suspension galvanometer as the null-point instrument, Figure 86. One is a modification of the Klett-Summerson colorimeter (p. 95).

The Spekker Fluorometer shown in Figure 87 is a null-point instrument. Ultraviolet light is furnished by a mercury vapor discharge lamp and a Wood's filter. One ray goes to the compensating photocell, the other through a calibrated variable aperture to the sample solution. The second photocell is near the sample solution and receives the fluorescence only. The same manufacturer offers the Hilger Vitameter A shown in Figure 88, designed solely for reading vitamin A.[8]

---

[3] Erich Loewenstein, *Ind. Eng. Chem., Anal. Ed.*, **15**, 658 (1943).

[4] N. C. Beese and J. W. Marsden, *J. Optical Soc. Am.*, **32**, 317-23 (1942).

[5] B. Tedeschi, *Atti. ist. veneto, sci.*, Pt. II, **100**, 13-36 (1941).

[6] Frederick Kavanaugh, *Ind. Eng. Chem., Anal. Ed.*, **13**, 108-11 (1941).

[7] F. Kavanagh, *Ind. Eng. Chem., Anal. Ed.*, **13**, 108-11 (1941).

[8] Frank Twyman and David H. Follett (Adam Hilger, Ltd.), British Patent 416,423 (1934).

Fig. 85. Coleman electronic photofluorometer

Fig. 86. Klett-Summerson fluorometer. (*Klett Manufacturing Co.*)

Another modifiable instrument is available from Pfaltz and Bauer, Inc., Figure 89. Primarily designed for fluorometry, by use of a low-

FIG. 87. Spekker photoelectric fluorometer. (*Adam Hilger, Ltd.*)

FIG. 88. Vitameter A. (*Adam Hilger, Ltd.*, London)

voltage tungsten bulb it is suitable for colorimetry. Permanent glass standards replace quinine sulfate and riboflavin as standards.

A design in the literature uses alternating current, vacuum photo-cells, and a conventional electronically stabilized, feedback amplifier.[9] Changing the lamp and filters of an inexpensive, compensating, two-photocell colorimeter converts it into a fluorometer.[10] The Beckman spectrophotometer may be modified for fluorometric purposes by providing a source of ultraviolet light and an optical cell compartment with filters. This adaptation uses the original receiving and amplifying system of the instrument and provides a sensitive method of measurement.[11]

FIG. 89.  Fluorometer.  (*Pfaltz & Bauer, Inc.*)

A simple instrument[12] with a test tube to hold the sample will measure the fluorescence with a barrier-layer cell and a high sensitivity galvanometer. Fluctuations of lamp intensity offer the main limitation to accuracy which is only one-tenth to one-fiftieth that of the galvanometer.[13] By use of a cuvette the accuracy of this design is increased.[14]

[9] Richard P. Krebs and H. J. Kersten, *Ind. Eng. Chem., Anal. Ed.,* **15,** 132-3 (1943).

[10] D. J. Hennessey and L. R. Cerecedo, *J. Am. Chem. Soc.,* **61,** 179-83 (1939); D. K. Froman and W. D. McFarlane, *Can. J. Research,* **18B,** 240-5 (1940); F. Kavanagh, *Ind. Eng. Chem., Anal. Ed.,* **13,** 108-11 (1941); A. H. Woodcock, *Can. J. Res.,* **19D,** 253-7 (1941).

[11] Mary H. Fletcher, Charles E. White and Milton S. Sheftel, *Ind. Eng. Chem., Anal. Ed.,* **18,** 204-5 (1946).

[12] R. F. Cohen, *Rev. tran. chim.,* **54,** 133-8 (1935).

[13] G. M. Hills, *Biochem. J.,* **33,** 1966-79 (1939).

[14] D. J. Hennessey and L. R. Cerecedo, *J. Am. Chem. Soc.,* **61,** 179-83 (1939); cf. D. B. Hand, *Ind. Eng. Chem., Anal. Ed.,* **11,** 306-9 (1939).

# CHAPTER XVI

## ACCURACY

OF THE factors limiting the accuracy of colorimetric methods, some are inherent in the nature of the comparison to be made and some in the specific procedure of a given determination. The limitations are much fewer for the series of standards and duplication methods than for the dilution method and balancing method. The photometric methods, especially when they become photoelectric, introduce a whole class of new possibilities of error inherent in the additional apparatus involved.

Colorimetric methods may be classified according to the reason for their use, which is in turn related to the accuracy expected. Some find their popularity because they are rapid. Accuracy is sacrificed for speed in obtaining the final result. A second class is used because it furnishes a method of determination of small amounts of substances with greater accuracy than is possible by gravimetric or volumetric methods. A third class contains methods where no gravimetric or volumetric method is available. Biological methods in particular are apt to be of this third class. Often the accuracy of this group is low, but that is not necessarily so. The determinations of the first class may all be carried out in a short time. It often happens that the method of preparation of the sample for the second and third classes takes hours to insure the accuracy desired. That colorimetric methods are in many cases more accurate for estimation of small quantities than the majority of volumetric or gravimetric methods is indicated by their use in specifications for the purity of chemicals.[1]

**General Limitations.**[2] For a colorimetric method to be accurate the color produced by the action of the given reagent on the test sub-stance should be the only color present in the solution. Therefore, a visual colorimetric estimation is frequently not possible if the original solution is colored, unless that color is produced by the test substance

---

[1] *A. C. S. Analytical Reagents; Specifications Recommended by the Committee on Analytical Reagents of the American Chemical Society*, 132 pp., American Chemical Society, Washington, D. C. (1941); cf. Edward Wichers, A. Q. Butler, W. D. Collins, P. H. Messinger, R. A. Osborn, Joseph Rosin, and J. F. Ross, *Ind. Eng. Chem., Anal. Ed.*, **16**, 281-8 (1944).

[2] R. Dolique, *Bull. soc. chim. biol.*, **17**, 1304-17 (1935); L. P. Romero and M. A. M. Romero, *pH* 1941, No. 23, 35-9.

or will be removed by the reagent used. In some particular instances, a slight contamination of one color may be equalized by coloring the standard. In a few types of determinations the color of the original solution is corrected by a similar colored layer in addition to the standard. Similarly, a colorimetric estimation is not usually possible if the solution to be examined contains anything other than the test substance which will give a precipitate or color with the given reagent. Occasionally, the bands are far enough apart so that by spectrophotometry or filter photometry one can be separated by filtering. A slight overlap in the latter case has been corrected by calculation.[3] It is desirable for the accuracy of these methods that the color produced be reasonably permanent and that the conditions under which it is produced be such that they can be duplicated without great difficulty. Thus, all or a standardized fraction of the test substance may be converted to the colored product. In an exceptional case comparisons of colors permanent for only 30 seconds have been successfully carried out.

Errors which would interfere in any analytical method, such as contamination in grinding,[4] separation of materials in sieving, and the like, are assumed to be substantially absent. Some errors in handling of small amounts, such as sorption in filtering or on glass during standing, can only be mentioned. If the test substance has a large molecular weight these errors can be important. Reaction with glass can usually be avoided by the use of Pyrex brand. The usual methods of concentration of very dilute samples and seperation of or from interfering substances are employed: precipitation of the test substance, precipitation of interfering substances, precipitation with a collector, electrodeposition, formation of a noninterfering complex with the interfering substance, sorption on a solid such as zeolite, extraction with an immiscible solvent, volatilization as in distillation of arsenic, antimonic, or germanic chlorides. Such separations are to be avoided, if possible, because they necessitate another operation which may introduce error.

**Limitations of Specific Methods.** Each of the following five types of methods is particularly applicable to certain special conditions, and not under other conditions.

The *Series of Standards Method* is the most widely applicable. If the color developed from the test substance fades, it can be estimated

---

3 Harold W. Knudson, Villiers W. Meloche and Chauncey Juday, *Ind. Eng. Chem., Anal. Ed.*, **12**, 715-19 (1940).

4 S. L. Hood, R. O. Parks and Charles Hurwitz, *Ind. Eng. Chem., Anal. Ed.*, **16**, 202-5 (1944).

by comparison with a series of standards prepared at the same time under the same conditions. This method does not assume that Beer's law holds.

The *Dilution Method* does not require that Beer's law should hold. Permanence for only a short time is necessary.

The *Balancing Method* depends on use of a variable thickness of layer instead of addition of water as in the dilution method. Beer's law is therefore assumed to hold. Ordinarily, the color developed must be reasonably permanent.

The *Absorption Method* accumulates the errors of reading in preparation of the standardization curves and in reading the sample. Instrumental errors may therefore be doubled, but as properly selected those errors are reduced in these methods. Beer's law need not hold.

The *Duplication Method,* as usually applied, is subject to the limitation that the color must develop at once and be permanent for a few minutes. It does not assume that Beer's law holds. If the color developed varies with the conditions under which mixing is carried out, this method cannot be used.

**Typical Sources of Error.** The following 16 sources of error would appear to be all inclusive:

1. Mechanical errors of the colorimeter.
2. Optical errors of the solutions.
3. Errors from varied light.
4. Errors in readings.
5. Errors of dilution.
6. Errors from varied temperatures.
7. Errors from varied times of standing.
8. Errors from variable quantities of chemicals present.
9. Errors from other solutes than the test substance present in the sample.
10. Unavoidable error of the individual operator.
11. Variable sensitivity of range.
12. Variable size of colloidal particles.
13. Dichromatism.
14. Turbidity.
15. Impurities in the reagents.
16. Errors in artificial standards.

With as varied sources of error as these it seems self-evident that calculations of the probable error in colorimetric methods[5] are incomplete.

**Mechanical Errors of the Colorimeter.** Errors due to inaccurate calibration can always be checked by comparison of two known solutions. This should be done with a new colorimeter before putting it into use, but the range of accuracy of the solutions used must be considered.

With the photoelectric colorimeter of any type, this introduces the possible lag of the photoelectric cell in reaching equilibrium, variable sensitivity of the cell in different ranges, reading of fluorescence by the tube if the fluorescence is in a range to which the tube is more or less sensitive than to the primary wave band,[6] change in luminosity of the light source with age of the usual bulb, and possible damage to the galvanometer or other instruments. These have been discussed in some detail under those types of instruments. Multiple reflections within the instrument must be avoided, a factor varying in different types of instruments. Unless the filters are matched within the accuracy of reading, care must be taken that they are not interchanged. Filters must be heat-stable, not of selenium glass for example.

In the types having two cups or two cuvettes, care must be taken that they are not interchanged due to possible variations in thickness of the bottoms or the space between the sides respectively. Provision must be made for exact replacement of the cup or cell in successive determinations. Dust in the eyepiece or stains on the cups or cuvettes will cause errors. Reflectors and color filters must likewise be free from dust or other deposits, and must be handled with care to avoid scratching. Depending on the design of the colorimeter as to detail, there is always a way of checking the zero point before using the instrument to be sure that no mechanical accident has altered it since last used. But the original zero point must have been right. Accuracy and reproducibility are not the same thing. An instrument which is out of adjustment may give totally inaccurate values which are faithfully reproducible at that degree of maladjustment. Only careful checking of the original calibration can insure accuracy.

---

5 Anders Ringbom, *Z. anal. Chem.*, **115**, 332-43 (1939); A. Schleicher, *Ibid.*, **125**, 386-405 (1943).

6 Kasson S. Gibson, *Proc. Am. Soc. Testing Materials*, **44**, 725-32 (1944).

**Optical Errors of the Solutions.** These may arise from color in the solution other than that of the test substance. Methods are usually so chosen as to prevent such errors. Other and more important errors are inherent in the design of instruments. In order that colors which appear identical may actually be so, they must be viewed at equal distances, and the lines of the major axes of the two must intersect at a point slightly behind the center of the retina. This is impossible of attainment, since optically a cylinder appears as a truncated cone. The condition is approached in practice by having the cylinders at a considerable distance from the eye. When an instrument is used for comparison the condition is further approached by close juxtaposition of portions of the centers of the fields at substantially equal distances from the eyepiece. If depths and cross sections are identical and observed at equal and reasonable distances from the eye the errors of optical distribution may be ignored.

When the cross section varies but the depth is the same, by viewing a limited area in the center of standard and sample the errors of cross section do not appear. When the depths of the two solutions vary, as in some instrumental work, other optical errors may arise. It is conceivable that the apparent size of molecules may vary, according to the same law that governs optical size of objects, inversely as the square of the distance from the point of vision. This can neither be proved nor disproved, hence the assumption is made for balancing and dilution methods that different columns of liquids of the same apparent tint contain the same number of molecules.

In equal colors of unequal depth, more molecules will be behind each other in the longer column than in the shorter. This is ignored and is a possible source of error in comparing a standard with a sample of widely varying concentration. It is minimized in practice by having the concentrations of the two reasonably close.

The proper shape of container for the solution is a section of a hollow sphere with the point of vision coinciding with the center. In comparing fairly long columns this condition is approximated. In comparing shallow solutions the error becomes greater and an appreciable difference in color between the edge and center of the field can be detected.

In case of considerable variation in concentration the following error[7] has been shown:

---
[7] William M. Dehn, *J. Am. Chem. Soc.*, **39**, 1392-9 (1917).

$a$ = distance from nearer surface

$a + b$ = distance from further surface

$r$ = radius of nearer surface

$c$ = distance that radius of nearer surface is moved toward the further surface

The ratio of the viewed volumes is assumed to be

$$1 : b - c/b \tag{I}$$

The actual ratio is

$$1 : \frac{a^2(a + b)^3 - (a + c)^3}{(a + c)^2(a + b)^3 - a^3} \tag{II}$$

If $a = 2$, $b = 2$ nd $c = 1$ the ratio according to equation I is $1:0.500$ and according to equation II is $1:0.290$, an error of 42 per cent. At $a = 20$, $b = 2$, $c = 1$ the ratio according to I is $1:0.475$ or equal to the assumed limitation of the colorimeter.

In the photoelectric colorimeter the tube is sufficiently far from the cuvette to minimize such errors, even though a very thin cell may be used.

**Errors from Varied Light.** Below a threshold level, which varies for different wave lengths, the precision with which the solutions in two tubes can be matched decreases as some direct function of the intensity of lighting. If two colors being compared are not alike in quality the results with varied light differ greatly; comparison of such solutions is not satisfactory at best. Considering possible qualities such as light from a blue sky, the brassy sky of summer, high white light, fog light, dark-cloud light, and the dull light of rainy days, it is not surprising that individual estimations may vary with the light. Variations of the same operator on the same method may range from 1 per cent to 10 per cent on different days, a powerful argument for standardization on the use of artificial light. Another comparison[8] of multiband vs. single wave length using the balancing method indicates 17 per cent error with white light, 3.3 per cent with filtered light and 2.0 per cent with monochromatic. Optimum conditions for accuracy were not selected. The use of color filters appreciably improves the accuracy with the Duboscq type of instrument[9] and the same factor of accurate selection of a narrow wave band makes spectrophotometric methods, whether of the full or abridged type, more accurate in this particular source of

[8] J. E. R. Winkler, *Schweiz. Arch. angew. Wiss. Tech.*, **6**, 199-201 (1940).

[9] W. D. Armstrong, *Ind. Eng. Chem., Anal. Ed.*, **5**, 300-2 (1933).

error. Spectrophotometers vary in the degree of accuracy with which the same band can be selected on different days.

The light of the sun that reaches us is more yellow than the original, due to some absorption of blue by the atmosphere. Blue skylight is the opposite extreme, with light reflected from white clouds intermediate. The evening sky and the light on misty days and in the city is often more yellow than direct sunlight. It is feasible to remove some of the red end of the spectrum from artificial light to duplicate sunlight but not to add blue light to make up the deficiency.

Many practical forms of lighting equipment are available. A light in a box, painted white inside and provided with a slit by which the light can illuminate the mirror of the colorimeter, is satisfactory. In some cases a microscope illuminator will serve the purpose, but it is better to have a colorimeter light such as those shown in Figure 90. There is an accelerated trend toward built-in lights in colorimeters and nearly all photoelectric instruments standardize on artificial light as a matter of course. As one type, a spiral of 6-mm. neon tubing, 45 mm. long and 35 mm. in external diameter, has been used with suitable glass filters as a light source.[10]

With photoelectric instruments, only careful choice of operating conditions can insure the highest accuracy, even if the best instruments are used. In a visual spectrophotometer the percentage error is at a minimum at an absorption between 1.5 and 2; in photoelectric instruments, at about 0.43.[11] Theoretically, photoelectric methods give much greater sensitivity of discrimnation than the eye. A simple and relatively inexpensive photoelectric instrument [12] properly used can be as accurate as a spectrophotometer for the relative measurements required for most colorimetric methods. There are exceptions.

**Errors in Readings.** Nearly all visual methods in the range for which they are designed claim an accuracy of 5 per cent or better. The sensitivity of perception of color varies in different wave lengths with green read most easily. However, generalization can lead to confusion. Thus, in promotion of photoelectric instruments the probable error in use of Nessler tubes has been rated at 3-8 per cent,[13] with the Duboscq instrument but little better. In contrast it is not uncommon to find the

---

[10] F. L. Matthews, R. H. Crist and A. Knoll, *Ind. Eng. Chem., Anal. Ed.,* **11,** 503 (1939).

[11] F. Twyman and G. F. Lothian, *Proc. Physical Soc.,* **45,** 643 (1933).

[12] N. Stafford, *Ann. Repts. Chem. Soc.,* **33,** 456-65 (1936).

[13] A. Thiel, *Ber.,* **68,** 1015 (1935); *Z. anal. Chem.,* **106,** 281 (1936).

accuracy of reading of photoelectric instruments estimated at 0.1 per cent. Aside from question as to the accuracy of such estimates in many cases, they relate only to reproducibility of readings in the range of maximum sensitivity. Thus, for maximum accuracy the galvanometer reading should fall in the central portion of the scale.[14] The relative significance of error in various ranges is shown in Fig. 91. It is probably a fair, general estimate that visual instrumental methods averaging several readings are accurate to 2 per cent, occasionally to 1 per cent, and that photoelectric methods under optimum

FIG. 90. Tag colorimeter stand and daylight illuminator with Saybolt chromometer in place. (*C. J. Taghabue Mfg. Co.*, Brooklyn, N. Y.)

Colorimeter lamp for attachment directly to colorimeter. (*Bausch & Lomb*)

[14] Robert H. Hamilton, *Ind. Eng. Chem.*, *Anal. Ed.*, **16**, 123-6 (1944).

conditions are susceptible of accuracy to much better than 1 per cent. When high accuracy is important and the range of maximum sensitivity is unknown it is desirable to compare at two or more different concentrations of sample and standard, or to read photoelectrically at more than one concentration.

When the accuracy of readings is in question, usually due to variations of the system from Beer's law and to individual error, a correction curve should be constructed. To do this, take a known solution of the test substance to be used. Prepare a series of dilutions such as 2.0, 1.8, 1.6, 1.4, 1.2, 0.8, 0.6, and 0.4 times the strength to be adopted as a reference standard. This reference standard is conveniently half that of the original solution. Adopt a height of reference standard similar to that of the unknowns to be tested and compare it against each of the diluted standards and a portion of the reference standard. The values obtained can then be plotted in comparison with the theoretical straight line, and deviations determined. Similar curves for 10, 15 and 20 mm. depths of reference standard are desirable. Provided these do not coincide with the reference standard, and they usually do over a fair range, the values can be correctly read from

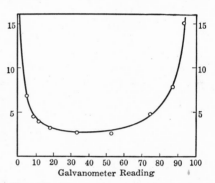

FIG. 91. Percentage error in results at various galvanometer readings from an error of 1 unit in reading the galvanometer

the curves so determined, rather than taken on the assumption that Beer's law holds. The alternative and preferable procedure is to discard all results outside of the range in which Beer's law is so shown to hold experimentally, provided it holds at all. The deviations from Beer's law will ordinarily follow the same formula as do nephelometric corrections (p. 118).

Published curves for correction values should not be used as they fail to account for factors which are difficult to define but which are probably partially inherent in the individual operator and his instrument.

In attempting to attain a high degree of acuracy by colorimetric methods, due account must be taken of other errors inherent in the methods. Accuracy to 0.1 per cent in such calibration curves is hardly justifiable if the concentration of unknown and the nature of the method prohibit accurate reading to closer than 5 per cent. Such deviations will be apparent in the construction of the correction curves. Construction of such curves is valuable experience for the student, or the analyst lacking experience with colorimetric methods.

It is desirable to avoid methods by which factors for formulae are worked out and used, as there is a tendency to over-extend the use of such formulae, a thing improbable when a visual comparison of the curves must be made. Substitution in Kober's formula $K = x(xy - s)/s(x - 1)$ permits comparison of curves obtained at different levels by the same worker or different workers. In this formula $y$ is the reading of the solution varied, $x$ the ratio of the concentrations of the known and unknown, and $s$ the setting for the solution which is not varied. This leaves only $K$, a constant for the solution being compared provided the values fall on a straight line.

**Errors of Dilution.** In many cases it is impossible to choose a sample having as small a content of the test substance as specified in the method, particularly if the substance being analyzed is an ore or alloy containing a fairly large percentage of the test substance. In that case the sample may be taken containing more of the test substance than specified for the method and dissolved as directed. This solution may then be accurately diluted and an aliquot taken. If the method specifies that a sample must contain less than 0.001 gram of the test substance and the smallest sample of the substance which can conveniently be weighed will contain nearly 0.1 gram of test substance, this may be dissolved as specified and diluted to one liter in a volumetric flask. Ten ml. of this may then be treated as directed. The weight of test substance found in that amount of solution multiplied by 100 will give the amount in the original sample.

When it is necessary to use such a method the final result cannot be as accurate in regard to the absolute amount of test substance by weight, but the results are as accurate so far as the percentage error is concerned. As an illustration, accuracy to 5 per cent with a weight of sample containing 0.001 gram of test substance would permit an error of 0.00005 gram of the test substance. If the sample contained 0.5 gram of test substance, an amount greater than would ordinarily be present in a weight of sample used, the corresponding accuracy to 5 per cent would permit an error of 0.025 gram. In the second case the amount of test substance in the sample is 500 times as large and the possible error in grams 500 times as great. Since comparion is by the same method, the larger sample being diluted for the purpose, the percentage error is the same in each.

The rapidity with which colorimetric readings may be made often admits of the attainment of considerably greater accuracy than estimated, by rapidly taking several readings and averaging the results obtained.

It is always desirable by the balancing method to compare a sample with a standard having a content of test substance varying from that of the sample by not over 50 per cent. In many cases the difference must be less. When several standards are available, a closer one can be selected. This depends on stability of the color developed, time required for preparation of standard, and effect of dilution on sample or standard. The only general rule which can be stated is that the accuracy of the balancing method will be greater if the standard does not differ greatly in concentration from that of the sample.

In some cases the solute molecule itself may be ionized and the color measured is that of one of the ions. In such a case the assumption is that ionization occurs to the same degree in standard and sample being measured. In general, this is correct. More commonly, the solute molecule is little, if at all, ionized.

**Errors from Varied Temperatures.** In many determinations the sample and standard are heated until the maximum intensity of color has been developed. In such cases the maximum color reached may vary with temperature. The intensity of color is also sometimes affected by the temperature of the solution being compared. If comparison is made with a standard which has been standing, the temperature of standard and sample may not be the same and may result in error. In some cases a change in intensity or quality of color with temperature has been noted in the outline of the method.

**Errors from Varied Times of Standing.** In many determinations the color develops only after standing for a definite period and sometimes starts to fade after reaching the optimum. If the comparison is made before sufficient time has expired, erroneous estimations are obtained against artificial standards. Such reactions are usually a matter of temperature, so that standing for five minutes in a room at 15° may not give at all the result of five minutes at 25°. This type of error may be avoided by preparation of the same quantity of sample and standard at the same time.

**Errors from Variable Quantities of Chemicals Present.** In many cases the color is influenced by the amount of chemicals added in the preparation of the sample or in development of the color. If the standard does not contain the same kinds and amounts of neutral salts as the sample, this may lead to error. In the development of color the concentration of reagent should not differ in sample and standard. In many cases the mass-action effect of a large excess of reagent will tend to darken the color. An example of this is one of the oldest colorimetric methods, that for ferric iron with thiocyanate. The general chemistry experiment whereby the intensity of red color is increased by addition of more thiocyanate, or lessened by addition of ammonium salts, is clearly a mass-action effect. The reaction is expressed in simple but not necessarily accurate form by the following equation.

$$FeR_3 + 3NH_4CNS \rightleftarrows Fe(CNS)_3 + 3NH_4R$$

If the structure of the colored material derived from the test substance permits, there may be different equilibria between the quinoid and benzoid forms and different degrees of hydration of the molecule. For many reactions careful control of the pH value is essential.

These errors are avoided by careful standardization of the method. In some cases the effect of variable concentration of reagent or of hydrolysis due to variable concentration of test substance is to produce dichromatic or polychromatic changes, after which the standard and sample are not comparable.

Since the maximum intensity of color is desired with the minimum amount of test substance, it follows that the use of inner complex structures is most effective.[15] The smaller the degree of dissociation the less the effect of variation of color with difference in amounts of reagents.

**Errors from Other Solutes Than the Test Substance Present in the Sample.** If the reaction used is a general rather than a specific one, the result obtained may be greatly in error. This is avoided as far as possible by naming the interfering substances. Cresol gives the same reaction with phosphotungstate as phenol. When both are present, neither can be accurately determined.

Phosphorus, silica and arsenic all give the same type of yellow color with molybdate reagent. Therefore, if arsenic is present, phosphorus cannot be determined by the molybdate method. The effect of iron alone or of phosphate alone on molybdate solutions used for estimation of silica is entirely different from the combined influence of the two, and from the effect of iron in the presence of silica. Broad statements that

---

[15] A. K. Babko, *Trudy Vzesoyuz. Konferentsii Anal. Khim.*, **2**, 227-32 (1943).

certain ions do not interfere because they do not react with the reagent are therefore unjustified, unless it is known that they also do not react with each other or with the test substance to form compounds which do react with the reagent.

The effect of alien ions present may take varied forms. In some cases they simply develop a similar color as in the examples just cited. In other cases they react with the reagent to give interfering turbidity. It is not unusual for them to react with the reagent to give a colorless compound and reduce the amount of reagent present to react with the test substance. They may react by oxidation or reduction with either the test substance or the reagent. They may react with the product of the reagent and test substance to cause fading.

Possible methods of avoidance, aside from removal of the interfering ions, are to filter out rays from the interfering substance and correct for it, to restrain the effect of the interfering substance by pH adjustment, or to transform the interfering ion into a complex.

In many cases of colloidal dispersions of test substances the size of aggregate will be affected by the kind and concentration of dissolved salts. An example is colloidal lead sulfide. This method although widely used is often unsatisfactory, giving yellow to brown colors in many cases which cannot be matched, because of variation in the salt effect of dissolved substances. To some extent this effect is overcome by addition of a protective colloid. The equal concentration of all chemicals in sample and standard is as important with colloidal sols as with true solutes.

Interference due to the natural color of a solution may occasionally be corrected by similarly coloring the standard comparison solution. A more satisfactory method is to superimpose the colored solution over the standard. This permits using a portion of the sample itself and is correspondingly more accurate. This principle is applied in the block comparator (p. 23).

In the last analysis, errors from this source may arise which are difficult to detect because of the presence of undetermined materials other than the test substance in the sample. If the test substance is one which can be isolated in a sufficient state of purity, comparing known amounts in solutions which contain possible interfering substances which may occur in the sample solution demonstrates the interference or noninterference of the latter. Some methods, mainly biological, are used as a matter of necessity without the effect of accompanying substances being known. Where substances are known to interfere, their effects are quoted with the method.

An exception to this source of error is that sometimes addition of another color will improve the sensitivity.[16] Thus, the amount of fuchsin to produce the same shade rather than intensity in a sample and standard of potassium dichromate is applied by the formula $x = C(a_x/a_c)$ where $C$ is the concentration of the standard, $a_x$ and $a_c$ are the volumes of the same fuchsin solution added to unknown and standard. In general, add red or blue to yellow or greenish yellow solutions, which are in the region of low sensitivity of the eye.

**Unavoidable Error of the Individual Operator.**[17] These errors are avoided by careful training of the operator and by checking of his accuracy by other operators. Thus, difficulty reported in reading flour color by variable sensitivity of different observers [18] could probably be overcome by training. Avoiding eye fatigue due to long continued operation is essential to accuracy. The best time of observation is of the order of 3-5 seconds; a series of short observations are preferable to prolonged gazing at a color. To avoid eye fatigue the intensity of illumination should not be greater than is necessary to make observations. The eye not in use should not be closed and a wearer of spectacles should not remove them, unless other means are provided for the correction of the eye.

Color blindness does not necessarily bar a man from colorimetry, as it usually exists for only a limited range of wave lengths and gives the man unusual accuracy in other wave bands. Some color is usually present in the range to which the eye is sensitive. Consequently changes are detected, and provided the transmission of the sample and standard are the same, accuracy may be expected to be limited only to the extent that the intensities being measured are less than the normal. This statement does not apply to visual spectrophotometry or abridged photometry where all the color may be in the wave bands to which the operator is blind. Gross errors may easily occur with artificial standards or in any case where standard and sample do not have the same form of transmission curve.[19] Color ignorance on the part of new workers, although important in classification of colors, does not affect their value in colorimetry. All people not color blind are normal after training,

---

16 E. K. Nikitin and V. I. Tikhonova, *J. Applied Chem.* (U.S.S.R.), **11**, 347-51 (1938).

17 A. J. Younger, *Phil. Mag.*, **19**, 1107-15 (1935).

18 H. K. Parker, *J. Assoc. Official Agr. Chem.*, **19**, 569-73 (1936).

19 F. Twyman and G. F. Lothian, *Proc. Phys. Soc.*, **45**, 643 (1936).

differences between individuals being due to physical conditions or lack of training.

So far as color blindness is concerned the photoelectric colorimeter is a complete answer. The photoelectric colorimeter is itself color blind in that two colors which appear the same to the eye may record quite differently photoelectrically. Therefore, the photoelectric instrument must never be used to compare with artificial standards. There are even arguments that visual instruments can be more accurate than photo-electric.[20]

**Variable Sensitivity of Range.** The assumption is sometimes made that a colorimetric method is equally sensitive throughout its entire range. That this is incorrect is indicated by consideration. If a method will just detect the difference between 0.001 and 0.0008 mg. of test substance it is impossible that it will detect the difference between 0.1000 and 0.9998 mg. On the other hand, the difference between 0.1000 and 0.0800 mg. should be much greater than between 0.001 and 0.0008 mg. It therefore appears that the law as to sensitivity is that of Weber, "The increment in stimulus that produces a just perceptible difference in sensation is always the same fraction of the total stimulus."

This factor has been studied quantitatively for solutions in the usual colorimetric range. The sensitivity of a colorimetric method has been defined as the reciprocal of the weight in milligrams of test substance which can just be differentiated with certainty. A more practical defi-nition of sensitivity, one more commonly used, is the difference expressed in weight, which can normally be detected over the range of concentration in which the method is applied. The personal equation may be disre-garded. The ease of determination may be measured by the variation from the mean when two concentrations are compared, with and without intermediate shades to aid in the comparison. Both the sensitivity and the ease of determination vary with the concentration. It is usually easier to distinguish a difference between two colors than between colorless and colored.

The following illustrates the variation in range of a typical color. With ammoniacal copper sulfate in concentrated solution, the fraction of the whole needed to detect a change in color is 5.5 per cent; in the inter-mediate range it is only 1 per cent; and in the dilute range it varies and becomes very large. This explains the variations in sensitivity found by different investigators with the same reaction, and to some extent the

[20] Benedikt Mader, *Chem. Tech.*, **16**, 165-7 (1943).

large variations in sensitivity between different methods, when the range has not been investigated in detail. Solutions of dyes have also been found to show perceptible differences according to a geometric series.

**Variable Size of Colloidal Particles.** In a much greater number of cases than usually indicated, the problem is one of measurement of a suspended precipitate which is either too fine for nephelometric measurement or else colorimetric measurement is preferred. Sulfide methods for copper and lead are good examples. According to all of our reasoning, these salts, insofar as they dissolve, are ionized and uncolored or slightly colored. The suspended colloid is therefore the source of color. Of some 20 inorganic methods picked at random, about 50 per cent will give a precipitate on addition of sufficient reagent to sufficient test substance. It is reasonable to expect that at an intermediate stage there is a colloidal dispersion.

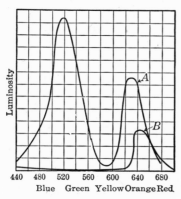

440  480  520  560  600  640  680
Blue  Green  Yellow Orange Red

FIG. 92 [21]. Luminosity curves, calculated by means of the transmission, the relative energy of standard white light and the relative visibility

In many cases the procedures used provide for a protective colloid or stabilizer. This may be of the neutral colloid type such as gelatin, gum acacia (arabic), starch, or egg albumin, or of the solution link-type such as hydrogen sulfide, ferric chloride and others. Such protective colloids cause and preserve greater uniformity in particle size where colloidal solutions are being compared colorimetrically. In many cases colorimetric comparison without them would be impossible.

**Dichromatism.** If the color of a solution is composed of two or more maxima of luminosity, and if the rate of change of these maxima is not the same, dichromatism occurs. A typical case is bromocresol purple at pH 7.6 The curve A in Figure 92 is obtained at a low concentration. If the depth of the solution be increased to 10 times that of the original, or if the concentration be multiplied by 10, the curve B is obtained. The curve A represents a blue or blue-green with a red tinge. Curve B is red.

Another effect is to be predicted for any test substance where one ion and the molecule are colored. If the molecule were yellow and the ion blue, the color of the solution would vary from yellow through green

---

[21] William Mansfield Clark, Determination of Hydrogen Ions, 3rd. Ed., p. 162, Williams and Wilkins Co., Baltimore, Md. (1928).

to blue according to the concentration of the solution. It follows that comparison of sample and standard at concentrations differing to any considerable extent would be impossible. A deep column of dilute solution would be blue, a shallow column of more concentrated solution would be green.

Dichromatism is not usual with natural standards but occurs with Nessler reagent. A solution of bichromate is another example; in dilute solution it is apparently a pure yellow; in more concentrated solution red lines are also present.

This dichromatism may be intensified or lessened by the use of artificial illuminants which are in general rich in red waves and deficient in blue. Thus, a dichromatic indicator will be redder in such artificial light and less blue. In many cases errors due to dichromatism are avoided by use of color filters for the comparison, the interfering color being absent from the colored light used. As an example, blue or yellow solutions may be compared in the light of a mercury arc to eliminate the red waves.

**Turbidity.** In a turbid solution there is some light which has entered, not been obstructed by any particle, and passed upward through the entire depth of the column. In addition, some light has entered from the side and been reflected by the particles, unless the sides of the tubes are opaque. Light entering from the side has passed through a lesser depth of column and therefore less absorption has occurred. The color registered by the eye is consequently greater than it would be if all the light reaching it had traveled through the full depth of the column of solution. Thus, sera and plasma may appear clear to the eye and yet have sufficient turbidity to cause gross error.

Correction for turbidity by addition of a similar turbidity to the standard is at best a poor substitute. The standard may be corrected by superimposing a turbid sample according to the Walpole technic (p. 22), although this, too, has several defects. The accuracy attainable in colorimetric technic with a turbid solution is therefore strictly limited. By adaptation of an integrating-sphere colorimeter, results are independent of turbidity.[22]

**Purity of Reagents.** It is almost unnecessary to add that all reagents used should be free from the test substance. This is usually checked by a blank determination, as no reagent can be considered to be above

[22] A. Dognon, *Rev. optique*, **19**, 205-12 (1940); *Compt. rend. soc. biol.*, **135**, 113-15 (1941).

suspicion until its purity has been proved when working with such small quantities. Although analytical reagents made to American Chemical Society standards should always be used there is hardly a chemist who has not traced at some time otherwise unexplainable results to contamination.

**Errors in Artificial Standards.** This has already received some specific discussion with respect to liquid standards (p. 59).

There is a tendency to use standardized sets of color glasses because of their convenience. If accurately calibrated, they may be entirely satisfactory. Several difficulties are to be noted. It is difficult to secure a permanent standard which will match the test solution over the entire range of dilution. Calibration of glass standards is difficult and expensive. Duplication of standards is difficult. At best, a set of glass standards apply only at a definite concentration of reagent, with interfering substances absent, so that they can be used only if the method is operating perfectly smoothly.

The spectral absorption curves of secondary standards, whether glasses or solutions, may be far different from those of the primary standards, even though apparently identical to the eye.[23] Only if the wave-length distribution of the secondary standard approximated that of the primary standard would this factor disappear.[24] This can only be determined by comparison of spectrophotometric distribution curves, and such distribution is exceedingly rare. It can occur as in the example of potassium chromate and silicomolybdic acid [25] shown in Figure 44 (p. 60).

**Importance of Sources of Error.** The sources of error have been discussed at length, mainly to provide a warning of the necessary factors to be considered in the development of new methods and to show why the procedure is so exactly defined in many cases. The operator, in using a colorimetric method, can only justify changes from the prescribed procedure when it is known, preferably by experimental determination, that an error will not be introduced by such changes. Many of the methods in the literature do not fully account for all of the possible sources of error.

---

[23] J. P. Mehlig and M. G. Mellon, *J. Phys. Chem.*, 35, 3397-3414 (1931); A. L. Bacharach and E. Lester Smith, *Analyst*, 59, 70-81 (1934).

[24] H. W. Swank and M. G. Mellon, *Ind. Eng. Chem., Anal. Ed.*, 6, 348-50 (1934); William D. McFarlane, *Ibid.*, 8, 124-6 (1936).

[25] M. G. Mellon, *Colorimetry for Chemists*, p. 25, G. Frederick Smith Chemical Co., Columbus, Ohio (1945).

# CHAPTER XVII

# CALCULATIONS

**Series of Standards.** When a series of standards is used the volumes of sample and standards should be the same, and the weight of test substance in the unknown estimated by the amount in the standard to which it corresponds. The percentage or the weight of test substance per unit volume is then readily calculated from this by dividing by the weight of sample used and multiplying by 100.

**Dilution Method.** The calculation of results when the dilution method is used is more complex. The darker of the two solutions is diluted until the colors of the two are identical when observed horizontally through tubes of uniform diameter. At this stage the content of test substance per milliliter is the same and the total content of test substance of one is to that of the other directly as their volumes. To illustrate:

Weight of standard used, 0.1 gram
Weight of unknown used, 0.2 gram
'Standard contains 0.16 per cent of test substance
Readings, standard 38 ml., unknown 45 ml.

This is estimated as follows:

Per cent in standard × weight of standard: Per cent in unknown × weight of unknown = volume of standard:

Volume of unknown.

$$0.016:0.2x = 38:45$$

$$7.6x = 0.72 \qquad\qquad x = 0.0947$$

Therefore, the sample being tested contains 0.0947 per cent of test substance.

Calculation of results by the dilution method does not always resolve itself into a mere comparison of percentage values, since frequently a known volume of standard solution with a known content of test substance per milliliter, is used as the standard. In that case, the weight of test substance in the standard must be calculated. From that, the weight in the sample and then the percentage present in the sample can be calculated. The method follows:

Weight of sample used = 2 grams
Standard used = 20 ml. of a solution containing 0.00002 gram of test substance per ml.
Readings, standard 20 ml., unknown 48 ml.

From the readings above, it follows that in this case the color of the sample was darker than that of the standard and therefore the sample was diluted. There would be no change in the method of calculation if the standard had been diluted.

Weight of test substance in standard: Weight of test substance in unknown = volume of standard: volume of unknown.
Weigh of test substance in standard is 20 × 0.00002 = 0.0004 gram.

$$0.0004 : x = 20 : 48$$
$$x = 0.00096$$

Therefore, the two grams of sample used contained 0.00096 gram of test substance and the percentage in the sample was 0.048.

**Balancing Method.** Results obtained by the balancing method are somewhat more complicated to calculate. When the two tubes are balanced the color observed vertically is the same but the depths of solutions are not necessarily identical. This method is applicable only if Beer's law holds. The tubes are calibrated in millimeters of depth, except in a few instruments which read in milliliters. These values may be substituted for millimeter of depth.

An example follows:

Weight of sample = 2 grams
Volume of sample after solution before addition to tube $A$ = 50 ml.
Height of sample in tube $A$ = 7.3 mm.
Height of standard in $B$ to balance = 8.4 mm.
Content of standard per ml. = 0.00001 gram of test substance

When the colors of $A$ and $B$ are balanced the concentrations of the solutions are inversely proportional to the height of the columns, thus:

Test substance per ml. in $A$ : test substance per ml. in $B$ = depth of liquid in $B$ : depth of liquid in $A$

$$x : 0.00001 = 8.4 : 7.3$$

$x = 0.0000115$ gram test substance per ml. in sample solution.

Then the total test substance in the sample is

$$50 \times 0.0000115 = 0.000575 \text{ gram}$$

This is 0.0002875 gram per gram of sample and the sample therefore contained 0.02875 per cent of test substance.

The general formula[1] for balancing-method calculations is

$$x = \frac{F}{R} \times S \times \frac{V_u}{V_s} \times \frac{D_2}{D_1} \times \frac{1}{V}$$

In this

$x$ = concentration of unknown in same terms as $S$
$F$ = scale reading of standard in mm.
$R$ = scale reading of unknown in mm.
$S$ = concentration of standard in standard terms
$V_u$ = volume of unknown solution matched against standard
$V_s$ = volume of standard solution matched
$D_1$ = volume of unknown taken for analysis
$D_2$ = volume to which $D_1$ was diluted when color was developed
$V$ = volume of $D_1$ taken for color development

In routine work this simplifies down to $x = (F/R) \times S$, or this multiplied by a simple factor, since the remaining terms are selected to give 1 or a small whole number for simplicity of calculation.

It is always advisable to select samples, particularly for routine work, so that calculations involved are only multiplication of readings obtained, by some simple factor. Manipulation by the balancing method is usually standardized at some setting of the standard and only the unknowns varied. In that case, a table or curve can be conveniently used for reading the concentration of test substance directly.

**Duplication Method.** Results by the method of duplication, sometimes called colorimetric titration are readily estimated. A standard solution is added to a blank containing the same reagents as the sample until the color of the sample is matched. Water and standard are then cautiously added, alternately, until the volume as well as the color of the two solutions is identical. The result as to how much test substance is present in the sample is given by the amount necessary to form an identical standard. The percentage in the sample is then calculated as follows:

---

[1] A. R. Rose, *Proc. Soc. Exp. Biol. Med.*, **23**, 219-20 (1925).

Weight of sample = 5 grams

Standard used contains 0.0002 gram of test substance per ml.

Volume of standard used for duplication = 2.3 ml.

Then, the total test substance used in preparation of the duplicate
was 2.3 × 0.0002 = 0.00046 gram.

Therefore, the sample contained 0.00046 ÷ 5 grams of test substance
per gram of sample or 0.000092, which is 0.0092 per cent.

**Absorbency or Transmittance Methods.** These methods give results with a minimum of calculation. If absorbency or the reverse value

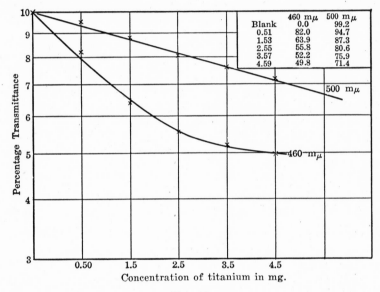

| | 460 mμ | 500 mμ |
|---|---|---|
| Blank | 0.0 | 99.2 |
| 0.51 | 82.0 | 94.7 |
| 1.53 | 63.9 | 87.3 |
| 2.55 | 55.8 | 80.6 |
| 3.57 | 52.2 | 75.9 |
| 4.59 | 49.8 | 71.4 |

FIG. 93

transmittance is plotted against concentration, on a linear-linear scale,
a curved line is always obtained. If the log of transmittance is plotted
against concentration and Beer's law holds, the result will be a straight
line. A convenient expedient for accomplishing the latter is to plot the
value of the transmittance on log-linear paper.

The curves shown in Figure 93 for titanium by the peroxide method
are selected because they illustrate that at one wave length, the 500 mμ
curve, the system may conform to Beer's law, yet at another wave length,
460 mμ, the slope of the curve is sharper, and even though the system
does not conform to Beer's law, results of greater accuracy can be read.
The results were obtained with a Coleman spectrophotometer. In Fig-

ure 94 a better curve is obtained on the same instrument at 700 m$\mu$ for the blue silicomolybdate. The correction for a reagent blank is included in the curve, that is, the straight line does not pass through the origin.

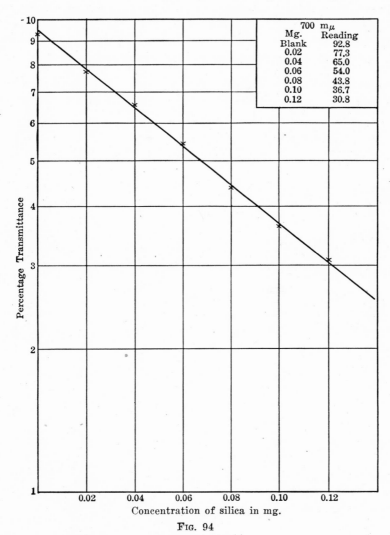

| 700 m$\mu$ | |
|---|---|
| Mg. | Reading |
| Blank | 92.8 |
| 0.02 | 77.3 |
| 0.04 | 65.0 |
| 0.06 | 54.0 |
| 0.08 | 43.8 |
| 0.10 | 36.7 |
| 0.12 | 30.8 |

Concentration of silica in mg.

Fig. 94

The curve is therefore valid only for the particular lot of reagents for which it was developed.

Identical curves would be obtained if the log transmittance were plotted on linear-linear paper and a companion curve of the same slope if log absorbency or extinction were plotted. This is illustrated in Figure 2.

Assume that a sample of 0.2 gram had been dissolved and made up to 1 liter, as had also the standards from which the curve was developed. A transmittance reading shows 57.3 From the curve this is 0.053 mg. of titanium. The percentage in the sample was therefore 0.0265 per cent. By far the majority of results are read in this way.

The alternative to such reading of the curve is to read the log transmittance from the instrument, having established that it is a straight line. This method will be applied to Figure 94. The first and last points covering a range of 0.12 mg. give these data:

$$\begin{array}{ll} \text{Logarithm of 92.8} & 1.96755 \\ \text{Logarithm of 30.8} & 1.48855 \\ \hline & \text{Difference } 0.47900 \end{array}$$

The logarithmic change in transmittance per mg. is 0.479/0.12 = 3.99. This is 0.0399 per 0.01 mg. which, within the accuracy of the method, would usually be taken as 0.04.

The blank is then equivalent to $2 - 1.96755 = 0.03245$ and $0.03245/0.04 = 0.00811$ mg. Given a reading of the log of the transmittance of 1.75815 the calculation can be applied as follows:

$$2 - 1.75815 = 0.24185$$
$$0.24185/0.04 = 6.046$$

This times 0.01 = 0.06046 mg. total titanium. Therefore,

$$0.06046 - 0.00811 = 0.05235 \text{ mg. of titanium in the sample.}$$

This will be seen to be the same value previously read from the curve as 0.053 mg.

The calculation from Beer's law can also be carried out from the molecular extinction coefficient as follows:[2]

Weight of sample = 0.2517 gram.

Transmittance of solution at 580m$\mu$ = 52.1 per cent
Transmittance of solvent at 580m$\mu$ = 89.1 per cent
Molecular extinction coefficient, $\Sigma$ = 52.99
Cell length — 1.958 cm.

$$(1) \qquad c = \frac{\log \dfrac{I_1}{I_2}}{\Sigma l} \text{ moles per liter}$$

[2] J. P. Mehlig, *Ind. Eng. Chem., Anal. Ed.*, 7, 387-9 (1935).

(2) $$c = \frac{\log \frac{I_1}{I_2} \times 63.57}{\Sigma l} \quad \text{grams of copper per liter}$$

(3) $$I = \frac{\text{transmittance of solution} \times 100}{\text{transmittance of solvent}} \times I_1 = 100$$

(4)
$$\log \frac{I_1}{I_2} = \log 100 - (\log \text{ transmittance of solution} \\ + \log 100 - \text{transmittance of solvent})$$

(5)
$$\log \frac{I_1}{I_2} = \log \text{ transmittance of solvent} - \log \text{ transmittance of solution}$$

(6)
$$\log \frac{I_1}{I_2} = \log 89.1 - \log 52.1 = 1.9499 - 1.7168 = 0.2331$$

Substituting in (2) gives

$$c = \frac{0.2331 \times 63.57}{52.99 \times 1.968} \quad \text{gram of copper per liter}$$

Introducing a volume of 250 ml. of solution as containing the sample gives a copper content of

$$\frac{0.2331 \times 63.57 \times 100}{52.99 \times 1.968 \times 4 \times 0.2517} = 14.12\%$$

# CHAPTER XVIII

## HYDROGEN-ION—GENERAL

THE titration of an acid is a measure of the total acidity of a solution. This, however, does not express its active acidity or intensity of acidity, which is the critical factor in determining the chemical properties of the solution.[1] This intensity is dependent upon the concentration of hydrogen-ion, $C_H$, which is a function of the concentration of acid and degree of ionization. This is equally applicable to bases, and, by suitable consideration of the equilibria involved, to hydrolysis accompanied by the ionization of a product of hydrolysis to yield hydrogen- or hydroxylions.

The hydrogen-ion concentration of a solution is often determined colorimetrically, particularly in control work. Improvements in the glass electrode, with accompanying results of high accuracy, are causing it to replace colorimetric methods. The use of the photometer for colorimetric work could reverse this trend. The simplicity of many colorimetric pH methods is a strong recommendation.

The values of $C_H$ may vary so greatly that charting on a linear scale is not practical. The values of $C_H$ are therefore commonly expressed as the pH value which is the logarithmic value of the reciprocal of the hydrogen-ion concentration, $\log_{10} \dfrac{1}{C_H}$

**Theory.** A simple acid, HA, in a polar solvent partially dissociates into $H^+$ and $A^-$. If other solutes are absent and the ionization of the solvent is negligible,

(1) $\qquad H^+ = A^-$

At a concentration C

(2) $\qquad C = HA + A^- = HA + H^+$

A familiar form of the law of mass action is

(3) $\qquad K_a = \dfrac{H^+ \times A^-}{HA}$

---

[1] E. Mundinger, *Molkerei Zig.* (Hildesheim), **49**, 2362-4, 2387-9 (1935).

Since $H^+ = A^-$, this may be expressed

(4) $\qquad K_a = \dfrac{H^{+2}}{C - H^+}$

The symbol $\alpha$ is conventionally used as a measure of the degree of dissociation and in this simple case $\alpha = \dfrac{H^+}{C} = \dfrac{A^-}{C}$

The usual solution for determination of pH is a solution of a salt containing some acid or base. In mixtures, (3) holds within limits. Variation of concentration may alter it. Within the limits in which (3) holds it may be restated

(5) $\qquad K_a = \dfrac{\alpha^2}{1-\alpha} = \dfrac{\alpha H^+}{1-\alpha}$

From this it follows that

(6) $\qquad H^+ = K_a \dfrac{1-\alpha}{\alpha}$

To express this in pH as defined, the logarithm of the reciprocal of each side of (6) gives

(7) $\qquad pH = \log \dfrac{1}{H^+} = \log \dfrac{1}{K_a} + \log \dfrac{\alpha}{1-\alpha}$

Similarly

(8) $\qquad pK_a = \log \dfrac{1}{K_a}$

From (7)

(9) $\qquad pH = pK_a + \log \dfrac{\alpha}{1-\alpha}, \quad \text{or} \quad pK = pH - \log \dfrac{\alpha}{1-\alpha}$

or if the ionization of the salt present is practically 100 per cent and the acid is but little ionized

(10) $\qquad pH = pK_a + \log \dfrac{C_{salt}}{C_{acid}}$

For convenience, it is customary to consider bases only as the negative form of acids, the values of $C_{OH}$, pOH and $pK_b$ being of use only in special cases. For convenience in referring to indicators, the pH at which the amounts of acid and alkaline forms are equal is called the pK value.

**Indicators.** Determination of hydrogen-ion concentration colorimetrically is made by indicators, provided the solution is not too highly colored, or too turbid. Indicators undergo complex molecular rearrangement with a change of pH. One form may be colorless or the two forms may differ in color. Acid-base indicators behave like weak acids or bases which change color upon dissociation. The change in the color of the sulfonphthalein indicators is usually associated with a tautomeric change in the molecule with the migration of the double bond, perhaps in the quinoid form.[2] The majority of the indicators are weak acids, where tautomeric change depends on their ionization and formation of the undissociated salt. The reaction in one direction is normally formation of a salt. Therefore, inherently it is a chemical reaction of the indicator with hydrogen- or hydroxyl-ion as one of the reacting substances. Evidence also attests to the fact that the color change of indicators with pH may be due to changes in colloidal particle size.[3]

When alcohol is added to an aqueous solution, the ionization constant of weak acids and bases diminishes. Indicator acids will become more sensitive to hydrogen-ions. In the presence of organic solvents, indicator acids become more sensitive to hydrogen-ions, and the color-change interval occurs at a higher pH value. However, under the same circumstances, indicator bases become less sensitive to hydrogen-ions, thus depressing the pH value at which the color-change interval takes place.[4]

**Transmittance.** If the indicator is colored in only one of its forms, the degree of transition at any point within the zone of color change may be expressed as the ratio of the intensity of the light transmitted at that point to that transmitted through an equal quantity of indicator under conditions insuring maximum intensity, or, more briefly, by measuring the transmittance. The logarithm of the ratio of incident light to transmitted light is the extinction coefficient. This is directly proportional to the concentration of the solution, if Beer's law is followed. It is affected by the thickness of the layer and the transparency of the solution.[5]

Two-color indicators [6] may also be defined in a similar manner or as

---

[2] J. F. McClendon, *Am. Naturalist*, **64**, 289-99 (1930).

[3] Maki Takata, *Tôhoku J. Exptl. Med.*, **25**, 9-30 (1935).

[4] I. M. Kolthoff and H. A. Laitinen, *pH and Electro Titrations*, 2nd ed., p. 30, John Wiley & Sons, Inc., New York (1941).

[5] A. Leclère, *Bull. biol. pharm.*, **1938**, 530-41; H. van Dam, *Ing. chim.*, **24**, 41-56 (1940).

[6] K. Maennchen, *Mitt. Leitz-Werke*, **1941**, No. 63, 47-50; *Physik. Ber.*, **22**, 1280 (1941).

the ratio of the intensities of absorption at two wave lengths selected at or near the respective maxima of the two absorption bands in question.[7] The logarithm of this ratio demonstrates a linear relationship when plotted.[8] The intensity ratio of the two absorption bands is independent of the total concentration of the indicator over wide ranges of concentration. This ratio of the two-color indicator is especially useful for pH determination, since the purity of indicators is variable, and low concentrations do not always yield reproducible results.[9] Calibration curves are prepared with buffers of known pH, thus permitting the conversion of transmittance readings into pH values. A wave-length variation of 0.1 m$\mu$ corresponds to a pH variation of 0.002-0.004.[10]

In the spectrophotometric study of phthalein and azo dyes at various hydrogen-ion concentrations, the absorption band generally changes in height and intensity, but does not shift in wave length. In a solution containing a standard amount of indicator, the height of the band varies, within certain limits, with the hydrogen-ion concentration, and may be compared against standard curves.[11] Any absorption due to a moderate color of the original solution may be counteracted and its effect removed by using the original solution as a blank in the comparison cell. Measuring the peak of the absorption band proves to be a more accurate method than determining the edge of the band with a simple spectroscope.

The absorption curve of the indicator is fundamental in colorimetric pH work. The use of a graph to coordinate dominant wave length with pH as a means of determining the pH of solutions [12] is applicable with accuracy only to sulfonphthalein indicators which show no purple characteristics. In cases where the dominant wave lengths fall in the purple on either side of the color-change range, this method has little value.[13]

The wave lengths of the absorption bands of some common indicators [14] are listed in Table 16. The variation of the absorption curve with pH is illustrated in Figure 95 which shows the curve for bromothymol blue, a dichromatic indicator. The values plotted are −log T as

[7] Walter C. Holmes, *J. Am. Chem. Soc.*, **46**, 627-31 (1924).

[8] Sigge Hähnel, *Svensk. Kem. Tid.*, **46**, 262-79 (1934).

[9] S. E. Q. Ashley, *Ind. Eng. Chem., Anal. Ed.*, **11**, 72-9 (1939).

[10] A. G. de Almeida, *Mikrochemie*, **26**, 9-21 (1939).

[11] Wallace R. Brode, *J. Am. Chem. Soc.*, **46**, 581-96 (1924).

[12] A. G. de Almeida, "Determinação fotométrica da concentração hidrogeniónica," *Dissertation Lisboa*, 91 pp. (1935).

[13] W. B. Fortune and M. G. Mellon, *J. Am. Chem. Soc.*, **60**, 2607-10 (1938).

[14] Wallace R. Brode, *J. Am. Chem. Soc.*, **46**, 581-96 (1924).

TABLE 16. WAVE LENGTHS OF DOMINANT ABSORPTION BANDS OF
SOME COMMON INDICATORS

| Indicator | Wave Length mμ | Indicator | Wave Length mμ |
|---|---|---|---|
| Thymol blue (acid) .......... | 544 | Cresol red ................... | 572 |
| Bromophenol blue ........... | 592 | Phenol red ...... ........... | 558 |
| Methyl red ................... | 530 | Thymol blue (alk.) .......... | 596 |
| Bromocresol purple .......... | 591 | Neutral red .................. | 533 |
| Bromothymol blue ........... | 617 | Phenolphthalein ............. | 553 |
| | | Thymolphthalein ............. | 598 |

determined at different wave lengths and different pH values. All values for a given curve are at the pH value indicated. The change in absorption which takes place with change of pH is ascribed to change of disso-

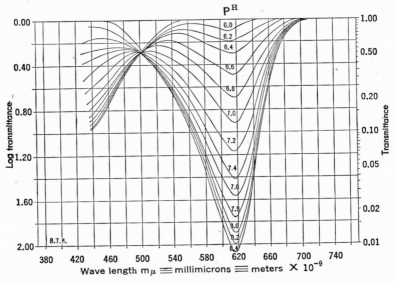

FIG. 95. Transmittance curve for bromothymol blue

ciation of the indicator. This is based on the justifiable assumption of distinctly different absorption by the ion and molecule of the indicator.

Transmittance curves prepared for methyl orange containing 0.006 gram per liter were found to exhibit a fixed isobestic point at 469 mμ. An increase in pH is accompanied by a consistent change in the intensity of absorption. At a pH of 2.62, the peak is located at 507 mμ. As the pH increases, the band shifts towards the blue so that at a pH of 4.0, the peak occurs at 472 m$\mu$.[15] This is shown in Figure 96.

Methyl red is often used analytically as an equivalent of methyl orange. The corresponding curves for it are shown in Figure 97.

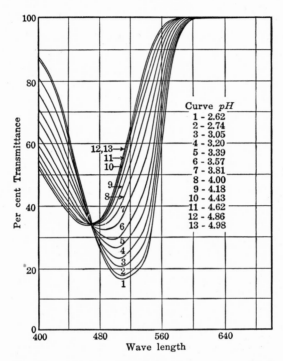

| Curve | pH |
|-------|------|
| 1 - | 2.62 |
| 2 - | 2.74 |
| 3 - | 3.05 |
| 4 - | 3.20 |
| 5 - | 3.39 |
| 6 - | 3.57 |
| 7 - | 3.81 |
| 8 - | 4.00 |
| 9 - | 4.18 |
| 10 - | 4.43 |
| 11 - | 4.62 |
| 12 - | 4.86 |
| 13 - | 4.98 |

FIG. 96. Spectral transmission curves for methyl orange solutions at different pH values: one cm. cell thickness and 0.375 ml. of a solution containing 0.4 g./1 diluted to 25 ml.

In the case of bromocresol green, an isobestic point is also evident, but the peak absorption remains constant at 615 m$\mu$ with changing pH as shown in Figure 98.

Equal parts of methyl red and bromocresol green exhibit an isobestic point at 580 m$\mu$ and a diffuse crossing at 450 m$\mu$.

The transmittance of energy by the ions may be expressed by

$$(11) \qquad \frac{I_i}{I_1} = 10^{-lc(1-a)K_m}$$

[15] W. B. Fortune and M. G. Mellon, *J. Am. Chem. Soc.*, **60**, 2607-10 (1938).

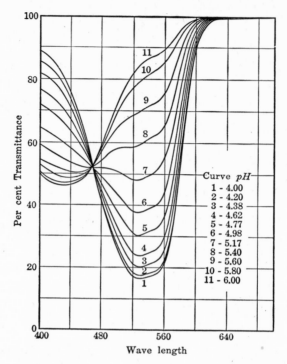

FIG. 97. Spectral transmission curves for methyl red solutions at different pH values: one cm. cell thickness and 0.375 ml. of a solution containing 0.4 g./1 diluted to 25 ml.

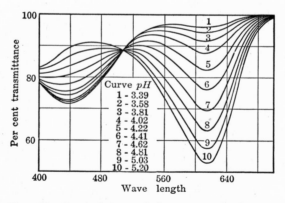

FIG. 98. Spectral transmission curves for bromocresol green solutions at different pH values: one cm. cell thickness and 0.375 ml. of a solution containing 0.4 g./1 diluted to 25 ml.

In this $I_1$ is the intensity of the light entering the solution, $I_i$ that not absorbed by the ions, $l$ is the depth of the solution, $c$ is the concentration of indicator present, $a$ is the degree of dissociation and $K_i$ is the molecular extinction coefficient of the ions.

Similarly the transmittance by the molecules may be expressed by

$$(12) \qquad \frac{I_m}{I_1} = 10^{-lc(1-a)K_m}$$

in which $I_m$ is the intensity of energy not absorbed by the molecules and $K_m$ is the molecular extinction coefficient of the molecules.

The total transmittance is given by

$$(13) \qquad T = \frac{I_2}{I_1} = \frac{I_i + I_m}{I_1} - 1$$

Applying the general form of Beer's law these result in

$$(14) \qquad -\log T = lc[aK_i + (1-a)K_m].$$

When $a$ is 1 the value for $K_m$ disappears and the simple form is obtained,

$$(15) \qquad -\log T = lcK_i$$

Similarly, if instead of a pH value where dissociation is complete, one is assumed without dissociation the simplified form due to disappearance of $K_i$ would be

$$(16) \qquad -\log T = lcK_m$$

At an intermediate point the curve must pass through a stage at which $a$ is 0.5. Equation (14) then becomes

$$(17) \qquad -\log T = 0.5lc(K_i + K_m)$$

The point at which this occurs is that through which all the curves for that indicator must pass. This isobestic point [16] is shown at about $\lambda = 510$ in Figure 95 for bromothymol blue. The occurrence of such a point is adequate evidence that the change occurring with change in pH is no more complex than the attainment of an equilibrium between two components. When such a point cannot be determined by spectrophotometric absorption curves of the indicators it is sufficient evidence that such a simple relationship does not exist for that indicator.

[16] E. B. R. Prideaux, *Chem. & Ind.*, **45**, 664, 678 (1926).

Knowing that such a relationship exists, it follows that when ionization of the indicator is approximately complete, (15) becomes approximately

$$(18) \qquad -\log T = lcaK_i$$

Having $-\log T_a$, the value when the absorption is at a maximum, the pH value of a well-buffered solution at a value where $a$ is 0.1–0.9, and $-\log T_d$ for the solution at the pH value determined, it follows that with the depth of layer, $l$, and concentration constant

$$(19) \qquad \frac{-\log T_d}{-\log T_a} = \frac{lcaK_i}{lcK_i} = a$$

If the concentration or depth of layer is altered, the more complex form

$$(20) \qquad a = \frac{(\log T_d) l_a\, c_a\, K_i}{(\log T_a) l_d\, c_d\, K_i} \text{ is obtained.}$$

Since only one wave length is used $K_i$ cancels from (20) and $c_a$ and $c_d$ need not be known if their ratio is known.

For calculation of the value of $a$ it is only necessary to have the transmittances of the solution at a wave length $\lambda_m$ which is not appreciably absorbed by the ion and at a value $\lambda_i$ which is not appreciably absorbed by the molecule. At $\lambda_m$, $K_i = 0$ and at $\lambda_i$, $K_m = 0$. From this it follows from (19) that

$$(21) \qquad a = \frac{(\log T_d)\lambda_i}{(\log T_a)\lambda_i} = R_i, \quad \text{and}$$

$$(22) \qquad 1 - a = \frac{(\log T_d)\lambda_m}{(\log T_a)\lambda_m} = R_m$$

Therefore, from (9)

$$(23) \qquad pH = pK + \log \frac{R_i}{R_m}$$

**Interpretation.** The dissociation of pure water is $0.0_61$ mole per liter. The concentration of hydrogen-ion is therefore $0.0_61$ and concentration of hydroxyl-ion is the same. If an acid is added the amount of hydrogen-ion is increased and the amount of hydroxyl-ion correspondingly reduced. According to the law of mass action

$$\frac{C_H \times C_{OH}}{C_{H_2O}} = \frac{0.0_61 \times 0.0_61}{1} = 0.0_{13}1$$

If the amount of acid were such as to increase the concentration of hydrogen-ion to 0.01 mole per liter, about 0.01 $M$ hydrochloric acid, the hydroxyl-ion would be correspondingly reduced. The very simple expression $C_H \times C_{OH} = 0.0_{13}1$ defines the concentration of either when the other is known.

The pH scale is by definition the negative exponent of 10 which will give the concentration of hydrogen-ion. The concentration of hydroxyl-ion is simultaneously defined. For a value of $C_H = 0.0_61$ the corresponding figure is $10^{-7.0}$ Therefore this is expressed as pH 7.0. For $C_H = 0.0_{11}1$ this is expressed as pH 12.0. Since the acidity is less than at neutrality the concentration of hydroxyl-ion is high and pH 12.0 is a relatively high alkalinity.

TABLE 17. INTERRELATION OF pH, $C_H$ AND $C_{OH}$

| $pH$ | $C_H$ Moles Per Liter | $C_{OH}$ Moles Per Liter | Moles $H^+$ Per Liter to Change from Previous pH | Moles $OH^-$ Per Liter to Change from Previous pH |
|---|---|---|---|---|
| 1 | $10^{-1} = 0.1$ | $10^{-13} = 0.0_{12}1$ | | |
| 2 | $10^{-2} = 0.01$ | $10^{-12} = 0.0_{11}1$ | $-0.09$ | $+0.0_{12}9$ |
| 3 | $10^{-3} = 0.0_21$ | $10^{-11} = 0.0_{10}1$ | $-0.0_29$ | $+0.0_{11}9$ |
| 4 | $10^{-4} = 0.0_31$ | $10^{-10} = 0.0_91$ | $-0.0_39$ | $+0.0_{10}9$ |
| 5 | $10^{-5} = 0.0_41$ | $10^{-9} = 0.0_81$ | $-0.0_49$ | $+0.0_99$ |
| 6 | $10^{-6} = 0.0_51$ | $10^{-8} = 0.0_71$ | $-0.0_59$ | $+0.0_89$ |
| 7 | $10^{-7} = 0.0_61$ | $10^{-7} = 0.0_61$ | $-0.0_69$ | $+0.0_79$ |
| 8 | $10^{-8} = 0.0_71$ | $10^{-6} = 0.0_51$ | $-0.0_79$ | $+0.0_69$ |
| 9 | $10^{-9} = 0.0_81$ | $10^{-5} = 0.0_41$ | $-0.0_89$ | $+0.0_59$ |
| 10 | $10^{-10} = 0.0_91$ | $10^{-4} = 0.0_31$ | $-0.0_99$ | $+0.0_49$ |
| 11 | $10^{-11} = 0.0_{10}1$ | $10^{-3} = 0.0_21$ | $-0.0_{10}9$ | $+0.0_39$ |
| 12 | $10^{-12} = 0.0_{11}1$ | $10^{-2} = 0.01$ | $-0.0_{11}9$ | $+0.0_29$ |
| 13 | $10^{-13} = 0.0_{12}1$ | $10^{-1} = 0.1$ | $-0.0_{12}9$ | $+0.09$ |

There remains only to indicate more specifically the relationship between pH and actual concentration of hydrogen- or hydroxyl-ion. $C_H$ is a linear relationship, each unit of change being the same as the previous. pH is a logarithmic relationship, each unit of change being ten times the previous one. This is more clearly shown by the accompanying Table 17. From this it will be noted that addition of $0.0_59$ mole of hydroxyl-ion will change the pH value from 8.0 to 9.0. Addition of another $0.0_59$ mole of hydroxyl-ion will not change the pH value from 9.0 to 10.0. Rather it will require 10 times that amount or $0.0_49$ moles to change to pH 10.0.

Table 18 gives the approximate pH of 0.1 $N$ solutions of some common acids, bases and salts as illustrations of the variation of pH among solutions of like concentration, and Table 19 gives the pH of some common substances.[17]

TABLE 18. pH VALUES FOR 0.1 $N$ SOLUTIONS, AT 20°, OF COMMON ACIDS AND BASES, ROUNDED TO THE FIRST DECIMAL

| Acids | pH Value | Bases | pH Value |
|---|---|---|---|
| Hydrochloric acid | 1.0 | Sodium bicarbonate | 8.4 |
| Sulfuric acid | 1.2 | Borax | 9.2 |
| Phosphoric acid | 1.5 | Ammonia | 11.1 |
| Sulfurous acid | 1.5 | Sodium carbonate | 11.6 |
| Acetic acid | 2.9 | Trisodium phosphate | 12.0 |
| Alum | 3.2 | Sodium metasilicate | 12.2 |
| Carbonic acid | 3.8 | Lime (saturated) | 12.3 |
| Boric acid | 5.2 | Sodium hydroxide | 13.0 |

TABLE 19. pH VALUES OF VARIOUS COMMON SUBSTANCES

| | | | |
|---|---|---|---|
| Apples | 2.9-3.3 | Limes | 1.8-2.0 |
| Apricots (dried) | 3.6-4.0 | Magnesia, milk of | 10.5 |
| Asparagus | 5.4-5.7 | Milk, cows | 6.4-6.8 |
| Beans | 5.0-6.0 | Molasses | 5.0-5.4 |
| Beers | 4.0-5.0 | Olives | 3.6-3.8 |
| Beets | 4.9-5.6 | Oranges | 3.0-4.0 |
| Blackberries | 3.2-3.6 | Peas | 5.8-6.4 |
| Bread, white | 5.0-6.0 | Peaches | 3.4-3.6 |
| Cabbage | 5.2-5.4 | Pears | 3.6-4.0 |
| Carrots | 4.9-5.2 | Pickles, dill | 3.2-3.5 |
| Cherries | 3.2-4.1 | Pickles, sour | 3.0-3.5 |
| Cider | 2.9-3.3 | Pimento | 4.7-5.2 |
| Corn | 6.0-6.5 | Plums | 2.8-3.0 |
| Crackers | 7.0-8.5 | Pumpkin | 4.8-5.2 |
| Dates | 6.2-6.4 | Raspberries | 3.2-3.7 |
| Flour, wheat | 6.0-6.5 | Rhubarb | 3.1-3.2 |
| Ginger ale | 2.0-4.0 | Salmon | 6.1-6.3 |
| Gooseberries | 2.8-3.1 | Sauerkraut | 3.4-3.6 |
| Grapefruit | 3.0-3.3 | Shrimp | 6.8-7.0 |
| Grapes | 3.5-4.5 | Spinach | 5.1-5.7 |
| Hominy (lye) | 6.9-7.9 | Squash | 5.0-5.3 |
| Human blood plasma | 7.3-7.5 | Strawberries | 3.1-3.5 |
| Human duodenal contents | 4.8-8.2 | Sweet potatoes | 5.3-5.6 |
| Human feces | 4.6-8.4 | Tomatoes | 4.1-4.4 |
| Human gastric contents | 1.0-3.0 | Tuna | 5.9-6.1 |
| Human milk | 6.6-7.6 | Turnips | 5.2-5.5 |
| Human saliva | 6.0-7.6 | Vinegar | 2.4-3.4 |
| Human spinal fluid | 7.3-7.5 | Water, distilled (equil. with air) | 5.8 |
| Human urine | 4.8-8.4 | Water, distilled ($CO_2$ free) | 6.8-7.0 |
| Jams, fruit | 3.5-4.0 | Water, mineral | 6.2-9.4 |
| Jellies, fruit | 3.0-3.5 | Water, sea | 8.0-8.4 |
| Lemons | 2.2-2.4 | Wines | 2.8-3.8 |

[17] J. L. St. John, *Food Industries*, **13**, No. 12, 67 (1941).

The uses of pH determination colorimetrically are so varied that a complete listing of references, even without discussion, is not feasible within the space available. Therefore, those discussed are only a selected few, illustrative of the types of application.

**Colorimetric Principles.** As the hydrogen-ion concentration of a solution containing a colorimetric pH indicator is changed, the color as well as the intensity of color is usually changed. There are some exceptions, the so-called monochromatic pH indicators.

All the usual types of methods are applicable, the series-of-standards, balancing, duplication, and dilution methods. The value for the series-of-standards method may be expressed as transmittance.

**Principle of Buffer Solutions.** At fixed points for standards it is necessary to prepare mixtures of related compounds such that on dilution with water there is to all practical purposes no change in the pH of the solution. Probably the most familiar of these is an acetic acid-sodium acetate mixture.

There are numerous series of such standard buffers as outlined by Sorensen, Walpole, Clark and Lubs, and others. The quoted pH of the buffer solution depends primarily on determination by electrometric methods.

Rather than duplicate in a buffer solution the actual pH found in the sample two other methods are possible according to the Ostwald theory. The first is to have definite volumes of acid and alkaline forms of the indicator, the two varying in concentration, the sum of the colors to be compared with the sample. The second is to vary the depths of acid and alkaline forms of the indicator in the same concentration as in the sample, the total depth of standard always being the same as that of the sample. The first is the method of Gillespie; the second is used in certain instrumental methods of measurement.

**Sources of Error.** In addition to the usual sources of error, in colorimetric determinations there are several which are particularly applicable to pH determinations.

*Dilution of Sample.* Some samples can be diluted with an equal volume of distilled water, or even several volumes of distilled water without affecting the pH. This is because they are heavily buffered. Similar dilution of slightly buffered samples will cause substantial error.

*Filtration of Sample.* Filtration of neutral distilled water through paper does not appreciably alter the pH. Filtration of a $N$ potassium chloride solution, even though the filter is first washed with distilled water, causes substantial error. If the filter is washed 4 times with $N$ potassium chloride solution and the first few ml. of filtrate from a $N$ potassium chloride extract are discarded the errors are largely avoided.

*Acid Contamination.* If ordinary paraffin is used for coating a bottle it gives a distinctly acid reaction and will affect an indicator or the buffer to be used. An alkaline buffer, or indicator adjusted on the alkaline side, will react with carbon dioxide of the air. This is serious above pH 8.0. If a tube is closed with the finger to shake it, distinctly acid contamination may occur from the soiling material on the skin, largely of a sebaceous nature.

*Alkaline Contamination.* Buffers or indicators stored in glass bottles are apt to react with the alkalinity of the glass. Water when boiled, even in a Pyrex flask, shows an alkaline reaction on standing for 12–24 hours.

*Salt Error.* Two solutions having different concentrations of salts and the same concentration of indicator do not always show the same pH value. Therefore, strictly speaking, sample and buffers used for comparison should contain the same concentration of the same salts, an obvious impossibility and a condition but rarely approached in practical use. The cause of this change of colorimetric pH by the presence of salts is unknown. Neither the acid nor alkaline colors of bromophenol blue, bromocresol green, bromothymol blue, phenol red, cresol red or thymol blue are affected. The acid colors of methyl orange, tropeolin 00, and methyl red, and the alkaline colors of various nitrophenols and salicyl yellow are intensified by the presence of salts.

Neutral salts affect the dissociation of indicators without change of pH due to the effect of the ionic strength on the activity coefficients of the indicator, and probably do not change the dissociation constant. The salt effect may be expressed in terms of change in the apparent dissociation constant. As the pH range of the indicator rises, the salt effect is more marked. The change in the shade of the indicator produced by boiling is attributed in part to the change in the ionization constant of water and in part to a change in the salt error. The salt error decreases with an increase in temperature, so that the error approaches zero at the boiling point of water.[18]

The same types of indicators do not always behave alike. Methyl red and methyl orange show very small salt errors under different conditions, probably due to their amphoteric character. Amphoteric indicators may

---

[18] Walter Neumann, *Z. anal. Chem.*, **101**, 89-101 (1935).

therefore be best. There are grave discrepancies for phenolphthalein, *o*-cresolphthalein, thymol blue and phenol red.

The theory of Debye and Hückel may be used as a quantitative expression of the relation between ionic strength and pK values on the assumption that all the salts are completely dissociated, and that the combined effect of their ions on the logarithm of an activity coefficient is proportional, as a first approximation, to the square root of the ionic strength.

Since the electrometric method is made the standard, the effect of salt is thrown on the indicator. It is well known that salt affects both the electrometric pH and the colorimetric value. Salt errors may be positive or negative. In sea water a 3.5 per cent salt content gives a value of pH 8.43 with phenolphthalein against a standard borate buffer when the electrometric value is 8.22. The error varies with the indicator. Table 20 shows the salt correction for various indicators at various ionic strengths [19] and Table 21 values at different molarities. Salts that dissociate into bivalent ions produce a greater salt error than those dissociating into univalent ions.[20] The salt error is three times greater for the indicator where the acid form is a monovalent anion than for the indicator whose acid form is uncharged. It would be possible to reduce the salt error with indicators whose acid and alkaline forms changed in the same manner with varying ionic strength.[21] Ionization of the indicator into a basic or acid hybrid ion and a monovalent ion, such as is exemplified by methyl orange, tends to reduce the salt error.

Weak bases, such as the methoxytriphenyl carbinols, which dissociate to form a monovalent cation, are particularly suitable as indicators for the determination of small concentrations of hydrogen-ion.

*Protein Error.* The effect of protein on colorimetric pH values is similar to the salt error. Blood serum is a good example. Colorimetric pH on diluted serum differs by varying amounts at 20° or 38° from that of the undiluted serum. The results are consistently 0.08 pH higher than those by the hydrogen electrode and 0.14 higher than by the quinhydrone electrode.

The positively charged protein, on the acid side of the isoelectric point, exerts a larger influence than the negatively charged protein. The diazo indicators are especially affected by the positively charged

---

19 I. M. Kolthoff and H. A. Laitinen, *pH and Electro Titrations*, 2nd ed., p. 50, John Wiley and Sons, Inc., New York (1941).

20 L. Michaelis and A. Gyemant, *Biochem. Z.*, **109**, 165-210 (1920).

21 I. M. Kolthoff, *Ind. Eng. Chem., Anal. Ed.*, **8**, 237-9 (1936).

TABLE 20. SALT CORRECTION FOR INDICATORS AT VARIOUS
IONIC STRENGTHS
(Ionic Strength of Buffer Solution Used for Comparison is 0.1)

| Ionic Strength | Thymol Blue [a] | Methyl Orange | Bromo-phenol Blue | Bromo-cresol Green | Methyl Red | Chloro-phenol Red |
|---|---|---|---|---|---|---|
| 0.0025 | .... | —0.04 | +0.15 | +0.21 | 0.00 | ..... |
| 0.005 | .... | —0.04 | +0.14 | +0.18 | 0.00 | +0.15 |
| 0.01 | 0.00 | —0.02 | +0.14 | +0.16 | 0.00 | +0.13 |
| 0.02 | 0.00 | 0.00 | +0.13 | +0.14 | 0.00 | +0.12 |
| 0.05 | 0.00 | 0.00 | +0.10 | +0.05 | 0.00 | +0.05 |
| 0.1 | 0.00 | 0.00 | 0.00 | 0.00 | 0.00 | 0.00 |
| 0.5 (KCl) | 0.00 | 0.00 | —0.10 | —0.12 | 0.00 | —0.16 |
| 0.5 (NaCl) | 0.00 | 0.00 | —0.18 | —0.16 | 0.00 | —0.19 |

[a] Thymol blue in its acid range (pH 1.3 — 2.8).

| Ionic Strength | Bromo-thymol Blue | Phenol Red | Thymol Blue | Phenol-phthalein | Thymol-phthalein | |
|---|---|---|---|---|---|---|
| 0.0025 | +0.14 | +0.14 | ..... | ..... | ..... | ..... |
| 0.005 | +0.12 | +0.12 | +0.16 | +0.18 | ..... | ..... |
| 0.01 | +0.11 | +0.11 | +0.12 | +0.12 | +0.11 | ..... |
| 0.02 | +0.07 | +0.07 | +0.09 | +0.10 | +0.09 | ..... |
| 0.05 | +0.04 | +0.04 | +0.05 | +0.05 | +0.05 | ..... |
| 0.1 | 0.00 | 0.00 | 0.00 | 0.00 | 0.00 | ..... |
| 0.5 (KCl) | —0.20 | —0.20 | —0.12 | —0.16 | —0.19 | ..... |
| 0.5 (NaCl) | —0.28 | —0.29 | —0.19 | —0.21 | ..... | ..... |

TABLE 21. SALT ERRORS WITH CLARK AND LUBS INDICATORS

| INDICATOR | CORRECTION | | |
|---|---|---|---|
| | 1 molar | 2 molar | 3 molar |
| Thymol blue (alkaline range)......................... | —0.22 | —0.29 | —0.34 |
| Cresol red............................................ | —0.28 | —0.32 | —0.37 |
| Phenol red........................................... | —0.21 | —0.26 | —0.29 |
| Bromothymol blue.................................... | —0.19 | —0.27 | —0.29 |
| Bromocresol purple................................... | —0.26 | —0.33 | —0.31 |
| Bromocresol green.................................... | —0.26 | —0.31 | —0.29 |
| Bromophenol blue..................................... | —0.28 | —0.37 | —0.43 |
| Thymol blue (acid range)............................. | —0.10 | —0.13 | —0.12 |
| Methyl red........................................... | —0.04 | —0.01 | +0.12 |

protein hydrates.[22] Nevertheless, it is possible to obtain reliable results with methyl red in casein and egg albumin solutions, where the pH is near the isoelectric point or about 5.0.

It is probable that this type of error is incorrecly named from one manifestation, since the same type of error occurs with some colorimetric indicators in soap solutions. In that case it is accentuated by increasing pH with the accompanying increase in colloidal micellar soap. A more general name for the effect would be colloidal error as signifying sorption and other phenomena occurring in colloidal dispersions.

*Indicator Error.* This anomalous designation refers to the fact that the indicator is itself a factor in the pH of the solution. In producing a definitely colored form of the indicator the pH of the solution has been altered. In heavily buffered solutions this is of no importance; in unbuffered solutions it introduces serious error unless the pH of the indicator is adjusted to match that of the sample before adding it. Such adjusted indicators known as "isohydric" indicators are in use.

*Temperature.* It is essential that the temperature of sample and standards be very nearly the same.

*Miscellaneous.* Some indicator solutions will fade if exposed to ultra-violet radiation. Such exposure has no effect on the crystals. Differences in the method of preparation of the indicator solutions may affect their color. Indicators from different sources have been found to show important variations. These last two do not have any bearing provided the same indicator solution is used for sample and standards.

Sorption of the acid or alkaline form of the indicator by a colloidal dispersion and reaction of the indicator with colloidal particles at the interface to give a colored product are also sources of error.

Among other errors that must be mentioned are the specific effects of certain buffers on indicators, slow change in color, and precipitation or change in size of colloidal particles.

**Accuracy.** The accuracy of the colorimetric method for pH has been estimated as 5 per cent, against an accuracy of 2.5 per cent for the electrometric method.[23] However, it has been stated that by plotting the dominant wave length against pH, the pH determination may be even more precise than the electrometric method.

---

[22] William Mansfield Clark, *The Determination of Hydrogen Ions*, 3rd ed., p. 184-5, Williams & Wilkins Co., Baltimore, Md. (1928).

[23] Martin Kilpatrick, Elwyn F. Chase and Leonard C. Riesch, *J. Am. Chem. Soc.*, **56**, 2051-3 (1934).

# CHAPTER XIX

## HYDROGEN-ION BUFFERS AND INDICATORS

**Simple Standard Buffer.** A buffer for pH 7.0 can be prepared very readily by mixing equivalent solutions of ammonium hydroxide and acetic acid. The acid and base have the same dissociation constant so that the buffer gives the neutral point. Bubbling air through the buffer for 5 minutes reduces the pH only 0.05 unit.

**Clark and Lubs Buffer Solutions.**[1] The series from pH 2.2 to 10.0 is satisfactorily covered by a series of buffers composed of potassium chloride, monopotassium phosphate, acid potassium phthalate, boric acid with potassium chloride, sodium hydroxide and hydrochloric acid. The solutions required are as follows:

*0.2 M Potassium Chloride.* Unless the salt is of unquestionable purity recrystallize 2-3 times. Dry at 120° for 2 days. Dissolve 14.912 grams in warm water, and when cool dilute to 1 liter.

*0.2 M Acid Potassium Phthalate.* For this, prepare acid potassium phthalate as follows: Dissolve 60 grams of pure potassium hydroxide in about 400 ml. of water. Add 50 grams of commercial resublimed phthalic anhydride. Commercial phthalic anhydride not resublimed may be seriously contaminated with benzoic acid, naphthols and quinones. As much as 10 recrystallizations may be required if a good commercial grade is not used. After the phthalic anhydride has dissolved and cooled, test a portion with phenolphthalein. If still alkaline add portions of phthalic anhydride until a diluted portion shows only a faint pink with phenolphthalein. If acid, add more potassium hydroxide solution to faint alkalinity.

When the solution has been adjusted to faint alkalinity add 60 grams more of phthalic anhydride, plus an amount equal to that added to remove excess alkalinity, and heat until solution is complete. Filter while hot into a crystallizing dish. Cover, and place where it will cool slowly. Filter with suction, and recrystallize twice from distilled water. Do not allow the temperature to go below 20° at any time or a more acid

---

[1] William Mansfield Clark and Herbert A. Lubs, *J. Biol. Chem.*, 25, 479-509 (1916); *J. Bacteriology*, 2, 1-34, 109-36, 191-236 (1917); William Mansfield Clark, *Determination of Hydrogen Ions*, 3rd ed., p. 196, Williams and Wilkins Co., Baltimore, Md. (1928).

salt, $2KHC_8H_4O_4 \cdot H_2C_8H_4O_4$, will deposit. This is in prismatic needles, easily distinguished from the 6-sided, orthorhombic plates of the usual acid salt. Dry at 110° to constant weight. Dissolve 40.836 grams in water, and dilute to 1 liter. If the purity of the salt is subject to any question, titrate a portion of this solution.

*0.2 M Monopotassium Phosphate.* Recrystallize the best available grade of monopotassium phosphate, $KH_2PO_4$, 3 times from distilled water. Dry to constant weight at 110°. Dissolve 27.312 grams in water and dilute to 1 liter. Test the solution to insure that it gives a distinct red with methyl red and a distinct blue with bromophenol blue.

If a sediment is deposited, it is largely colloidal iron and aluminum compounds, free from silica. The use of hard and soft glass, paraffin or silver has apparently no relation to this. As a satisfactory method of further purification, if necessary, prepare an approximately 0.2 *M* solution. Seal in a flask, to prevent excessive loss of water, and heat at 75-85° for 24 hours. Filter through very fine paper and evaporate the filtrate to crystallization. Addition of an equal volume of 95 per cent alcohol will facilitate crystallization of this partially concentrated solution.

*0.2 M Boric Acid—0.2 M Potassium Chloride.* Recrystallize boric acid several times from distilled water. Air-dry in thin layers between filter papers. It begins to lose water of constitution above 50°. Insure constant weight by drying weighed samples in thin layers over calcium chloride in a desiccator. Dissolve 12.4048 grams of boric acid and 14.912 grams of pure potassium chloride (p. 170) in water, and dilute to 1 liter.

*0.2 M Sodium Hydroxide.* Absence of any substantial amount of carbonate in the final solution is essential. Dissolve 100 grams of the best quality sodium hydroxide in 100 ml. of distilled water in a Pyrex flask. Cover the mouth of the flask, and allow to stand overnight for the carbonate to settle.

If the separation is complete by sedimentation it need not be filtered. Otherwise, treat a hardened filter paper with warm 1:1 sodium hydroxide solution. After a few minutes, decant and wash the paper once with absolute alcohol, twice with 50 per cent alcohol, and several times with distilled water. Place in a Büchner funnel and apply gentle suction until nearly dry, but not dry enough to curl. Pour the concentrated alkali on the middle of the paper, and spread carefully with a glass rod, using gentle suction to make the paper adhere properly to the funnel. Filter, and dilute after rough calculation to about 1.2 *M*. Standardize this exactly against a standard acid, using not less than 10 ml. as sample. From the average of not less than three standardizations agreeing within 0.001 $M$ calculate the dilution to an exactly 0.2 $M$ solution. Carry out the dilution with the least possible exposure, and transfer to a heavily paraffined bottle to which are attached a 50 ml, buret and a soda-lime guard tube as shown in Figure 99.

Weigh out several portions of acid potassium phthalate, and dissolve in water. Pass a stream of air free of carbon dioxide through the solution, add phenolphthalein, and titrate with the alkali to a faint pink.

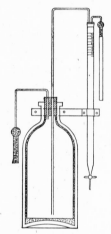

If the solution varies from 0.2 $M$ use a factor rather than adjust to exactly 0.2 $M$.

*0.2 M Hydrochloric Acid.* Dilute pure hydrochloric acid to approximately 0.2 $M$, and standardize with 0.2 $M$ sodium hydroxide solution.

**Kolthoff and Vleeschhouwer Buffer Solutions.[2]** For high pH values, up to 12.0, other buffer solutions can be used.

*0.05 M. Borax.* Recrystallize the commercial material twice from water. Dry over hydrated sodium bromide, $NaBr \cdot 2H_2O$, to constant weight. Dissolve 19.10 grams in water, and dilute to 1 liter.

*0.05 M Sodium Carbonate.* Dry the best quality of sodium carbonate to constant weight at 160°. Dissolve 5.30 grams in water, and dilute to 1 liter.

*0.1 M Citric Acid.* The citric acid should give a clear solution in water, show no test for chloride or sulfate, and give practically no ash. To purify, recrystallize the commercial grade 1-2 times from water.

Fig. 99. Paraffined bottle with buret and soda-lime guard tube for standard alkali solution

Dry to constant weight over hydrated sodium bromide, $NaBr \cdot 2H_2O$. To check the amount of water of hydration, dry at 20-30 mm. pressure at 70°. The acid should remain colorless and lose $8.58 \pm 0.1$ per cent of moisture. As buffer, dissolve 21.008 grams in water, and dilute to 1 liter. As a further check, it is advisable to titrate a portion of the solution with 0.2 $N$ barium hydroxide solution to a distinct red with phenolphthalein.

A series of wide-range buffers, covering the concentrations of hydrogen-ion from 2.2-8.0, has been produced [3] employing 0.2 $M$ disodium phosphate and 0.1 $M$ citric acid.

[2] I. M. Kolthoff and J. J. Vleeschhouwer, *Biochem. Z.*, **179**, 410-13 (1926); **189**, 191 (1927).

[3] T. C. McIlvaine, *J. Biol. Chem.*, **49**, 183-6 (1921).

**Manipulation.** It is convenient to prepare 200 ml. of each buffer at a time. Place in 250-ml. bottles. Perforate the stoppers with an opening which will just take a 10-ml. pipet, and leave the pipet in the stopper. If the bottles are to stand for any length of time cover the pipets to prevent collection of dust.

**Buffer Mixtures.** By proper admixture of buffer solutions according to Tables 22-29 buffers of any value from pH 1.0-12.0 can be prepared. As these tables overlap, buffers from one set can be compared with another to insure accuracy.

TABLE 22.  BUFFER MIXTURES FOR pH 1.0-2.2

| pH | Ml. of 0.2$M$ Potassium Chloride | Ml. of 0.2$M$ Hydrochloric Acid | Dilute to (ml.) |
|---|---|---|---|
| 1.0 | 0.00 | 59.50 | 100 |
| 1.1 | 2.72 | 47.28 | 100 |
| 1.2 | 12.45 | 37.55 | 100 |
| 1.3 | 20.16 | 29.84 | 100 |
| 1.4 | 26.30 | 23.70 | 100 |
| 1.5 | 31.18 | 18.82 | 100 |
| 1.6 | 35.03 | 14.95 | 100 |
| 1.7 | 38.12 | 11.88 | 100 |
| 1.8 | 40.57 | 9.43 | 100 |
| 1.9 | 42.51 | 7.49 | 100 |
| 2.0 | 44.05 | 5.95 | 100 |
| 2.1 | 45.27 | 4.73 | 100 |
| 2.2 | 46.24 | 3.76 | 100 |

TABLE 23.  BUFFER MIXTURES FOR pH 2.2-3.8

| pH | Ml. of 0.2$M$ Potassium Acid Phthalate | Ml. of 0.2$M$ Hydrochloric Acid | Dilute to (ml.) |
|---|---|---|---|
| 2.2 | 50 | 46.60 | 200 |
| 2.4 | 50 | 39.60 | 200 |
| 2.6 | 50 | 33.00 | 200 |
| 2.8 | 50 | 26.50 | 200 |
| 3.0 | 50 | 20.40 | 200 |
| 3.2 | 50 | 14.80 | 200 |
| 3.4 | 50 | 9.95 | 200 |
| 3.6 | 50 | 6.00 | 200 |
| 3.8 | 50 | 2.65 | 200 |

TABLE 24.  BUFFER MIXTURES FOR pH 4.0-6.2

| pH | Ml. of 0.2$M$ Potassium Acid Phthalate | Ml. of 0.2$M$ Sodium Hydroxide | Dilute to (ml.) |
|---|---|---|---|
| 4.0 | 50 | 0.40 | 200 |
| 4.2 | 50 | 3.65 | 200 |
| 4.4 | 50 | 7.35 | 200 |
| 4.6 | 50 | 12.00 | 200 |
| 4.8 | 50 | 17.50 | 200 |
| 5.0 | 50 | 23.65 | 200 |
| 5.2 | 50 | 29.75 | 200 |
| 5.4 | 50 | 35.25 | 200 |
| 5.6 | 50 | 39.70 | 200 |
| 5.8 | 50 | 43.10 | 200 |
| 6.0 | 50 | 45.40 | 200 |
| 6.2 | 50 | 47.00 | 200 |

TABLE 25.  BUFFER MIXTURES FOR pH 5.8-8.0

| pH | Ml. of 0.2$M$ Monopotassium Phosphate | Ml. of 0.2$M$ Sodium Hydroxide | Dilute to (ml.) |
|---|---|---|---|
| 5.8 | 50 | 3.66 | 200 |
| 6.0 | 50 | 5.64 | 200 |
| 6.2 | 50 | 8.55 | 200 |
| 6.4 | 50 | 12.60 | 200 |
| 6.6 | 50 | 17.74 | 200 |
| 6.8 | 50 | 23.60 | 200 |
| 7.0 | 50 | 29.54 | 200 |
| 7.2 | 50 | 34.90 | 200 |
| 7.4 | 50 | 39.34 | 200 |
| 7.6 | 50 | 42.74 | 200 |
| 7.8 | 50 | 45.17 | 200 |
| 8.0 | 50 | 46.85 | 200 |

TABLE 26.  BUFFER MIXTURES FOR pH 7.8-10.0

| pH | Ml. of 0.2M Boric Acid, 0.2M Potassium Chloride | Ml. of 0.2M Sodium Hydroxide | Dilute to (ml.) |
|---|---|---|---|
| 7.8 | 50 | 2.65 | 200 |
| 8.0 | 50 | 4.00 | 200 |
| 8.2 | 50 | 5.90 | 200 |
| 8.4 | 50 | 8.55 | 200 |
| 8.6 | 50 | 12.00 | 200 |
| 8.8 | 50 | 16.40 | 200 |
| 9.0 | 50 | 21.40 | 200 |
| 9.2 | 50 | 26.70 | 200 |
| 9.4 | 50 | 32.00 | 200 |
| 9.6 | 50 | 36.85 | 200 |
| 9.8 | 50 | 40.80 | 200 |
| 10.0 | 50 | 43.90 | 200 |

TABLE 27.  BUFFER MIXTURES FOR pH 9.2-11.0

| pH | Ml. of 0.05M Sodium Carbonate | Ml. of 0.05M Borax |
|---|---|---|
| 9.2 | 0.00 | 100.00 |
| 9.4 | 35.70 | 64.30 |
| 9.6 | 55.50 | 44.50 |
| 9.8 | 66.70 | 33.30 |
| 10.0 | 75.40 | 24.60 |
| 10.2 | 82.15 | 17.85 |
| 10.4 | 86.90 | 13.10 |
| 10.6 | 91.50 | 8.50 |
| 10.8 | 94.75 | 5.25 |
| 11.0 | 97.30 | 2.70 |

TABLE 28.  BUFFER MIXTURES FOR pH 11.0-12.0

| pH | Ml. of 0.1M Disodium Phosphate | Ml. of 0.1M Sodium Hydroxide | Dilute to (ml.) |
|---|---|---|---|
| 11.0 | 25 | 4.13 | 50 |
| 11.2 | 25 | 6.00 | 50 |
| 11.4 | 25 | 8.67 | 50 |
| 11.6 | 25 | 12.25 | 50 |
| 11.8 | 25 | 16.65 | 50 |
| 12.0 | 25 | 21.60 | 50 |

TABLE 29. BUFFER MIXTURES FOR pH 2.2-8.0

| pH | Ml. of 0.2M Disodium Phosphate | Ml. of 0.1M Citric Acid |
|---|---|---|
| 2.2 | 0.40 | 19.60 |
| 2.4 | 1.24 | 18.76 |
| 2.6 | 2.18 | 17.82 |
| 2.8 | 3.17 | 16.83 |
| 3.0 | 4.11 | 15.89 |
| 3.2 | 4.94 | 15.06 |
| 3.4 | 5.70 | 14.30 |
| 3.6 | 6.44 | 13.56 |
| 3.8 | 7.10 | 12.90 |
| 4.0 | 7.71 | 12.29 |
| 4.2 | 8.28 | 11.72 |
| 4.4 | 8.82 | 11.18 |
| 4.6 | 9.35 | 10.65 |
| 4.8 | 9.86 | 10.14 |
| 5.0 | 10.30 | 9.70 |
| 5.2 | 10.72 | 9.28 |
| 5.4 | 11.15 | 8.85 |
| 5.6 | 11.60 | 8.40 |
| 5.8 | 12.09 | 7.91 |
| 6.0 | 12.63 | 7.37 |
| 6.2 | 13.22 | 6.78 |
| 6.4 | 13.85 | 6.15 |
| 6.6 | 14.55 | 5.45 |
| 6.8 | 15.45 | 4.55 |
| 7.0 | 16.47 | 3.53 |
| 7.2 | 17.39 | 2.61 |
| 7.4 | 18.17 | 1.83 |
| 7.6 | 18.73 | 1.27 |
| 7.8 | 19.15 | 0.85 |
| 8.0 | 19.45 | 0.55 |

Capsules of buffer salts [4] and compressed buffer tablets [5] are also available in the pH range from 2.0-12.0 in increments of 0.2. The buffer tablet dissolved volumetrically in 100 ml. of water will give a buffer solution accurate to ± 0.02 pH. The buffer tablets are compressed from appropriate mixtures of the following salts:

[4] R. P. Cargille, 118 Liberty St., New York, N. Y.
[5] Coleman Electric Company, New York, N. Y.

| pH Range | Composition |
|---|---|
| 2.0 | Oxalic acid |
| 2.2–3.6 | Potassium acid phthalate |
|  | Tartaric acid |
| 3.8–6.0 | Potassium acid phthalate |
|  | Sodium phosphate |
| 6.2–9.0 | Sodium tetraborate |
|  | Potassium phosphate |
| 9.2–10.8 | Sodium tetraborate |
|  | Sodium carbonate |
| 11.0–12.0 | Sodium phosphate |
|  | Sodium hydroxide |

Prepared buffer solutions are also widely sold by laboratory supply houses.

**Indicator Solutions.** There are four important classes of indicators: phthaleins, sulfophthaleins, nitrophenols and azo compounds. Each class has characteristic extinction curves. Clark [6] lists 185 colorimetric indicators. Many of these are valueless, yet they are a selection of those recorded as used at some time and are only a small part of the number available. As an example, 33 derivatives of dinitroanilines have been listed as usable for indicators. The absorption spectra of the Clark and Lubs indicators reveal that the ratio of the two different color components of the indicator is dependent solely on the hydrogen-ion concentration and not on the amount of indicator.

Three well-selected tables of indicators are available. The first is that of Sorensen given in Table 30. In the Sorensen pH range between 4.5 and 6.0, thymolsulfonephthalein, known as thymol blue, exists in its yellow midform, with an absorption band in the violet portion of the spectrum. As the alkalinity increases from 6.0-12.0, the color is transformed to a blue-violet, with an absorption band in the yellow and red portions of the spectrum, the maximum of which lies at 596 m$\mu$. Within this range, the degree of transition at any point may be determined by spectrophotometric measurements, and expressed in a ratio which gives the degree of development of the band of the alkaline form of the indicator. It may also be expressed as the ratio which records the relative intensities of the respective bands of the mid-form and the alkaline form. The apparent dissociation constants of the indicator are 1.5 in the acid and 8.91 in the alkaline ranges. The dissociation of the indicator, however, is retarded after the mid-point in its acid range has been passed.

[6] William Mansfield Clark, *Determination of Hydrogen Ions*, 3rd ed., pp. 76-90, Williams and Wilkins Co., Baltimore, Md. (1928).

TABLE 30. INDICATORS OF SORENSON

| | Composition of Test Solution | Useful Range pH | Sensitivity to Neutral Salts | USEFULNESS IN PRESENCE OF | | | Stability on Standing |
|---|---|---|---|---|---|---|---|
| | | | | True proteins | High conc. of products of proteolysis | Chloroform and toluene | |
| Methyl violet 6B .... | 0.01-0.05 per cent aqueous | y 0.1- 3.2 v | high | fair | good | with chloroform not, with toluene useful | acid solutions fade |
| Mauve .......... | 0.01-0.05 per cent aqueous | 0.1- 2.9 | high | fair | good | as above | as above |
| Benzene-azo-diphenylamine ...... | 0.01 gram in 1 ml. N HCl + 50 ml. alcohol + 49 ml. water | p 1.2- 2.1 y | low | not | fair | not | moderate |
| Tropeolin OO (sodium salt of diphenylaminoazo-p-benzenesulfonic acid). | 0.01 per cent aqueous | r 1.4- 2.6 y | low | not | fair | good | good |
| Metanil yellow (sodium salt of m-sulfonate-azo-diphenylamine) ......... | 0.01 per cent aqueous | r 1.2- 2.3 y | low | not | fair | good | good |
| Benzene-azo-benzylaniline ......... | 0.02 gram in 1 ml. 0.1N HCl + 50 ml. alcohol + 49 ml. water | p 2.3- 3.3 y | low | not | good | not | moderate |
| p-benzenesulfonicacid-azo-benzylaniline... | 0.01 per cent aqueous | r 1.9- 3.3 y | low | not | fair | good | good |
| p-benzenesulfonic acid-azo-m-chlorodiethylaniline ......... | 0.01 per cent aqueous | r 2.6- 4.0 y | low | not | fair | good | good |
| Benzene-azo-dimethylaniline ......... | 0.01 gram in 0.1 ml. 0.1N HCl + 80 ml. alcohol + 20 ml. water | r 2.9- 4.0 y | low | not | good | not | moderate |

| Indicator | Preparation | Color & pH range | | | | | |
|---|---|---|---|---|---|---|---|
| Methyl orange (sodium salt of dimethylaminoazo-benzenesulfonic acid) | 0.01 per cent aqueous | r 3.1– 4.4 y | low | not | fair | good | good |
| Benzene-azo-α-naphthylamine | 0.01 gram in 0.4 ml. 0.1 N HCl + 30 ml. alcohol + 70 ml. water | r 3.7– 5.0 y | low | not | good | not | moderate |
| p-benzenesulfonic acid-azo-α-naphthylamine | 0.01 gram in 60 ml. alcohol + 40 ml. water | r 3.5– 5.7 y | low | not | good | good | good |
| Methyl red (dimethylaminoazo-benzene-o-carbonic acid) | 0.02 gram in 60 ml. alcohol + 40 ml. water | r 4.2– 6.3 y | low | S.C. | good | good | moderate |
| p-nitrophenol | 0.04 gram in 6 ml. alcohol + 94 ml. water | c 5.0– 7.0 y | moderate | good | good | good | good |
| Neutral red (dimethyldiaminophenasin-chloride) | 0.01 gram in 50 ml. alcohol + 50 ml. water | r 6.8– 8.0 y | low | S.C. | good | S.C. | good |
| Rosolic acid | 0.04 gram in 40 ml. alcohol + 60 ml. water | br 6.9– 8.0 r | low | fair | good | fair | good |
| Tropeolin OOO No. 1 (sodium salt of p-sulfobenzeneazo-β naphthol) | 0.01 per cent aqueous | v 7.6– 8.9 p | low | good | good | good | good |
| p-α-naphtholphthalein | 0.1 gram in 150 ml. alcohol + 100 ml. water | y 7.3– 8.7 b | moderate | S.C. | good | good | fair |
| Phenolphthalein | 0.05 gram in 50 ml. alcohol + 50 ml. water | c 8.3–10.0 r | moderate | S.C. | good | good | good—fades in strong alkali |
| Thymolphthalein | 0.04 gram in 50 ml. alcohol + 50 ml. water | c 9.3–10.5 b | moderate | S.C. | good | good | fades in moderate alkali |
| Alizarin yellow R (sodium salt of benzeneazo-salicylic acid) | 0.01 per cent aqueous | y 10.1–12.1 y | | good | good | | good |
| Tropeolin O (sodium salt of azo-benzene-4'-sulfonate) | 0.01 per cent aqueous | y 11.1–12.7 o | | | fair | fair | good |

S.C. = useful in special cases.  b = blue; br = brown; c = colorless; o = orange; p = pink; r = red; v = violet; y = yellow.

The absorption band for thymol blue is narrow and sharp, and the primary and secondary bands, which are in equilibrium, are sufficiently intense and distinct for facile reading. A mixture of methyl red and bromothymol blue may be employed to supplement the intermediate range not covered by thymol blue for the determination of hydrogen-ion concentrations from 1-10.

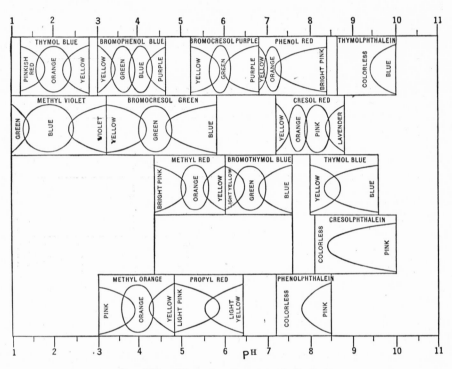

FIG. 100. pH range of common indicators

At the transition interval, bromophenol blue exhibits dichromatism, wherein the color of the indicator varies with concentration and depth of solution. The indicator is inaccurate in solutions that exhibit turbidity or contain alcohol or alkaloids.

Tetrabromophenoltetrabromosulfonephthalein [7] has been proposed to replace bromophenol blue, under the name of tetrabromophenol blue. It shows a color change from yellow to blue but is free from dichromatism.

[7] Wilton C. Harden and Nathan L. Drake, *J. Am. Chem. Soc.*, **51**, 562-6, 2278-9 (1929).

Tetrabromo-m-cresolsulfonephthalein, known as bromocresol green, was found to have an apparent dissociation constant of 4.68 for the pure material.[8]

In Figure 100 are given the ranges and color changes of indicators available from the Eastman Kodak Co. A useful chart of the range of color changes of common indicators has been prepared and is shown in Figure 101. A second table (Table 31) gives a set of one-color indicators.

TABLE 31.  MONOCHROMATIC INDICATORS OF MICHAELIS

| | | | | | pK Value |
|---|---|---|---|---|---|
| Picric acid | colorless | 0.0- | 1.3 | yellow | ... |
| 2,4-Dimitrophenol, α-dinitrophenol | colorless | 2.0- | 4.7 | yellow | 4.06 |
| 2,6-Dinitrophenol, β-dinitrophenol | colorless | 1.7- | 4.4 | yellow | 3.69 |
| 2,5-Dinitrophenol, γ-dinitrophenol | colorless | 4.0- | 6.0 | yellow | 5.15 |
| m-Nitrophenol | colorless | 6.3- | 9.0 | yellow | 8.33 |
| p-Nitrophenol | colorless | 4.7- | 7.9 | yellow | 7.18 |
| Phenolphthalein | colorless | 8.5- | 10.5 | red | 9.73 |
| Alizarin yellow GG, salicyl yellow | colorless | 10.0- | 12.0 | yellow | ... |

Numerous indicators have been examined for high pH ranges and been found unsatisfactory. The most promising, as given in Table 31, are supplemented by Table 32. Several indicators whose pH range is

TABLE 32.  INDICATORS FOR HIGH pH VALUES

| Common Name | Chemical Name | Color Change | | | |
|---|---|---|---|---|---|
| Alizarin Yellow GG | m-Nitrobenzeneazosalicylic acid | Lemon Yellow | 10.0 | Yellow | 12.0 |
| Alizarin Yellow R | p-Nitrobenzeneazosalicylic acid | Yellow | 10.0 | Orange | 12.0 |
| Tropeolin O | p-Sulfobenzeneazoresorcin | Yellow | 11.0 | Orange | 13.0 |
| Azo blue | Ditolyldisazo-bis-α-naphthol-4-sulfonic acid | Violet | 10.0 | Purple | 11.0 |
| ............ | α-Naphthol benzein | Yellow | 9.0 | Green | 10.6 |

above 10 have been included under their commercial brands because of the availability of data on their use. The third table (Table 33) is a selection of indicators of Clark and Lubs, enlarged by Cohen, and further amplified by these proprietary indicators over a range not otherwise covered.

Comparison of the Clark and Lubs indicators with those of Michaelis (Table 31) has shown differences of 0.1-0.2 pH. Use of Clark and Lubs indicators with the Pulfrich spectrophotometer yields a value accurate to 0.1 pH.[9] The differences are in unbuffered solution and are due to the varying alkaline content of the dye or to variations in its constitution.

[8] Walter C. Holmes and Edward F. Snyder, *J. Am. Chem. Soc.*, 47, 226-9 (1925).
[9] H. van Dam, *Ing. chim.*, 24, 41-56 (1940).

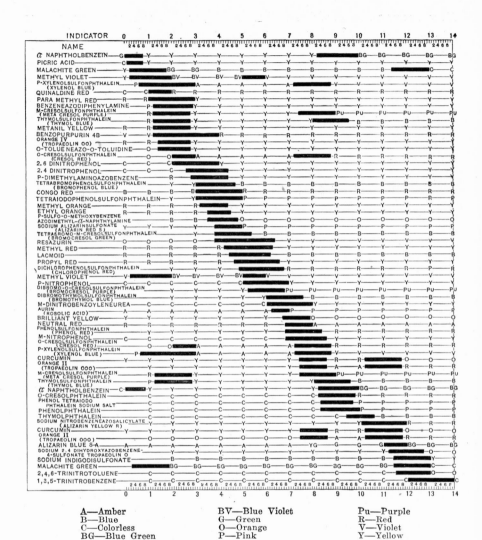

A—Amber                   BV—Blue Violet           Pu—Purple
B—Blue                    G—Green                  R—Red
C—Colorless               O—Orange                 V—Violet
BG—Blue Green             P—Pink                   Y—Yellow

The pH range shown are approximations and are intended to aid in selecting the proper indicator.
Further details can be obtained from such books as:
1. Hydrogen Ions—by Hubert T. S. Britton (1929).
2. The Determination of Hydrogen Ions—by William M. Clark (1928).
3. Indicators—by I. M. Kolthoff (1926).
4. The Theory and Use of Indicators—by E. B. R. Prideaux (1917).

FIG. 101. Hydrogen-ion concentration ranges and color changes of organic
chemical indicators. (*Eastman Kodak Co.*)

TABLE 33.   INDICATORS OF CLARK AND LUBS, COHEN [10] AND LA MOTTE CHEMICAL PRODUCTS CO.

| Common Name | Molecular Weight | ml. 0.01 N NaOH per 0.1 g. Indicator | pK | Range pH | Color Change Acid – Alkaline | pH Required for Full Acid Color | pH Required for Full Alkaline Color | Absorption Maximum Acid mμ | Absorption Maximum Alk. mμ |
|---|---|---|---|---|---|---|---|---|---|
| m-Cresol purple | 382 | 26.2 | 1.51 | 1.2–2.8 | red-yellow | conc. HCl | 6 | 533 | |
| Thymol blue | 466 | 21.5 | 1.5 | 1.2–2.8 | red-yellow | conc. HCl | 6 | 544 | |
| Bromophenol blue | 669 | 14.9 | 3.98 | 3.0–4.6 | yellow-blue | 0 | 7 | | 592 |
| Bromocresol green | 698 | 14.3 | 4.67 | 3.8–5.4 | yellow-blue | 1 | 8 | | 617 |
| Chlorophenol red | 423 | 23.6 | 5.98 | 4.8–6.4 | yellow-red | 2 | 9 | | 573 |
| Bromophenol red | 512 | 19.5 | 6.16 | 5.2–6.8 | yellow-red | 3 | 10 | | 574 |
| Bromocresol purple | 540 | 18.5 | 6.3 | 5.2–6.8 | yellow-purple | 3 | 10 | | 591 |
| Bromothymol blue | 624 | 16.0 | 7.0 | 6.0–7.6 | yellow-blue | 4 | 10 | | 617 |
| Phenol red | 354 | 28.2 | 7.9 | 6.8–8.4 | yellow-red | 5 | 11 | | 558 |
| Cresol red | 382 | 26.2 | 8.3 | 7.2–8.8 | yellow-red | 5 | 11 | | 572 |
| m-Cresol purple | 382 | 26.2 | 8.32 | 7.4–9.0 | yellow-purple | 5 | 11 | | 580 |
| Thymol blue | 466 | 21.5 | 8.9 | 8.0–9.6 | yellow-blue | 6 | 12 | | 596 |
| Cresolphthalein | | | 9.4 | 8.2–9.8 | colorless-red | 6 | 12 | | |
| La Motte purple | | | | 9.6–11.2 | blue-violet | | | | |
| Nitro yellow | | | | 10.0–11.6 | colorless-deep yellow | | | | |
| Sulfo orange | | | | 11.0–12.6 | pale yellow-deep orange | | | | |
| La Motte violet | | | | 12.0–13.6 | red-blue | | | | |

[10] Barnett Cohen, *Public Health Repts.*, **41**, 3051-74 (1926).

Nitrophenols and dinitrophenols undergo no change in character of color with deviating pH but vary in intensity from colorless to yellow as the pH increases. The acidity may be estimated within 0.05 pH using a photometer. p-Nitrophenol is quite suitable for unbuffered solutions. A study of the α, β, and γ forms of dinitrophenol demonstrated that the β form is most suitable in the pH range 1.30-3.70, the α form in the range 2.50-4.33, and the γ form for pH 3.62-5.74.[11]

Pinachrom (M), p-ethoxyquinaldin-p-ethoxyquinolin ethylcyanine, when dissolved in dilute hydrochloric acid, is an excellent one-color indicator for the range 5.8-7.8, changing from colorless in acid medium to red in alkaline medium. The color develops fully after about two minutes. It is recommended for tap water and distilled water. At low electrolyte content the salt error is negligible. At high salt cnocentrations the reaction indicated is too acid.

For use by the balancing method the pK value of the indicator must be known. The values are given with the necessary tables for the Clark and Lubs-Cohen series in Table 33.

When the red sodium salt of quinizarin-6-sulfonic acid is added to an acid solution, a yellow color is formed. Addition of alkali to this solution produces first a sharp change to the pink and more gradually to the blue-violet form. The $pK_A$ for the first hydrogen is 8.2, and for the second hydrogen 10.7.[12]

Alizarin yellow GG changes from pale yellow to deep yellow at pH 9.5-11.5. Permanent color standards for comparison may be prepared from 1 per cent potassium chromate, 10 per cent cobaltic sulfate heptahydrate, and 10 per cent sulfuric acid by volume. This indicator has been used with particular effectiveness to determine pH in brass-plating solutions containing cyanide.[13] Dibromonaphthazarine is far more stable than napthazarine, and is a more satisfactory indicator in the pH range 7-12.[14] The pH of azobilirubin for one-half the dissociation of the indicator is 2.45, and the isobestic point is shown to be at a wave length of 520 mμ.[15]

Figure 102 gives the dissociation constants of many one-color indicators in readily usable form.[16]

[11] E. Lucchi, *Giorn. biol. ind. agrar. aliment.*, **7**, 154-63 (1937).

[12] J. H. Green, *Ind. Eng. Chem., Anal. Ed.*, **14**, 249 (1942).

[13] S. G. Clarke and W. N. Bradshaw, *Analyst*, **68**, 245-6 (1943).

[14] Ladislao Brüll and Pierleone Girotti, *Ann. chim. applicata*, **26**, 19-24 (1936).

[15] A. Thiel and H. Logemann, *Biochem. Z.*, **284**, 347-52 (1936).

[16] J. F. McClendon, *Am. Naturalist*, **64**, 289-99 (1930).

**pH of Indicator Solutions.** Unless the sample solution is well buffered, dilution by the indicator solution and reaction of the indicator with hydrogen-ion or hydroxyl-ion will affect the pH. For slightly buffered solutions, therefore, the pH of the indicator solution must be adjusted to about the middle of the transition range.[17] In exceedingly dilute solutions or in weakly buffered solutions of high neutral salt content a new definition of colorimetric pH must therefore be written. It is that the pH of the solution is that of the indicator solution, which does not change color when added to the unknown.[18] Salt and protein errors must still be given consideration. If the pH of the indicator solution is within 0.5 pH of that being determined, substantial accuracy is obtained. This would not apply to a case like distilled water, but neither would the other details of the usual technique.

The isohydric indicator solutions can also be pre-

[17] W. H. Pierre and J. F. Fudge, *J. Am. Chem. Soc.*, **50**, 1254-62 (1928).

[18] S. F. Acree and Edna H. Fawcett, *J. Bacteriology*, **17**, 163-204 (1929); *Ind. Eng. Chem., Anal. Ed.*, **2**, 78-85 (1930).

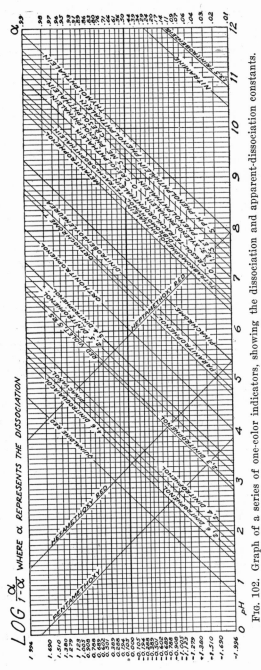

Fig. 102. Graph of a series of one-color indicators, showing the dissociation and apparent-dissociation constants.

pared by purification of the indicator until condustimetric titration gives theoretical results, and by calculation from the ionization constant of the indicator to the amount of sodium hydroxide necessary for solutions of definite pH. Estimations with isohydric indicators can also be conveniently carried out by use of a series of indicators having a range of pH values, not necessarily accurately known.[19] If the pH value determined remains constant when an additional amount of indicator is added the indicator is isohydric. This is a simpler technique.

**Universal Indicator.** For rough, preliminary estimation the so-called "universal indicator" undoubtedly has a use. The required indicator, with a narrow pH range, may then be applied. One such indicator has the following composition: phenolphthalein 100 mg., methyl red 200 mg., dimethylaminoazo benzene 300 mg., bromothymol blue 400 mg., thymol blue 500 mg. For preparation, dissolve in 500 ml. of absolute alcohol, and add 0.1 N sodium hydroxide solution until the red disappears and the solution indicates a pH of 6.0 by a yellow color. The color changes are as follows:

| Color | Red | Orange | Yellow | Green | Blue |
|---|---|---|---|---|---|
| pH | 2.0 | 4.0 | 6.0 | 8.0 | 10.0 |

Another contains 0.1 per cent solutions of the following: 15 ml. of dimethyl yellow, 5 ml. of methyl red, 20 ml. of bromothymol blue, 20 ml. of phenolphthalein, 20 ml. of thymolphthalein. The following colors are obtained:

| Color | Rose | Red-Orange | Orange | Yellow-Orange | Lemon-Yellow |
|---|---|---|---|---|---|
| pH | 1.0 | 3.0 | 4.0 | 5.0 | 6.0 |

| Color | Yellow Green | Green | Blue-Green | Violet |
|---|---|---|---|---|
| pH | 7.0 | 8.0 | 9.0 | 10.0 |

Another has the composition: tropeolin 00 70 mg. methyl orange 100 mg., methyl red 80 mg., bromothymol blue 400 mg., phenolphthalein 500 mg., alizarin yellow R 100 mg. in 100 ml. of 50 per cent alcohol. One drop is used in 10 ml. of solution to give the following colors.

| Color | Orange-Red | Red-Orange | Orange | Yellow-Orange | Orange-Yellow | Yellow | Green-Yellow |
|---|---|---|---|---|---|---|---|
| pH | 2.0 | 3.0 | 4.0 | 5.0 | 6.0 | 6.5 | 7.0 |

[19] I. M. Kolthoff and Tohru Kameda, *J. Am. Chem. Soc.*, **53**, 825-32 (1931).

| Color | Green | Green-Blue | Violet-Blue to Blue-Violet | Violet | Violet to Violet-Red | Violet-Red |
|---|---|---|---|---|---|---|
| pH | 8.0 | 9.0 | 9.5 | 10.0 | 11.0 | 12.0 |

By comparison with various buffers throughout the range an approximate pH can be obtained to be amplified by a more careful estimation

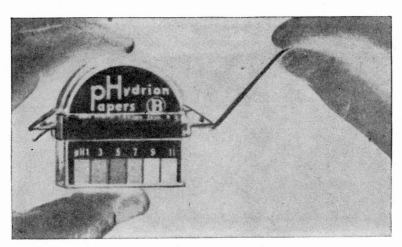

FIG. 103. Handy unit for determination of pH by universal indicator papers

over a small range. For many rough, preliminary purposes one of the universal indicators is sufficiently accurate.

The indicators are also available commercially in the form of impregnated paper, as shown in Figure 103.

# CHAPTER XX

# HYDROGEN-ION—PREPARATION OF SAMPLES

THIS subject is so broad that of necessity many kinds of samples are not mentioned. By analogy the methods given can be applied to many other forms with or without preliminary treatment. A major field is for examination of biological samples where colorimetric values usually check those obtained electrometrically within ± 0.3 pH units.[1]

**Water.** Use the water as received without dilution. Undue air exposure may alter the pH by absorption or loss of carbon dioxide according to the pH level. Colorimetric pH is suitable for controlling coagulation in water purification, especially if lime has to be added with the aluminum sulfate.

Aside from the usual methods, an approximation without standards may be made in the usual range of pH 8-9. Add 0.5 ml. of 0.5 per cent phenolphthalein solution to 100 ml. and mix. Compare the intensity as follows:

| Color | Estimated pH Equivalent |
|---|---|
| Indistinguishable from blank | not over 7.8 |
| Indistinguishable without comparison with blank | 8.0 |
| Faintly pink | 8.2 |
| Pink | 8.4 |
| Strongly pink | 8.6 |
| Very strongly pink | 8.8 |
| Red | 9.0 |

It is preferable that estimations of pH on water be made at the temperature of the water at its source.[2] Comparison of colorimetric methods with electrometric methods indicates that colorimetric results on water range from 0.2-0.4 pH units lower.[3]

**Sea Water.**[4] To every 100 ml. add 4 drops of 2.5 per cent mercuric chloride solution. Leave a small air space in the bottles. Use cresol red as indicator. The sample will keep for 2 weeks at 12° or 2 days at 33°.

---

[1] Albert Gluabiger and K. George Falk, *J. Lab. Clin. Med.,* **25,** 369-76 (1940).

[2] Luis Pró y Castillo, *Bol. soc. quím. Peru,* **2,** 7-8 (1936).

[3] Rustico Tengco, *Philippine J. Sci.,* **69,** 1-5 (1939).

[4] O. Gormez Ibanez, *J. Marine Biol. Assoc.,* **17,** 483-8 (1931).

**Electroplating Solutions.** These samples are usually colored and therefore commonly require the Walpole technique (p. 22). For cyanide brass-plating solutions, alizarin yellow GG is a suitable indicator.[5] Corresponding permanent standards may be prepared from 1 per cent potassium dichromate, 10 per cent cobalt sulfate, and 10 per cent sulfuric acid by volume.

For nickel-plating solutions, use as indicator a 0.1 per cent solution of bromocresol purple in 20 per cent ethanol.[6] To overcome interference by the deep green of the solution, special glass discs are available for use in the Lovibond comparator with nickel-plating solutions having a hydrogen-ion concentration of 5.2-6-8 as determined with bromocresol purple as the indicator. One disc compensates for 120 grams of crystalline nickel sulfate per liter of solution, and the other for approximately twice that amount.

Sufficient accuracy in iron electroplating baths has been found by impregnating filter paper strips with xylene blue, Congo red, metanil yellow, or indigo carmine and immersing these strips in the solution.[7]

Comparison of colorimetric with electrometric methods indicates that the presence of high salt concentrations may cause the results to vary as much as 0.6 pH unit on this type of sample.

**Soils.** The pH of a soil is that of the aqueous extract which can be made from it. Select representative samples of soil, preferably from around the roots of the living plant. A soil sampler may be used.[8] Water used for extraction of soil acidity should be as free from carbon dioxide as possible. Distilled water is best, although high-grade ground water may be used. To 4-5 grams of soil add 15 ml. of water. Shake and allow the solid matter to settle, or preferably separate in a centrifuge.[9] Decant or pipet the more or less clear liquid and use as sample. High-grade barium sulfate is sometimes added to sorb colloidal matter before centrifuging.

As the volume of a soil solution is diluted from that corresponding to its moisture-holding capacity the pH changes. The change varies with the type of soil, exceeding 0.5 pH in some soils on 60 times

[5] S. G. Clarke and W. N. Bradshaw, *Analyst*, **68**, 245-6 (1943).

[6] E. S. Tinovskaya, *Zavodskaya Lab.*, **9**, 914-15 (1940).

[7] V. I. Afanas'eva and T. L. Mitnitskaya, *Poligraf. Proizvodstvo*, **1940**, 41-2.

[8] A. H. Eddins and W. H. Schovilk, *Soil Sci.*, **43**, 219-20 (1937).

[9] Felix G. Gustafson, *Ecology*, **9**, 360-3 (1928); cf. W. Heukeshoven, *Angew. Chem.*, **49**, 742-3 (1936); cf. Paul Funke & Co., German Patent 661,588 (1938).

dilution.[10] Such dilution reduces the pH of most alkaline soils and increases that of most acid soils. It is best to keep the amount of water used for extraction at a minimum.

Numerous modifications of the conventional methods are used, commonly with lowered accuracy. One is to shake 6 grams of soil with 12 ml. of $N$ potassium chloride solution and 6 drops of a 0.2 per cent solution of bromocresol green and compare with buffers containing the same amount of the same indicator after 15 minutes. If the solution is too turbid, prepare a larger sample, filter through paper and test successive portions of the filtrate until two give the same pH. Avoid absorption of carbon dioxide as far as possible.

Several other methods have been developed employing bromothymol blue [11] or a mixture of 1 part 0.02 per cent solution of methyl red and 2 parts of 0.04 per cent solution of bromothymol blue, covering the pH range 4.0-8.0.[12] Ordinarily, mixtures of inorganic salt solutions (p. 55) are employed as permanent standards. The colorimetric method has been found dependable for estimation of the hydrogen-ion concentration of soils.[13]

**Bacteriological Culture Media.** Nutrient agar is of itself a buffer so that it will stand sevenfold dilution, at which concentration it is liquid, without change of pH. It may then be used for a sample by the usual technics.[14] Indicators must be selected carefully because complex amino acids occasionally react with the indicators, voiding the results. Alizarin yellow GG is satisfactory, except with samples containing copper, but thymolphthalein fades rapidly and bromocresol green gives high results.[15] If the pH ranges from 6.8-7.8, solutions of cobalt acetate and of potassium chromate in various concentrations may be used as permanent standards.[16]

**Blood, Serum or Plasma.** Temperature and protein concentration modify the pH. Normally, the determination should be at 38°. In colorimetric determinations at room temperature on 103 samples, results of

---

[10] J. C. Wilcox, *Sci. Agr.*, **16**, 225-32 (1936).

[11] E. Gaspart, *IV Congr. intern. tech. chim. ind. agr. Bruxelles*, **2**, 296-9 (1935).

[12] N. I. Alyamovskiĭ, *Chemisation Socialistic Agr.* (U.S.S.R.), **8**, No. 1, 84-6 (1939).

[13] P. L. Hibbard, *J. Assoc. Official Agr. Chem.*, **19**, 256-62 (1936).

[14] Martin W. Lisse, Otto G. Jensen and Ralph P. Tittsler, *J. Bact.*, **21**, 383-94 (1931).

[15] A. B. Cox, *Soc. Chem. Ind. Victoria, Proc.*, **35**, 1001-5 (1935).

[16] Chun Chieh Young, *Trans. 9th Congr. Far East Assoc. Trop. Med.*, **1**, 377-8 (1935); *Ber. ges. Physiol. exptl. Pharmakol.*, **87**, 228.

85 per cent of the cases checked with electrometric data, taken at 38°, within 0.04 pH, if a temperature correction factor of 0.22 pH was subtracted from the colorimetric value.[17] In a study of dog serum concentrated by ultrafiltration through cellophane under 150 lb. per sq. in., it was found that the correction to be applied in the pH determination varies directly with the log of the protein concentration. The correction for the protein concentration for humans and for dogs is 0.243 unit of pH.[18]

Bromothymol blue is unsuitable for use with serum. Satisfactory values for blood may be obtained with $p$-nitrophenol, although it is a rather strong precipitating agent for proteins. Special cups with tight-fitting covers must be used, the plasma introduced under the indicator solution, causing it to overflow, and the cover put in place.

Dichromatic indicators have not been found entirely suitable for use with blood. Cyanine cannot be used because it is affected by proteins.

A special procedure is required for the technic given because a special saline indicator is required. The technic is approximately that of the Gillespie-Hatfield method (p. 201). The standards are 0.01-0.02 pH more acid with the saline solution than in the absence of salt. The standards remain practically unchanged for 8 days. The colorimetric results agree within 0.02 pH with electrometric determination at the same temperature. The acid and alkaline solutions as used are according to Gillespie and obviate the necessity of phosphate buffers. The corpuscles do not interfere so that the results obtained are those of the plasma, even when whole blood is used. No more than negligible error is introduced by the twenty-one-fold dilution required.

*Reagents.* Dissolve 0.9 gram of sodium chloride in freshly redistilled water in a 100 ml. volumetric flask. Dilute 15 ml. of 0.1 per cent pheno! red solution to 200 ml. to give a 0.0075 per cent solution. For use with whole blood add 11 ml. of this indicator solution to the saline solution, and dilute to 100 ml. For use with plasma prepare a similar solution using 10.5 ml. of indicator solution. Prepare a similar solution by dilution of 11 ml. of distilled water to 100 ml. with the saline solution for use in the control tubes. Adjust the reaction of the saline indicators to approximately that of blood by covering the solution with mineral oil and adding 0.01 $N$ sodium hydroxide solution containing the same concentration of indicator and salt, drop by drop, until the pH is approximately 7.4. So adjusted, there is little change on standing for a few

17 Victor C. Myers and Edward Muntwyler, *J. Biol. Chem.*, **78**, 243-55 (1928).

18 Howard W. Robinson, J. Waide Price and G. E. Cullen, *J. Biol. Chem.*, **114**, 321-40 (1936).

hours. As standard acid use 0.0001 $N$ hydrochloric acid, and as alkali 0.01 $N$ sodium hydroxide solution.

*Procedure.*—Prepare the series of pH standards given in Table 34.

*Serum or Plasma.* Put 4 ml. of adjusted saline indicator in a test tube under oil. Add 0.2 ml. of blood serum or plasma to the indicator, and stir. Prepare a control using the sample and saline solution without indicator. Replace the oil by paraffin, and place a thermometer in the cork with the bulb dipping into the control or a tube of water.

TABLE 34. pH VALUES AT 20° AND 38° AT 0.05° INTERVALS, WITH
CORRESPONDING AMOUNTS OF 0.0075 PER CENT PHENOL RED
AND 0.01 $N$ NaOH OR 0.0001 $N$ HCl.

| pH 20° | Alkali tube | | Acid tube | | pH 38° | Alkali tube | | Acid tube | |
|---|---|---|---|---|---|---|---|---|---|
| | *ml. dye* | *ml. alkali* | *ml. dye* | *ml. acid* | | *ml. dye* | *ml. alkali* | *ml. dye* | *ml. acid* |
| 6.70 | 0.19 | 24.81 | 2.31 | 22.69 | 6.70 | 0.25 | 24.75 | 2.25 | 22.75 |
| 6.75 | 0.21 | 24.79 | 2.29 | 22.71 | 6.75 | 0.28 | 24.72 | 2.22 | 22.78 |
| 6.80 | 0.24 | 24.76 | 2.26 | 22.74 | 6.80 | 0.31 | 24.69 | 2.19 | 22.81 |
| 6.85 | 0.26 | 24.74 | 2.24 | 22.76 | 6.85 | 0.34 | 24.66 | 2.16 | 22.84 |
| 6.90 | 0.29 | 24.71 | 2.21 | 22.79 | 6.90 | 0.38 | 24.62 | 2.12 | 22.88 |
| 6.95 | 0.32 | 24.68 | 2.18 | 22.82 | 6.95 | 0.42 | 24.58 | 2.08 | 22.92 |
| 7.00 | 0.36 | 24.64 | 2.14 | 22.86 | 7.00 | 0.46 | 24.54 | 2.04 | 22.96 |
| 7.05 | 0.39 | 24.61 | 2.11 | 22.89 | 7.05 | 0.50 | 24.50 | 2.00 | 23.00 |
| 7.10 | 0.43 | 24.57 | 2.07 | 22.93 | 7.10 | 0.55 | 24.45 | 1.95 | 23.05 |
| 7.15 | 0.48 | 24.52 | 2.02 | 22.98 | 7.15 | 0.60 | 24.40 | 1.90 | 23.10 |
| 7.20 | 0.52 | 24.48 | 1.98 | 23.02 | 7.20 | 0.65 | 24.35 | 1.85 | 23.15 |
| 7.25 | 0.57 | 24.43 | 1.93 | 23.07 | 7.25 | 0.71 | 24.29 | 1.79 | 23.21 |
| 7.30 | 0.62 | 24.38 | 1.88 | 23.12 | 7.30 | 0.77 | 24.23 | 1.73 | 23.27 |
| 7.35 | 0.68 | 24.32 | 1.82 | 23.18 | 7.35 | 0.84 | 24.16 | 1.66 | 23.34 |
| 7.40 | 0.74 | 24.26 | 1.76 | 23.24 | 7.40 | 0.90 | 24.10 | 1.60 | 23.40 |
| 7.45 | 0.80 | 24.20 | 1.70 | 23.30 | 7.45 | 0.97 | 24.03 | 1.53 | 23.47 |
| 7.50 | 0.86 | 24.14 | 1.64 | 23.36 | 7.50 | 1.04 | 23.96 | 1.46 | 23.54 |
| 7.55 | 0.93 | 24.07 | 1.57 | 23.43 | 7.55 | 1.11 | 23.89 | 1.39 | 23.61 |
| 7.60 | 1.00 | 24.00 | 1.50 | 23.50 | 7.60 | 1.18 | 23.82 | 1.32 | 23.68 |
| 7.65 | 1.07 | 23.93 | 1.43 | 23.57 | 7.65 | 1.25 | 23.75 | 1.25 | 23.75 |
| 7.70 | 1.14 | 23.86 | 1.36 | 23.64 | 7.70 | 1.32 | 23.68 | 1.18 | 23.82 |
| 7.75 | 1.21 | 23.79 | 1.29 | 23.71 | 7.75 | 1.39 | 23.61 | 1.11 | 23.89 |
| 7.80 | 1.28 | 23.72 | 1.22 | 23.78 | 7.80 | 1.46 | 23.54 | 1.04 | 23.96 |
| 7.85 | 1.35 | 23.65 | 1.15 | 23.85 | 7.85 | 1.53 | 23.47 | 0.97 | 24.03 |
| 7.90 | 1.42 | 23.58 | 1.08 | 23.92 | 7.90 | 1.60 | 23.40 | 0.90 | 24.10 |
| 7.95 | 1.49 | 23.51 | 1.01 | 23.99 | 7.95 | 1.67 | 23.33 | 0.83 | 24.17 |
| 8.00 | 1.56 | 23.44 | 0.94 | 24.06 | 8.00 | 1.73 | 23.27 | 0.77 | 24.23 |

Prepare tubes similarly protected by paraffin containing 5 ml. portions of the standards to be used at the same time. Heat to 38.5-39° and when the temperature has dropped to 38° make the comparison promptly, using the technique of the Gillespie-Hatfield method for colored samples The standards may be heated or not according to the series used. The standards may be kept for 5 weeks without fading.

*Blood.* Following the above procedure except that the indicator of a different concentration for blood is used. After mixing, centrifuge to settle the corpuscles before proceeding.

**Urine.** The method for colored solutions is used (p. 220). With phenol red, bromocresol purple and bromocresol green with urine at 1:5 dilution, at room temperature, a correction of −0.2 pH is necessary for the approximate pH. About half is for temperature and half for salt and buffer effects. Comparison with results on undiluted samples at 38° shows that no single correction constant holds, that for accurate results the urine must not be diluted, and that work must be done at 38°. In contrast with this, dilution with a saline diluent of definite pH has been carried out satisfactorily by the balancing method, the determinations being carried out under oil at 25°. Correction factors for conversion to 38° were phenol red 0.24 pH, bromothyol blue 0.20 pH, bromocresol purple 0.20 pH, bromocresol green 0.22 pH. Electrometric values are considered the more accurate in normal urine. In protein-free urine below pH 6.5, all methods are satisfactory. Strongly colored urines render the colorimetric method difficult, if not impossible. Decolorizing with animal charcoal is not permissible.

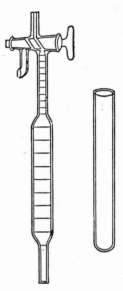

Fig. 104. Apparatus for handling spinal fluid in pH determination

**Gastric Contents.** The treatment varies with the degree of acidity. Below pH 2.1 use the clear filtrate directly. Above pH 2.1 and below 3.0 dialyze the sample against normal salt solution and use the dialysate.

The variations between electrometric and colorimetric methods are rather large. Below pH 3.0 the differences are never more than 0.5 and usually less. Above pH 3.0 differences of 1.0 pH are not uncommon, therefore, the electrometric method is preferable.

**Cerebrospinal Fluid.**[19] The sample must never come into contact with the air or it will lose carbon dioxide and give too high a value. A special apparatus is required. To one end of a tube the same size as used for the standards, fuse a 3-way stopcock. The other end carries a capillary tube. The tube is suitably calibrated, as shown in Figure 104.

19 I. McQuarrie and A. T. Shohl, *J. Biol. Chem.*, **66**, 367-74 (1925).

Place the indicator in the sampling pipet before taking the sample. Fill the sampling pipet with mercury. Connect the 3-way stopcock to the lumbar puncture needle by a suitably sterilized glass adapter and rubber tubing. Let the fluid escape under its own pressure until the air has been removed from the capillary tube. Then turn the stopcock so that the fluid enters the apparatus. In this operation immerse the sampling bulb in mercury so that the mercury level inside the bulb is at or very slightly above that outside. This is to avoid drawing too great a suction and possible leakage. When sufficient sample has been drawn, turn the stopcock and close the lower capillary with a pinchcock. Immerse the sample with indicator and standards in a water bath at 38° for 5 minutes before comparison. Using phenol red as indicator, the normal pH was found to be 7.35 to 7.40 ± 0.02.

**Dairy Products.** Determination of the pH in whole milk is nearly impossible due to the turbidity of the sample. Methods using dialysis eliminate turbidity and protein error but introduce a Donnan equilibrium, a salt error and a dilution effect. Dilution methods decrease turbidity and are suitable, provided the corrections are known. In 1:20 dilution, extreme accuracy is not possible but results within 0.1 pH can be attained, the average error being 0.06 pH. Colorimetric results on milk are usually 0.15-1.07 pH units lower than electrometric. The difference is usually less in fresh milk than in sour milk.

Prepared indicator paper may be used to determine the pH of milk and whey in the ranges below 6.6. Down to 5.4 the accuracy is to ±0.1 pH unit; below 5.4, to ±0.2 pH unit.[20] Strips of water-diffusable membrane containing indicators also may be placed in the liquid for 1.5 minutes, rinsed and compared with standards. Results for whey agree with potentiometric methods within 0.1 pH, with a slightly greater difference for milk.[21]

Standards have also been prepared in sealed tubes by adding increasing amounts of sour milk to normal sweet milk.[22] Treat with 30 ml. of methanol for every 20 ml. of milk. Refrigerate for 30 days, and filter. Determine the pH electrometrically. The indicator solution used was prepared by dissolving 20 mg. of bromocresol blue, 50 mg. of methyl red and 100 mg. of bromocresol purple in a liter of neutral methanol. Add 1 ml. of indicator to 10 ml. of serum, and place in

---

[20] L. Seekles, *J. Dairy Research*, 11, 79-83 (1940).

[21] R. Aschaffenburg, *J. Dairy Research*, 9, 335-8 (1938).

[22] G. Schwarz and Ottmar Fischer, *Milchw. Forsch.*, 17, 158-69 (1935).

sealed tubes for comparison. Titratable acidity is considered more important than pH.[23]

*Whole and Skim Milk.* If casein has started to separate, break up the curd thoroughly and mix with the whey before sampling. Pipet 5 ml. into a 100 ml. graduated cylinder, and dilute to volume. Pipet 10 ml. of sample into a tube and add indicator. Let casein separate if necessary. Compare, using a tube of diluted milk in back of the standard to correct for turbidity. The general procedure is therefore that for colored samples (p. 220). Apply correction from Table 35.

*Heated Milk.* When heated to boiling without loss of water treat the same as whole milk.

*Whey.* Proceed in the same way as for whole milk. If only part of the casein has separated, the correction factors in Table 35 do not apply, and the degree of separation of the casein must be estimated.

*Cream.* Obtain skim milk from the cream by centrifuging and determine as above. Assume that the value for the cream is the same as that obtained for the skim milk. If the cream has soured so that part of the casein is thrown down in centrifuging the correction factors do not apply.

*Powdered Milk.* Add distilled water so that the average total of solids, not fat, corresponds to whole milk. Proceed as for milk.

*Evaporated Milk.* Dilute 5 ml. with distilled water to 200 ml. and proceed as for milk. The pH of the evaporated milk before reconstituting can be obtained by subtracting 0.13 pH from the corrected value obtained for the reconstituted milk.

*Sweetened Condensed Milk.* Dilute with water so that the average of solids, not fat, corresponds to whole milk. Proceed as for whole milk except that correction factors in Table 35 do not apply. Instead, subtract 0.85 pH from the value obtained to get the pH of the reconstituted product or 1.15 pH to get the value for the original product.

**Brewery Products.** Variations in pH in the brewing industry are small, and the importance of small changes is great. Often an accuracy of 0.02-0.03 pH is necessary and this cannot be obtained colorimetrically. However, dilution of wort 5-10 times, and of stout 40 times does not involve serious error. Thymol blue, bromophenol blue, methyl red and bromothymol blue are used as indicators. Various errors include sorption by colloids, and reduction or oxidation of the indicator. These might be minimized by comparing with a mixture of buffer, indicator and water.

[23] E. Mundinger, *Molkerei-Ztg.* (Hildesheim), **49**, 2362-4, 2387-9 (1935).

TABLE 35. CORRECTION FACTORS FOR COLORIMETRIC DETERMINATION OF
HYDROGEN-ION CONCENTRATION OF MILK AND WHEY
BY DILUTION METHOD.[24]

| Colorimetric Reading | Whole Milk and Skim Milk | | Whey | | Indicator |
|---|---|---|---|---|---|
| | Correction Factor | Original Undiluted | Correction Factor | Original Undiluted | |
| pH | pH | pH | pH | pH | |
| 7.4 | 0.54 | 6.86 | | | Phenol red |
| 7.3 | 0.54 | 6.76 | | | |
| 7.2 | 0.54 | 6.66 | 0.26 | 6.94 | |
| 7.1 | 0.54 | 6.56 | 0.26 | 6.84 | |
| 7.0 | 0.54 | 6.46 | 0.26 | 6.74 | |
| 6.9 | 0.54 | 6.36 | 0.26 | 6.64 | |
| 6.8 | 0.54 | 6.26 | 0.26 | 6.54 | |
| 6.7 | 0.54 | 6.16 | 0.26 | 6.44 | |
| 6.6 | 0.54 | 6.06 | 0.26 | 6.34 | Bromocresol purple |
| 6.5 | 0.54 | 5.96 | 0.26 | 6.24 | |
| 6.4 | 0.54 | 5.86 | 0.25 | 6.15 | |
| 6.3 | 0.54 | 5.76 | 0.25 | 6.05 | |
| 6.2 | 0.54 | 5.66 | 0.24 | 5.96 | Chlorophenol red |
| 6.1 | 0.53 | 5.57 | 0.23 | 5.87 | |
| 6.0 | 0.52 | 5.48 | 0.23 | 5.77 | |
| 5.9 | 0.50 | 5.40 | 0.22 | 5.68 | |
| 5 8 | 0.48 | 5.32 | 0.22 | 5.58 | |
| 5.7 | 0.46 | 5.24 | 0.22 | 5.48 | |
| 5.6 | 0.43 | 5.17 | 0.22 | 5.38 | |
| 5.5 | 0.39 | 5.11 | 0.22 | 5.28 | |
| 5.4 | 0.35 | 5.05 | 0.22 | 5.18 | |
| 5.3 | 0.31 | 4.99 | 0.22 | 5.08 | |
| 5.2 | 0.28 | 4.92 | 0.22 | 4.98 | |
| 5.1 | 0.24 | 4.86 | 0.22 | 4.88 | |
| 5.0 | 0.22 | 4.78 | 0.22 | 4.78 | |
| 4.9 | 0.19 | 4.71 | 0.22 | 4.68 | Bromocresol green |
| 4.8 | 0.18 | 4.62 | 0.22 | 4.58 | |
| 4.7 | 0.17 | 4.53 | 0.22 | 4.48 | |
| 4.6 | 0.16 | 4.44 | 0.22 | 4.38 | |
| 4.5 | 0.16 | 4.34 | 0.22 | 4.28 | |
| 4.4 | 0.15 | 4.25 | 0.22 | 4.18 | Bromophenol blue |
| 4.3 | 0.15 | 4.15 | 0.22 | 4.08 | |
| 4.2(?) | 0.15 | 4.05 | 0.22 | 3.98 | |
| 4.1(?) | 0.16 | 3.94 | 0.22 | 3.88 | |
| 4.0(?) | 0.16 | 3.84 | 0.22 | 3.78 | |

[24] The product is diluted 1 to 19 with distilled water and the colorimetric determination made in the conventional way with turbidity blank. The colorimetric pH reading is located in the first column, then the pH of the undiluted milk or whey is found in the corresponding row.

**Meat Extract.** Extract 10 grams of fat-free, finely ground meat for 15 minutes with 100 ml. of boiled distilled water. Filter and use the filtrate as sample. The pH is 6.2 for meat of good quality, except for pork which gives 6.4.

**Molasses.** Dilute the sample with 9 volumes of distilled water. The results agree within experimental error with those obtained by electrometric methods.

**Flour, Baked Goods, and Alimentary Pastes.** Hydrogen-ion concentration may be determined in extracts of cereal products with p- or m-nitrophenol, or 2,5-dinitrophenol using the Walpole technique [25] (p. 22). The use of sulfonephthalein indicators is preferable.[26] Use 0.4 per cent solutions of bromocresol green, chlorophenol red, bromothymol blue, and phenol red. To 10 grams of flour or cereal or 15 grams of comminuted bread, add 100 ml. of cold, recently boiled water, and digest for 30 minutes at 25°, shaking occasionally. Allow the mixture to stand for 15 minutes. Decant the supernatant liquid through a hard filter paper, discarding the first 5 ml. and collecting 20 ml. in each of three 20 mm. test tubes. To 20 ml. of solution, add 0.5 ml. of indicator and compare with standards. The Gillespie comparator (p. 22) may be used to assist in reading the pH.[27]

**Sugar Solutions.** Dilute a solution of sugar to $22 \pm 0.5°$ Bé. This concentration is a compromise. The pH is less affected by dilution the more concentrated the solution used. The solution must be diluted to such an extent that it can be measured readily and mixed with the indicator. Compare with the methyl red series of indicators after suitable treatment.

**Soap Solutions.** The pH affects detergency.[28] Experience indicates the lack of reliability of simple estimation of pH in soap solutions. Some indicators are reliable and some are not.[29] If two indicators check as to

[25] George Garnatz, *J. Assoc. Official Agr. Chem.*, **19**, 542-6 (1936); *Ibid.*, **20**, 355-60 (1937).

[26] George Garnatz, *J. Assoc. Official Agr. Chem.*, **23**, 482-9 (1940); *Ibid.*, **24**, 583-6 (1941).

[27] *Official and Tentative Methods of Analysis*, 6th Ed., pp. 242-4, Association of Official Agricultural Chemists, Washington, D. C. (1945).

[28] Malcolm Dole, *Am. Dyestuff Reptr.*, **30**, No. 9; *Proc. Am. Assoc. Textile Chem. Colorists*, 231-8 (1941).

[29] Leslie R. Bacon, James W. Hensley and Thomas H. Vaughn, *Ind. Eng. Chem.*, **33**, 723-30 (1941).

the pH it is generally correct. The error is believed to be due to sorption of indicator by micelles of soap not having the pH of the main solution. Indicators not so sorbed would give correct readings. The errors in all cases result in low values.

**Sulfated Fatty Alcohols.** Estimation of the pH of solutions of the sulfated fatty alcohols and sulfonated synthetic detergents may be in error as much as one unit. The error is normally on the acid side, and is probably due to the same factors as in soap solutions.

**Gelatin Solutions.**[30] Colorimetric determination of the pH of buffered gelatin solutions indicates the average deviation to be ± 0.1 unit. For unbuffered solutions of purified gelatin, the deviation is ± 0.15 pH, and for nonpurified solution ± 0.50.

**Glue.** The natural color of even a 1 per cent solution of glue requires that the Walpole technic (p. 22) be used. Compare a 6 ml. sample solution to which 1 ml. of indicator has been added. Compensate by viewing the standard through 6 ml. of sample to which no indicator has been added, and view the sample through a tube of water.

**Sulfonated Oils.**[31] pH values taken with indicator strips are independent of the amount of dilution. The undiluted sample runs about 0.8 pH higher by this method than results obtained electrometrically, but colorimetric values for diluted solutions check those for undiluted. In diluting emulsions, the temperature of the mixing does not affect the pH value of the subsequently cooled emulsion. Sulfonated oils exert practically no buffering action in the presence of electrolytes.

**Textile Assistants.**[32] When determining colorimetric pH in the presence of textile assistants such as sulfonated oils, sulfated and sulfonated alcohols, sodium alkynaphthalene sulfonates, etc., they exert a specific effect on most indicators, leading to an error of as much as 1.0 unit.

**Unbuffered Solutions.** For pH in unbuffered solutions the liquid must be protected from atmospheric carbon dioxide. The solution of the indicator used must have been adjusted to the pH of the solution to

[30] I. Petrov and A. Pasuinskiǐ, *J. Applied Chem.* (U.S.S.R.), **8**, 165-70 (1935).

[31] G. Parsy, *J. Intern. Soc. Leather Trades Chem.*, **21**, 261-74 (1937).

[32] J. Edward Smith and Harold L. Jones, *J. Phys. Chem.*, **38**, 243-4 (1934); Harold L. Jones and J. E. Smith, *Am. Dyestuff Reptr.*, **23**, 423-7 (1934).

be examined. Such indicators are called adjusted or isohydric. This can be done conveniently by using the indicator solution at different pH values, not necessarily accurately known. If the pH after adding different amounts of indicator is the same the indicator was isohydric.

Introduce a sample of pure water into the Pyrex cell, Figure 105. Pass air through soda-lime, sulfuric acid and several wash bottles of pure water, then through B into the water in the cell. The water is carbon dioxide-free when successive determinations of pH do not show any change. Remove the stopper of the cell and quickly add the indicator with air flowing through the cell. Then after the color is homogeneous close B and A and compare with the same amount of indicator in a similar volume of buffer solution in another cell. After the reading pass more air through and add more indicator. Repeat with a third addition of indicator. The correct indicator mixture will show the same reading with the addition of different volumes of indicator.

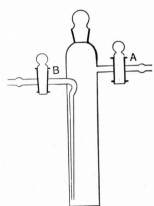

Fig. 105. Apparatus for estimation of pH in unbuffered solutions

For salt solutions or sodium hydroxide solution add the weighed amount of solute to the carbon dioxide-free water and dissolve it in the cell.

# CHAPTER XXI

# HYDROGEN-ION—METHODS OF DETERMINATION

COLORIMETRIC pH is usually accurate to 0.1 unit of pH. That degree of accuracy is readily attainable with some small amount of experience. Procedures have been developed for higher accuracy. For most samples the approximate range of pH is already known or can be quickly obtained by addition of a drop of a few well-known and readily available indicators: phenolphthalein, methyl orange, litmus, Congo red, or the use of corresponding impregnated papers. A useful variation is to determine the approximate range with a universal indicator, either as a solution or in paper form (p. 186). In either case, select an indicator for pH from such preliminary knowledge or test of the approximate range.

**Standard Tubes.** Colorimetric comparisons of standards for pH are usually made in uniform tubes, for which test tubes without lips are most suitable. A convenient size is 1.5 cm. in diameter and 15 cm. long. For making a selection add 10 ml. of water to a series of tubes which appear to be uniform. A variation of 5 per cent in height is permissible. Discard those varying more than that amount from the general average.

## COMPARISON WITH STANDARD BUFFERS

For estimation by this method a series of standard buffers is prepared. The same amount of the same indicator is added to each and to the standard of the same volume. Therefore, the selected buffer of known pH gives a color with the properly selected indicator which is characteristic of the pH of the buffer. It may either be a variation of a single color, with a monochromatic indicator, or a range of variation of two colors with a polychromatic indicator. Figure 106 illustrates a slide comparator suitable for this type of determination. The pH is read by direct comparison, provided the sample is not colored. Otherwise, use the Walpole method (p. 22).

**Procedure.** In a series of uniform tubes, usually Pyrex test tubes, place 10 ml. portions of the various buffer solutions to cover the desired range. To each add 0.2 ml. of standard and 0.05 per cent indicator solution and mix well. By hermetically sealing the buffer standards they will keep indefinitely, unless reaction occurs with the glass. Commercial sets of buffers developed with specified indicators and sealed may be purchased.

To 10 ml. of the sample add 0.2 ml. of the appropriate indicator solution from a pipet, mix well, and compare with the series of standard buffers.

### ESTIMATION WITHOUT BUFFERS

For a few estimations of pH, preparation of buffers takes a needless amount of time. The Gillespie comparator method [1] has been modi-

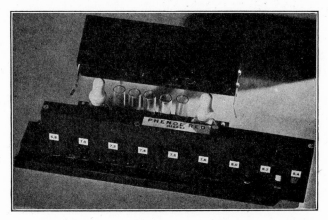

FIG. 106. Slide comparator for series of liquid standards.
(*Holmes I. Mettee, Baltimore, Md.*)

fied,[2] varied,[3] and further improved.[4] Accurate buffers are not required. Results are reproducible within 1 per cent.[5] Even in the original form the method could be applied by the average water works operator.[6] For monochromatic indicators this is quite simple since the additive value is of two tubes of the same color. For two-color indicators, this method

---

[1] Kamenosuke Sinowara, *Chem. Rev.* (Japan), **6**, 87-102 (1940); Louis J. Gillespie, *J. Am. Chem. Soc.*, **42**, 742-8 (1920); *Soil Science*, **9**, 115-35 (1920); cf. Endre Erendits, *Mezőgazdasági Kutatások*, **14**, 112-14 (1941).

[2] N. K. Smith, *Bull. Bur. Bio-Technology*, **4**, 105-7 (1921).

[3] H. L. Hind, *J. Inst. Brewing*, **30**, 57-60 (1924); cf. F. J. Watson, *Chem. Eng. Mining Rev.*, **19**, 381-3 (1927).

[4] William D. Hatfield, *J. Am. Chem. Soc.*, **45**, 940-3 (1923).

[5] E. A. Guggenheim and T. D. Schindler, *J. Phys. Chem.*, **38**, 543-56 (1934).

[6] William D. Hatfield, *J. Ind. Eng. Chem.*, **14**, 1038-40 (1922).

depends on the fact that the sum of the acid and basic color of an indicator is a linear function over the range of the indicator. Instead of using a buffer, a predetermined amount of indicator and acid may be placed in one tube to give the acid color and a predetermined amount of indicator and base in another tube to give the basic color. The sum of the colors of the two tubes is the same as that which would be given by the indicator with a buffer solution at a calculated pH. Comparisons should be made of equal volumes at equal depths. A bicolorimeter may be used to increase the accuracy. Another variation is based on the production of a color scale by mixing the acid and alkaline colors on the spot.

Use 1 drop of 0.2 per cent sodium hydroxide solution in 5 ml. of water for the alkaline colors and 1 ml. of 0.05 $N$ hydrochloric acid diluted to 5 ml. for the acid standards. The approximately 0.05 $N$ hydrochloric acid is prepared by dilution of 1 ml. of concentrated hydrochloric acid to 240 ml. Approximately 0.2 per cent sodium hydroxide solution is prepared directly from stick sodium hydroxide.

When a one-color indicator is added to a sample solution, the depth of color obtained is between the maximum color of a strongly alkaline solution and the almost colorless one of an extremely acid solution. When this color is compared with the maximum color obtained in alkaline solution, a difference in the depth of color is obtained. Figures check the electrometric method to 0.05 pH.[7] This holds true for most of the one-color indicators except phenolphthalein, because the first and second steps of the ionization overlap. Empirical data are available for this indicator.[8] If the solution is highly colored, measurement of the hydrogen-ion concentration may be made in a Gillespie comparator (p. 22). Such comparisons are useful for pH determinations of solutions that poison a hydrogen electrode.[9]

In the determination of pH without buffers, stable, inorganic, colored salt solutions may be used as standards.[10] A stable colorimetric scale over the pH range 4.0-8.0 may be obtained by mixing ferric chloride, cobaltous chloride, cupric chloride and copper sulfate in suitable pro-

---

[7] Amandus Hahn and Arthur Kretschmann, *Z. Biol.*, **97**, 585-9 (1936).

[8] L. Michaelis and A. Gyemant, *Biochem. Z.*, **109**, 165-210 (1920).

[9] W. B. Pleass, *Leather World*, **26**, 131 (1934); *J. Am. Leather Chem. Assoc.*, **30**, 197 (1935).

[10] J. Guillaume, *Bull, assoc. chim. sucr, dist.*, **47**, 450-4 (1930).

portions.[11]  Permanent colored glass discs also are employed as standards in conjunction with a Lovibond comparator,[12] Figure 107.  Values for

FIG. 107.  Lovibond comparator for pH determination.
*(British Drug House, Ltd.)*

pH between 0.1 and 14 have been determined colorimetrically within 0.1 pH unit.[13]

---

[11] N. I. Alyamovskiĭ, *Chemisation Socialistic Agr.* (U.S.S.R.), **8**, No. 1, 84-6 (1939).

[12] British Drug Houses, Ltd., London, England.

[13] Fr. Sierp and F. Fränsemeier, *Z. Ver. deut. Ing.*, **1942**, 24; *Wasser u. Abwasser*, **40**, 53 (1942).

**Indicators.** The indicators most commonly used are the neutralized sulfonphthalein series, often referred to as the Clark and Lubs indicators. The compositions to be used are given in Table 36.

TABLE 36. INDICATORS FOR USE WITH GILLESPIE-HATFIELD METHOD

| Indicator | pH Range | Weight in Grams | Ml. 0.01N Sodium Hydroxide | Dilute to (ml.) |
|---|---|---|---|---|
| Bromophenol Blue ..... | 3.10–5.00 | 0.02 | 3.28 | 250 |
| Methyl Red .......... | 4.05–5.95 | 0.02 | ... | 250 |
| Bromocresol Purple ... | 5.30–7.20 | 0.03 | 8.34 | 250 |
| Bromothymol Blue .... | 6.15–8.05 | 0.02 | 3.54 | 250 |
| Phenol Red .......... | 6.75–8.65 | 0.01 | 3.10 | 250 |
| Cresol Red .......... | 7.15–9.05 | 0.02 | 5.76 | 250 |
| Thymol Blue ......... | 7.85–9.75 | 0.02 | 4.76 | 250 |

**Buffer Solutions.** Four buffers are required which can be prepared from reagent-grade chemicals without further purification.

*Acetic Acid.* Dilute 57.7 ml. of glacial acetic acid to 1 liter.

*Monopotassium Phosphate.* Dissolve 7.0 grams of monopotassium phosphate in water and dilute to 1 liter.

*Disodium Phosphate.* Dissolve 18.0 grams of disodium phosphate in water and dilute to 1 liter.

*Sodium Carbonate.* Dissolve 1.0 gram of anhydrous sodium carbonate in water and dilute to 1 liter.

FIG. 108. Series of liquid color standards.
(*Holmes I. Mettee, Baltimore, Md.*)

**Standard Color Tubes.** The materials for use in the standard color tubes are outlined in Tables 37-43. Uniform test tubes are required. (Figure 108.)

To prepare, place in a test tube the desired fraction of a milliliter of the indicator solution. To this add the desired buffer to make a total of 1 ml. Add 10 ml. of buffer to each tube. Add 2 to 3 drops of toluene to act as preservative and stopper with paraffined corks.

Toluene will extract the acid color of methyl red and thus shift the apparent color. To avoid this allow the acid color tubes of methyl red to stand loosely stoppered for a few days before paraffining the stoppers. In that time the excess toluene will evaporate.

TABLE 37. BROMOPHENOL BLUE STANDARDS.

| | Acid Tube | | Basic Tube | |
|---|---|---|---|---|
| pH | Ml. of Indicator Solution | Ml. of Acetic Acid | Ml. of Indicator Solution | Ml. of Disodium Phosphate |
| 3.1 | 0.10 | 10.90 | 0.90 | 10.10 |
| 3.3 | 0.15 | 10.85 | 0.85 | 10.15 |
| 3.5 | 0.20 | 10.80 | 0.80 | 10.20 |
| 3.7 | 0.30 | 10.70 | 0.70 | 10.30 |
| 3.9 | 0.40 | 10.60 | 0.60 | 10.40 |
| 4.1 | 0.50 | 10.50 | 0.50 | 10.50 |
| 4.3 | 0.60 | 10.40 | 0.40 | 10.60 |
| 4.5 | 0.70 | 10.30 | 0.30 | 10.70 |
| 4.7 | 0.80 | 10.20 | 0.20 | 10.80 |
| 4.8 | 0.85 | 10.15 | 0.15 | 10.85 |
| 5.0 | 0.90 | 10.10 | 0.10 | 10.90 |

TABLE 38. METHYL RED STANDARDS.

| | Acid Tube | | Basic Tube | |
|---|---|---|---|---|
| pH | Ml. of Indicator Solution | Ml. of Acetic Acid | Ml. of Indicator Solution | Ml. of Disodium Phosphate |
| 4.05 | 0.10 | 10.90 | 0.90 | 10.10 |
| 4.25 | 0.15 | 10.85 | 0.85 | 10.15 |
| 4.4 | 0.20 | 10.80 | 0.80 | 10.20 |
| 4.6 | 0.30 | 10.70 | 0.70 | 10.30 |
| 4.8 | 0.40 | 10.60 | 0.60 | 10.40 |
| 5.0 | 0.50 | 10.50 | 0.50 | 10.50 |
| 5.2 | 0.60 | 10.40 | 0.40 | 10.60 |
| 5.4 | 0.70 | 10.30 | 0.30 | 10.70 |
| 5.6 | 0.80 | 10.20 | 0.20 | 10.80 |
| 5.75 | 0.85 | 10.15 | 0.15 | 10.85 |
| 5.95 | 0.90 | 10.10 | 0.10 | 10.90 |

**Procedure.** To a similar test tube add 10 ml. of sample and 1 ml. of indicator solution. Mix, and compare it and a similar tube containing distilled water with the two tubes representing the color.

Instead of using the measurements by milliliter as given, the assumption may be made that 1 drop is 0.05 ml. Fractions of milliliters can then be taken by drops with a fair degree of accuracy, and if desired, the volumes of sample and standards cut to half those specified.

TABLE 39. BROMOCRESOL PURPLE STANDARDS.

| | Acid Tube | | Basic Tube | |
|---|---|---|---|---|
| pH | Ml. of Indicator Solution | Ml. of Mono-potassium Phosphate | Ml. of Indicator Solution | Ml. of Sodium Carbonate |
| 5.3 | 0.10 | 10.90 | 0.90 | 10.10 |
| 5.5 | 0.15 | 10.85 | 0.85 | 10.15 |
| 5.7 | 0.20 | 10.80 | 0.80 | 10.20 |
| 5.9 | 0.30 | 10.70 | 0.70 | 10.30 |
| 6.1 | 0.40 | 10.60 | 0.60 | 10.40 |
| 6.3 | 0.50 | 10.50 | 0.50 | 10.50 |
| 6.5 | 0.60 | 10.40 | 0.40 | 10.60 |
| 6.7 | 0.70 | 10.30 | 0.30 | 10.70 |
| 6.9 | 0.80 | 10.20 | 0.20 | 10.80 |
| 7.0 | 0.85 | 10.15 | 0.15 | 10.85 |
| 7.2 | 0.90 | 10.10 | 0.10 | 10.90 |

TABLE 40. BROMOTHYMOL BLUE STANDARDS.

| | Acid Tube | | Basic Tube | |
|---|---|---|---|---|
| pH | Ml. of Indicator Solution | Ml. of Mono-potassium Phosphate | Ml. of Indicator Solution | Ml. of Sodium Carbonate |
| 6.15 | 0.10 | 10.90 | 0.90 | 10.10 |
| 6.35 | 0.15 | 10.85 | 0.85 | 10.15 |
| 6.5 | 0.20 | 10.80 | 0.80 | 10.20 |
| 6.7 | 0.30 | 10.70 | 0.70 | 10.30 |
| 6.9 | 0.40 | 10.60 | 0.60 | 10.40 |
| 7.1 | 0.50 | 10.50 | 0.50 | 10.50 |
| 7.3 | 0.60 | 10.40 | 0.40 | 10.60 |
| 7.5 | 0.70 | 10.30 | 0.30 | 10.70 |
| 7.7 | 0.80 | 10.20 | 0.20 | 10.80 |
| 7.85 | 0.85 | 10.15 | 0.15 | 10.85 |
| 8.05 | 0.90 | 10.10 | 0.10 | 10.90 |

TABLE 41.   PHENOL RED STANDARDS.

| | Acid Tube | | Basic Tube | |
|---|---|---|---|---|
| pH | Ml. of Indicator Solution | Ml. of Mono-potassium Phosphate | Ml. of Indicator Solution | Ml. of Sodium Carbonate |
| 6.75 | 0.10 | 10.90 | 0.90 | 10.10 |
| 6.95 | 0.15 | 10.85 | 0.85 | 10.15 |
| 7.1 | 0.20 | 10.80 | 0.80 | 10.20 |
| 7.3 | 0.30 | 10.70 | 0.70 | 10.30 |
| 7.5 | 0.40 | 10.60 | 0.60 | 10.40 |
| 7.7 | 0.50 | 10.50 | 0.50 | 10.50 |
| 7.9 | 0.60 | 10.40 | 0.40 | 10.60 |
| 8.1 | 0.70 | 10.30 | 0.30 | 10.70 |
| 8.3 | 0.80 | 10.20 | 0.20 | 10.80 |
| 8.45 | 0.85 | 10.15 | 0.15 | 10.85 |
| 8.65 | 0.90 | 10.10 | 0.00 | 10.90 |

TABLE 42.   CRESOL RED STANDARDS.

| | Acid Tube | | Basic Tube | |
|---|---|---|---|---|
| pH | Ml. of Indicator Solution | Ml. of Mono-potassium Phosphate | Ml. of Indicator Solution | Ml. of Sodium Carbonate |
| 7.15 | 0.10 | 10.90 | 0.90 | 10.10 |
| 7.35 | 0.15 | 10.85 | 0.85 | 10.15 |
| 7.5 | 0.20 | 10.80 | 0.80 | 10.20 |
| 7.7 | 0.30 | 10.70 | 0.70 | 10.30 |
| 7.9 | 0.40 | 10.60 | 0.60 | 10.40 |
| 8.1 | 0.50 | 10.50 | 0.50 | 10.50 |
| 8.3 | 0.60 | 10.40 | 0.40 | 10.60 |
| 8.5 | 0.70 | 10.30 | 0.30 | 10.70 |
| 8.7 | 0.80 | 10.20 | 0.29 | 10.80 |
| 8.85 | 0.85 | 10.15 | 0.15 | 10.85 |
| 9.05 | 0.90 | 10.10 | 0.10 | 10.90 |

TABLE 43. THYMOL BLUE STANDARDS.

| pH | Acid Tube Ml. of Indicator Solution | Ml. of Mono- potassium Phosphate | Basic Tube Ml. of Indicator Solution | Ml. of Sodium Carbonate |
|---|---|---|---|---|
| 7.85 | 0.10 | 10.90 | 0.90 | 10.10 |
| 8.05 | 0.15 | 10.85 | 0.85 | 10.15 |
| 8.2 | 0.20 | 10.80 | 0.80 | 10.20 |
| 8.4 | 0.30 | 10.70 | 0.70 | 10.30 |
| 8.6 | 0.40 | 10.60 | 0.60 | 10.40 |
| 8.8 | 0.50 | 10.50 | 0.50 | 10.50 |
| 9.0 | 0.60 | 10.40 | 0.40 | 10.60 |
| 9.2 | 0.70 | 10.30 | 0.30 | 10.70 |
| 9.4 | 0.80 | 10.20 | 0.20 | 10.80 |
| 9.55 | 0.85 | 10.15 | 0.15 | 10.85 |
| 9.75 | 0.90 | 10.10 | 0.10 | 10.90 |

BALANCING METHOD

For this method a special type of colorimeter is required, in which the total depth of the two standards is maintained at uniformly that of the sample. The ratio of the acid and alkaline standard colors is then varied. If the sample is turbid or colored, auxiliary cups are used according to the Walpole technic. A schematic diagram of a modified Duboscq colorimeter for this purpose is shown in Figure 109 and a photograph in Figure 39. The use of one-color indicators is preferred with the latter instrument.

Procedure.[14] In the right-hand cup place the sample with a suitable concentration of indicator so selected that the color falls within the useful range. In the two cups on the left hand, place the alkaline form of the indicator in the lower cup and the acid form in the upper cup, each with the same amount of indicator that was added to the sample. Adjust the cup containing standard and that containing the alkaline form of the indicator so that they are at the same definite distance from the plunger. Values of 10 mm., 15 mm. and 20 mm. are considered in the accompanying tables. Turn the right-hand empty cup up until it touches the plunger. By adjustment of the upper left-hand cup the depths of acid and alkaline color are varied but the total sum of their depths remains constant.

[14] J. J. Beaver, *J. Optical Soc. Am.*, 18, 41-9 (1929).

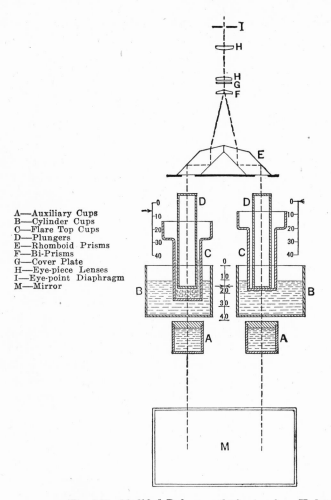

A—Auxiliary Cups
B—Cylinder Cups
C—Flare Top Cups
D—Plungers
E—Rhomboid Prisms
F—Bi-Prisms
G—Cover Plate
H—Eye-piece Lenses
I—Eye-point Diaphragm
M—Mirror

Fig. 109.  Modified Duboscq colorimeter for pH determination

**Calculation.** When a match is obtained the pH is calculated from the pK value. For this, the value of $pK_a = \log \dfrac{1}{k_a}$, the dissociation exponent,[15] is necessary, in which $K_a$ is the mass action constant. Having the pK value,

$$pH = pK_a + \log \frac{a}{1-a}$$

---

[15] N. Bjerrum, *Z. physik. Chem.*, **104**, 147 (1923); *Ibid.*, **106**, 219 (1923).

As applied to the balancing method the depth of acid color is a measure of $1 - a$ and the depth of alkaline color a measure of $a$. From these values the pH values in the tables have been solved. Therefore, by reference to Tables 44-48 the results from readings of this type of colorimeter may be obtained without calculation.

### DUPLICATION METHOD

The conventional colorimetric method for duplication of the color of test substance is applicable to pH determination. This differs from the usual technics in that the added solution is the indicator rather than the test substance. Only monochromatic indicators may be used. The application of the technic depends on the change in color being uniform over the range of pH to which the indicator is applicable.

To 10 ml. of the unknown in a test tube add 1 ml. of indicator solution. To another test tube add 9 ml. of a solution giving the maximum color with the indicator such as 0.02 N sodium hydroxide or hydrochloric acid. Add indicator, which may be either of full concentration or suitably diluted as to 0.5, 0.2 or 0.1 concentration, from a buret or pipet. Finally, adjust the volume of the standard so that the sample is matched in both color and volume.

*Calculation.* The result is obtained from the formula

$$pH = pK + \log \frac{C}{1 - C}$$

where pK is the constant for the indicator (p. 183, Table 33), and $C$ is the ratio of the amount of undiluted indicator solution added to the sample to that added to the standard.

### TABLE 44. READINGS FOR BALANCING TYPE COLORIMETER

Solution of the factor $\log \frac{y-x}{x}$ for 10 mm. depth

y = 10

| x | 0.0 | 0.1 | 0.2 | 0.3 | 0.4 | 0.5 | 0.6 | 0.7 | 0.8 | 0.9 |
|---|-----|-----|-----|-----|-----|-----|-----|-----|-----|-----|
| 1.0 | 0.95 | 0.91 | 0.86 | 0.82 | 0.79 | 0.75 | 0.72 | 0.69 | 0.66 | 0.63 |
| 2.0 | 0.60 | 0.57 | 0.55 | 0.52 | 0.50 | 0.48 | 0.45 | 0.43 | 0.41 | 0.39 |
| 3.0 | 0.37 | 0.35 | 0.33 | 0.31 | 0.29 | 0.27 | 0.25 | 0.23 | 0.21 | 0.19 |
| 4.0 | 0.17 | 0.16 | 0.14 | 0.12 | 0.10 | 0.09 | 0.07 | 0.05 | 0.03 | 0.02 |
| 5.0 | 0.00 | 9.98 | 9.96 | 9.95 | 9.93 | 9.91 | 9.89 | 9.88 | 9.86 | 9.84 |
| 6.0 | 9.82 | 9.80 | 9.79 | 9.77 | 9.75 | 9.73 | 9.71 | 9.69 | 9.67 | 9.65 |
| 7.0 | 9.63 | 9.61 | 9.59 | 9.57 | 9.55 | 9.52 | 9.50 | 9.48 | 9.45 | 9.42 |
| 8.0 | 9.40 | 9.37 | 9.34 | 9.31 | 9.28 | 9.25 | 9.21 | 9.17 | 9.13 | 9 09 |
| 9.0 | 9.05 | 8.91 | 8.87 | | | | | | | |

TABLE 44.   READINGS FOR BALANCING TYPE COLORIMETER—*Continued.*

Solution of the factor log $\frac{y-x}{x}$ for 15 mm. depth

y = 15

| x | 0.0 | 0.1 | 0.2 | 0.3 | 0.4 | 0.5 | 0.6 | 0.7 | 0.8 | 0.9 |
|---|---|---|---|---|---|---|---|---|---|---|
| 1.0 | 1.15 | 1.10 | 1.06 | 1.02 | 0.99 | 0.95 | 0.92 | 0.89 | 0.86 | 0.84 |
| 2.0 | 0.81 | 0.79 | 0.76 | 0.74 | 0.72 | 0.70 | 0.68 | 0.66 | 0.64 | 0.62 |
| 3.0 | 0.60 | 0.58 | 0.57 | 0.55 | 0.53 | 0.52 | 0.50 | 0.48 | 0.47 | 0.45 |
| 4.0 | 0.44 | 0.42 | 0.41 | 0.40 | 0.38 | 0.37 | 0.35 | 0.34 | 0.33 | 0.31 |
| 5.0 | 0.30 | 0.29 | 0.28 | 0.26 | 0.25 | 0.24 | 0.22 | 0.21 | 0.20 | 0.19 |
| 6.0 | 0.18 | 0.16 | 0.15 | 0.14 | 0.13 | 0.12 | 0.10 | 0.09 | 0.08 | 0.07 |
| 7.0 | 0.06 | 0.05 | 0.03 | 0.02 | 0.01 | 0.00 | 9.99 | 9.98 | 9.97 | 9.95 |
| 8.0 | 9.94 | 9.93 | 9.92 | 9.91 | 9.90 | 9.88 | 9.87 | 9.86 | 9.85 | 9.84 |
| 9.0 | 9.82 | 9.81 | 9.80 | 9.79 | 9.78 | 9.76 | 9.75 | 9.74 | 9.72 | 9.71 |
| 10.0 | 9.70 | 9.69 | 9.67 | 9.66 | 9.65 | 9.63 | 9.62 | 9.60 | 9.59 | 9.58 |
| 11.0 | 9.56 | 9.55 | 9.53 | 9.52 | 9.50 | 9.48 | 9.47 | 9.45 | 9.43 | 9.42 |
| 12.0 | 9.40 | 9.38 | 9.36 | 9.34 | 9.32 | 9.30 | 9.28 | 9.26 | 9.24 | 9.21 |
| 13.0 | 9.19 | 9.16 | 9.14 | 9.13 | 9.08 | 9.05 | 9.01 | 8.98 | 8.94 | 8.90 |
| 14.0 | 8.85 | | | | | | | | | |
| 15.0 | | | | | | | | | | |

Solution of the factor log $\frac{y-x}{x}$ for 20 mm. depth.

y = 20

| x | 0.0 | 0.1 | 0.2 | 0.3 | 0.4 | 0.5 | 0.6 | 0.7 | 0.8 | 0.9 |
|---|---|---|---|---|---|---|---|---|---|---|
| 1.0 | 1.28 | 1.23 | 1.19 | 1.16 | 1.12 | 1.09 | 1.06 | 1.03 | 1.00 | 0.98 |
| 2.0 | 0.95 | 0.93 | 0.91 | 0.89 | 0.87 | 0.84 | 0.82 | 0.81 | 0.79 | 0.77 |
| 3.0 | 0.75 | 0.74 | 0.72 | 0.70 | 0.69 | 0.67 | 0.65 | 0.64 | 0.63 | 0.62 |
| 4.0 | 0.60 | 0.59 | 0.58 | 0.56 | 0.55 | 0.54 | 0.52 | 0.51 | 0.50 | 0.49 |
| 5.0 | 0.48 | 0.46 | 0.45 | 0.44 | 0.43 | 0.42 | 0.41 | 0.40 | 0.39 | 0.38 |
| 6.0 | 0.37 | 0.36 | 0.35 | 0.34 | 0.33 | 0.32 | 0.31 | 0.30 | 0.29 | 0.28 |
| 7.0 | 0.27 | 0.26 | 0.25 | 0.24 | 0.23 | 0.22 | 0.21 | 0.20 | 0.19 | 0.18 |
| 8.0 | 0.18 | 0.17 | 0.16 | 0.15 | 0.14 | 0.13 | 0.12 | 0.11 | 0.10 | 0.10 |
| 9.0 | 0.09 | 0.08 | 0.07 | 0.06 | 0.05 | 0.04 | 0.03 | 0.03 | 0.02 | 0.01 |
| 10.0 | 0.00 | 9.99 | 9.98 | 9.97 | 9.96 | 9.96 | 9.95 | 9.94 | 9.93 | 9.92 |
| 11.0 | 9.91 | 9.90 | 9.89 | 9.89 | 9.88 | 9.87 | 9.86 | 9.85 | 9.84 | 9.83 |
| 12.0 | 9.82 | 9.81 | 9.81 | 9.80 | 9.79 | 9.78 | 9.77 | 9.76 | 9.75 | 9.74 |
| 13.0 | 9.73 | 9.72 | 9.71 | 9.70 | 9.69 | 9.68 | 9.67 | 9.66 | 9.65 | 9.64 |
| 14.0 | 9.63 | 9.62 | 9.61 | 9.60 | 9.59 | 9.58 | 9.57 | 9.56 | 9.55 | 9.53 |
| 15.0 | 9.52 | 9.51 | 9.50 | 9.49 | 9.47 | 9.46 | 9.45 | 9.44 | 9.42 | 9.41 |
| 16.0 | 9.40 | 9.38 | 9.37 | 9.36 | 9.34 | 9.33 | 9.31 | 9.30 | 9.28 | 9.26 |
| 17.0 | 9.25 | 9.23 | 9.21 | 9.19 | 9.18 | 9.16 | 9.14 | 9.12 | 9.09 | 9.07 |
| 18.0 | 9.05 | 9.02 | 8.99 | 8.97 | 8.94 | 8.91 | 8.88 | 8.84 | 8.80 | 8.76 |
| 19.0 | 8.72 | 8.67 | 8.62 | 8.56 | 8.49 | 8.41 | 8.31 | 8.18 | 8.00 | 7.70 |

TABLE 45. READINGS FOR BALANCING TYPE COLORIMETER WHEN STANDARD COLUMN IS 10 MM.

| Colorimeter Readings in mm. | pH m-Cresol Purple | pH Thymol Blue (acid) | pH Bromophenol Blue | pH Bromocresol Green | pH Chlorophenol Red | pH Bromophenol Red | pH Bromocresol Purple | pH Bromothymol Blue | pH Phenol Red | pH m-Cresol Purple | pH Thymol Blue |
|---|---|---|---|---|---|---|---|---|---|---|---|
| 1.0 | 2.46 | 2.45 | | | | | | | | | |
| 1.2 | 2.37 | 2.36 | | | | | | | | | |
| 1.4 | 2.30 | 2.29 | | 5.46 | | | | | | | |
| 1.6 | 2.23 | 2.22 | | 5.39 | | | | | | 9.05 | 9.62 |
| 1.8 | 2.17 | 2.16 | 4.64 | 5.33 | | | | | | 8.99 | 9.56 |
| 2.0 | 2.11 | 2.10 | 4.58 | 5.27 | | | | 7.60 | | 8.93 | 9.50 |
| 2.2 | 2.06 | 2.05 | 4.53 | 5.22 | 6.53 | | | 7.55 | | 8.87 | 9.45 |
| 2.4 | 2.01 | 2.00 | 4.48 | 5.17 | 6.48 | | 6.80 | 7.50 | 8.40 | 8.82 | 9.40 |
| 2.6 | 1.96 | 1.95 | 4.43 | 5.12 | 6.43 | | 6.75 | 7.45 | 8.35 | 8.77 | 9.35 |
| 2.8 | 1.92 | 1.91 | 4.39 | 5.08 | 6.39 | | 6.71 | 7.41 | 8.31 | 8.73 | 9.31 |
| 3.0 | 1.88 | 1.87 | 4.35 | 5.04 | 6.35 | | 6.67 | 7.37 | 8.27 | 8.69 | 9.27 |
| 3.2 | 1.84 | 1.83 | 4.31 | 5.00 | 6.31 | | 6.63 | 7.33 | 8.23 | 8.65 | 9.23 |
| 3.4 | 1.80 | 1.79 | 4 27 | 4.96 | 6.27 | | 6.59 | 7.29 | 8.19 | 8.61 | 9.19 |
| 3.6 | 1.76 | 1.75 | 4 23 | 4.92 | 6.23 | 6.41 | 6.55 | 7.25 | 8.15 | 8.57 | 9.15 |
| 3.8 | 1.72 | 1.71 | 4.19 | 4.88 | 6.19 | 6.37 | 6.51 | 7.21 | 8.11 | 8.53 | 9.11 |
| 4.0 | 1.68 | 1.67 | 4.15 | 4.84 | 6.15 | 6.33 | 6.47 | 7.17 | 8.07 | 8.49 | 9.07 |
| 4.2 | 1.65 | 1.64 | 4.12 | 4.81 | 6.12 | 6.30 | 6.44 | 7.14 | 8.04 | 8.46 | 9.04 |
| 4.4 | 1.61 | 1.60 | 4.08 | 4.77 | 6.08 | 6.26 | 6.40 | 7.10 | 8.00 | 8.42 | 9.00 |
| 4.6 | 1.58 | 1.57 | 4 05 | 4.74 | 6.05 | 6.23 | 6.37 | 7.07 | 7.97 | 8.39 | 8.97 |
| 4.8 | 1.54 | 1 53 | 4 01 | 4.70 | 6.01 | 6.19 | 6.33 | 7.03 | 7.93 | 8.35 | 8.93 |
| 5.0 | 1.51 | 1.50 | 3.98 | 4.67 | 5.98 | 6.16 | 6.30 | 7.00 | 7.90 | 8.32 | 8.90 |
| 5.2 | 1.47 | 1.46 | 3.94 | 4.63 | 5.94 | 6.12 | 6.26 | 6.96 | 7.86 | 8.28 | 8.86 |
| 5.4 | 1.44 | 1.43 | 3.91 | 4.60 | 5.91 | 6.09 | 6.23 | 6.93 | 7.83 | 8.25 | 8.83 |
| 5.6 | 1.40 | 1.39 | 3.87 | 4.56 | 5.87 | 6.05 | 6.19 | 6.89 | 7.79 | 8.21 | 8.79 |
| 5.8 | 1.37 | 1.36 | 3.84 | 4.53 | 5.84 | 6.02 | 6.16 | 6.86 | 7.76 | 8.18 | 8.76 |
| 6.0 | 1.33 | 1.32 | 3.80 | 4.49 | 5.80 | 5.98 | 6.14 | 6.84 | 7.74 | 8.16 | 8.74 |
| 6.2 | 1.30 | 1.29 | 3.77 | 4.46 | 5.77 | 5.95 | 6.11 | 6.81 | 7.71 | 8.13 | 8.71 |
| 6.4 | 1.26 | 1.25 | 3.73 | 4.42 | 5.73 | 5.91 | 6.07 | 6.77 | 7.67 | 8.09 | 8.67 |
| 6.6 | 1.22 | 1.21 | 3.69 | 4.38 | 5.69 | 5.87 | 6.03 | 6.73 | 7.63 | 8.05 | 8.63 |
| 6.8 | 1.18 | 1.17 | 3.65 | 4.34 | 5.65 | 5.83 | 5.99 | 6.69 | 7.59 | 8.01 | 8.59 |
| 7.0 | 1.14 | 1.13 | 3.61 | 4.30 | 5.61 | 5.79 | 5.95 | 6.65 | 7.55 | 7.97 | 8.55 |
| 7.2 | 1.10 | 1.09 | 3.57 | 4.26 | 5.57 | 5.75 | 5.91 | 6.61 | 7.51 | 7.93 | 8.51 |
| 7.4 | 1.06 | 1.05 | 3.53 | 4.22 | 5.53 | 5.71 | 5.87 | 6.57 | 7.47 | 7.89 | 8.47 |
| 7.6 | | | 3.48 | 4.17 | 5.48 | 5.66 | 5.82 | 6.52 | 7.42 | 7.84 | 8.42 |
| 7.8 | | | 3.43 | 4.12 | 5.43 | 5.61 | 5.77 | 6.47 | 7.37 | 7.79 | 8.37 |
| 8.0 | | | 3.38 | 4.07 | 5.38 | 5.56 | 5.72 | 6.42 | 7.32 | 7.74 | 8.32 |
| 8.2 | | | 3.32 | 4.01 | 5.32 | 5.50 | 5.66 | 6.36 | 7.26 | 7.68 | 8.26 |
| 8.4 | | | 3.26 | 3.95 | 5.26 | 5.44 | 5.60 | 6.30 | 7.20 | 7.62 | 8.20 |
| 8.6 | | | 3.19 | 3.88 | 5.19 | 5.37 | 5.53 | 6.23 | 7.13 | 7.55 | 8.13 |
| 8.8 | | | 3.11 | 3.80 | 5.11 | 5.29 | 5.45 | 6.15 | 7.05 | 7.47 | 8.05 |
| 9.0 | | | 3.03 | | 5.03 | 5.21 | 5.37 | 6.07 | 6.97 | 7.39 | 7.97 |

TABLE 46. READINGS FOR BALANCING TYPE COLORIMETER WHEN STANDARD COLUMN IS 15 MM.

| Colorimeter Readings in mm. | pH m-Cresol Purple | pH Thymol Blue (acid) | pH Bromophenol Blue | pH Bromocresol Green | pH Chlorophenol Red | pH Bromophenol Red | pH Bromocresol Purple | pH Bromothymol Blue | pH Phenol Red | pH m-Cresol Purple | pH Thymol Blue |
|---|---|---|---|---|---|---|---|---|---|---|---|
| 1.0 | 2.66 | 2.65 | | | | | | | | | |
| 1.2 | 2.57 | 2.56 | | | | | | | | | |
| 1.4 | 2.50 | 2.49 | | | | | | | | | |
| 1.6 | 2.43 | 2.42 | | | | | | | | | |
| 1.8 | 2.37 | 2.36 | | | | | | | | | |
| 2.0 | 2.32 | 2.31 | | | | | | | | | |
| 2.2 | 2.27 | 2.26 | | 5.43 | | | | | | | |
| 2.4 | 2.23 | 2.22 | | 5.39 | | | | | | 9.04 | 9.62 |
| 2.6 | 2.19 | 2.18 | | 5.35 | | 6.84 | | | | 9.00 | 9.58 |
| 2.8 | 2.15 | 2.14 | 4.62 | 5.31 | | 6.80 | | | | 8.96 | 9.54 |
| 3.0 | 2.11 | 2.10 | 4.58 | 5.27 | | 6.76 | | 7.60 | | 8.92 | 9.50 |
| 3.2 | 2.08 | 2.07 | 4.55 | 5.24 | | 6.73 | | 7.57 | | 8.89 | 9.47 |
| 3.4 | 2.04 | 2.03 | 4.51 | 5.20 | | 6.69 | 6.83 | 7.53 | | 8.85 | 9.43 |
| 3.6 | 2.01 | 2.00 | 4.48 | 5.17 | | 6.66 | 6.80 | 7.50 | 8.40 | 8.82 | 9.40 |
| 3.8 | 1.98 | 1.97 | 4.45 | 5.14 | | 6.63 | 6.77 | 7.47 | 8.37 | 8.79 | 9.37 |
| 4.0 | 1.96 | 1.95 | 4.43 | 5.12 | 6.43 | 6.60 | 6.74 | 7.44 | 8.34 | 8.76 | 9.34 |
| 4.2 | 1.93 | 1.92 | 4.40 | 5.09 | 6.40 | 6.57 | 6.71 | 7.41 | 8.31 | 8.73 | 9.31 |
| 4.4 | 1.89 | 1.88 | 4.36 | 5.05 | 6.36 | 6.54 | 6.68 | 7.38 | 8.28 | 8.70 | 9.28 |
| 4.6 | 1.86 | 1.85 | 4.33 | 5.02 | 6.33 | 6.51 | 6.65 | 7.35 | 8.25 | 8.67 | 9.25 |
| 4.8 | 1.84 | 1.83 | 4.31 | 5.00 | 6.31 | 6.49 | 6.63 | 7.33 | 8.23 | 8.65 | 9.23 |
| 5.0 | 1.81 | 1.80 | 4.28 | 4.97 | 6.28 | 7.46 | 6.60 | 6.30 | 8.20 | 8.62 | 9.20 |
| 5.2 | 1.79 | 1.78 | 4.26 | 4.95 | 6.26 | 6.44 | 6.58 | 7.28 | 8.18 | 8.60 | 9.18 |
| 5.4 | 1.76 | 1.75 | 4.23 | 4.92 | 6.23 | 6.41 | 6.55 | 7.25 | 8.15 | 8.57 | 9.15 |
| 5.6 | 1.73 | 1.72 | 4.20 | 4.89 | 6.20 | 6.38 | 6.52 | 7.22 | 8.12 | 8.54 | 9.12 |
| 5.8 | 1.71 | 1.70 | 4.18 | 4.87 | 6.18 | 6.36 | 6.50 | 7.20 | 8.10 | 8.52 | 9.10 |
| 6.0 | 1.69 | 1.68 | 4.16 | 4.85 | 6.16 | 6.34 | 6.48 | 7.18 | 8.08 | 8.50 | 9.08 |
| 6.2 | 1.66 | 1.65 | 4.13 | 4.82 | 6.13 | 6.31 | 6.45 | 7.15 | 8.05 | 8.47 | 9.05 |
| 6.4 | 1.64 | 1.63 | 4.11 | 4.80 | 6.11 | 6.29 | 6.43 | 7.13 | 8.03 | 8.45 | 9.03 |
| 6.6 | 1.61 | 1.60 | 4.08 | 4.77 | 6.08 | 6.26 | 6.40 | 7.10 | 8.00 | 8.42 | 9.00 |
| 6.8 | 1.59 | 1.58 | 4.06 | 4.75 | 6.06 | 6.24 | 6.38 | 7.08 | 7.98 | 8.40 | 8.98 |
| 7.0 | 1.57 | 1.56 | 4.04 | 4.73 | 6.04 | 6.22 | 6.36 | 7.06 | 7.96 | 8.38 | 8.96 |
| 7.2 | 1.54 | 1.53 | 4.01 | 4.70 | 6.01 | 6.19 | 6.33 | 7.03 | 7.93 | 8.35 | 8.93 |
| 7.4 | 1.52 | 1.51 | 3.99 | 4.68 | 5.99 | 6.17 | 6.31 | 7.01 | 7.91 | 8.33 | 8.91 |
| 7.5 | 1.51 | 1.50 | 3.98 | 4.67 | 5.98 | 6.16 | 6.30 | 7.00 | 7.90 | 8.32 | 8.90 |
| 7.6 | 1.50 | 1.49 | 3.97 | 4.66 | 5.97 | 6.15 | 6.29 | 6.99 | 7.89 | 8.31 | 8.89 |
| 7.8 | 1.48 | 1.47 | 3.95 | 4.64 | 5.95 | 6.13 | 6.27 | 6.97 | 7.87 | 8.29 | 8.87 |
| 8.0 | 1.45 | 1.44 | 3.92 | 4.61 | 5.92 | 6.10 | 6.24 | 6.94 | 7.84 | 8.26 | 8.84 |
| 8.2 | 1.43 | 1.42 | 3.90 | 4.59 | 5.90 | 6.08 | 6.22 | 6.92 | 7.82 | 8.24 | 8.82 |
| 8.4 | 1.41 | 1.40 | 3.88 | 4.57 | 5.88 | 6.06 | 6.20 | 6.90 | 7.80 | 8.22 | 8.80 |
| 8.6 | 1.38 | 1.37 | 3.85 | 4.54 | 5.85 | 6.03 | 6.17 | 6.87 | 7.77 | 8.19 | 8.77 |
| 8.8 | 1.36 | 1.35 | 3.83 | 4.52 | 5.83 | 6.01 | 6.15 | 6.85 | 7.75 | 8.17 | 8.75 |
| 9.0 | 1.33 | 1.32 | 3.80 | 4.49 | 5.80 | 5.98 | 6.12 | 6.82 | 7.72 | 8.14 | 8.72 |
| 9.2 | 1.31 | 1.30 | 3.78 | 4.47 | 5.78 | 5.96 | 6.10 | 6.80 | 7.70 | 8.12 | 8.70 |
| 9.4 | 1.29 | 1.28 | 3.76 | 4.45 | 5.76 | 5.94 | 6.08 | 6.78 | 7.68 | 8.10 | 8.68 |
| 9.6 | 1.26 | 1.25 | 3.73 | 4.42 | 5.73 | 5.91 | 6.05 | 6.75 | 7.65 | 8.07 | 8.65 |
| 9.8 | 1.23 | 1.22 | 3.70 | 4.39 | 5.70 | 5.88 | 6.02 | 6.72 | 7.62 | 8.04 | 8.62 |
| 10.0 | 1.21 | 1.20 | 3.68 | 4.37 | 5.68 | 5.86 | 6.00 | 6.70 | 7.60 | 8.02 | 8.60 |
| 10.2 | 1.18 | 1.17 | 3.65 | 4.34 | 5.65 | 5.83 | 5.97 | 6.67 | 7.57 | 7.99 | 8.57 |
| 10.4 | | | 3.63 | 4.32 | 5.63 | 5.81 | 5.95 | 6.65 | 7.55 | 7.97 | 8.55 |
| 10.6 | | | 3.60 | 4.29 | 5.60 | 5.78 | 5.92 | 6.62 | 7.52 | 7.94 | 8.52 |
| 10.8 | | | 3.57 | 4.26 | 5.57 | 5.75 | 5.89 | 6.59 | 7.49 | 7.91 | 8.49 |

TABLE 46. READINGS FOR BALANCING TYPE COLORIMETER WHEN
STANDARD COLUMN IS 15 MM.—*Continued*

| Colori-meter Read-ings in mm. | pH m-Cresol Purple | pH Thymol Blue (acid) | pH Bromo-phenol Blue | pH Bromo-cresol Green | pH Chloro-phenol Red | pH Bromo-phenol Red | pH Bromo-cresol Purple | pH Bromo-thymol Blue | pH Phenol Red | pH m-Cresol Purple | pH Thymol Blue |
|---|---|---|---|---|---|---|---|---|---|---|---|
| 11.0 | | | 3.54 | 4.23 | 5.54 | 5.72 | 5.86 | 6.56 | 7.46 | 7.88 | 8.46 |
| 11.2 | | | 3.51 | 4.20 | 5.51 | 5.69 | 5.83 | 6.53 | 7.43 | 7.85 | 8.43 |
| 11.4 | | | 3.48 | 4.17 | 5.48 | 5.66 | 5.80 | 6.50 | 7.40 | 7.82 | 8.40 |
| 11.6 | | | 3.45 | 4.14 | 5.45 | 5.63 | 5.77 | 6.47 | 7.37 | 7.79 | 8.37 |
| 11.8 | | | 3.41 | 4.10 | 5.41 | 5.59 | 5.73 | 6.43 | 7.33 | 7.75 | 8.33 |
| 12.0 | | | 3.38 | 4.07 | 5.38 | 5.56 | 5.70 | 6.40 | 7.30 | 7.72 | 8.30 |
| 12.2 | | | 3.34 | 4.03 | 5.34 | 5.52 | 5.66 | 6.36 | 7.26 | 7.68 | 8.26 |
| 12.4 | | | 3.30 | 3.99 | 5.30 | 5.48 | 5.62 | 6.32 | 7.22 | 7.64 | 8.22 |
| 12.6 | | | 3.26 | 3.95 | 5.26 | 5.44 | 5.58 | 6.28 | 7.18 | 7.60 | 8.18 |
| 12.8 | | | 3.22 | 3.91 | 5.22 | 5.40 | 5.54 | 6.24 | 7.14 | 7.56 | 8.14 |
| 13.0 | | | 3.17 | 3.86 | 5.17 | 5.35 | 5.49 | 6.19 | 7.09 | 7.51 | 8.09 |
| 13.2 | | | 3.12 | 3.81 | 5.12 | 5.30 | 5.44 | 6.14 | 7.04 | 7.46 | 8.04 |
| 13.4 | | | 3.06 | 3.75 | 5.06 | 5.24 | 5.38 | 6.08 | 6.98 | 7.40 | 7.98 |
| 13.6 | | | 2.99 | | 4.99 | 5.17 | 5.31 | 6.01 | 6.91 | 7.33 | |
| 13.8 | | | | | 4.92 | 5.10 | 5.24 | 5.94 | 6.84 | | |
| 14.0 | | | | | 4.83 | | 5.15 | | 6.75 | | |

TABLE 47. READINGS FOR BALANCING TYPE COLORIMETER WHEN STANDARD COLUMN IS 20 MM.

| Colorimeter Readings in mm. | pH m-Cresol Purple | pH Thymol Blue (acid) | pH Bromo-phenol Blue | pH Bromo-cresol Green | pH Chloro-phenol Red | pH Bromo-phenol Red | pH Bromo-cresol Purple | pH Bromo-thymol Blue | pH Phenol Red | pH m-Cresol Purple | pH Thymol Blue |
|---|---|---|---|---|---|---|---|---|---|---|---|
| 1.0 | 2.79 | 2.78 | | | | | | | | | |
| 1.2 | 2.70 | 2.69 | | | | | | | | | |
| 1.4 | 2.63 | 2.62 | | | | | | | | | |
| 1.6 | 2.57 | 2.56 | | | | | | | | | |
| 1.8 | 2.51 | 2.50 | | | | | | | | | |
| 2.0 | 2.46 | 2.45 | | | | | | | | | |
| 2.2 | 2.42 | 2.41 | | | | | | | | | |
| 2.4 | 2.38 | 2.37 | | | | | | | | | |
| 2.6 | 2.33 | 2.32 | | | | | | | | | |
| 2.8 | 2.30 | 2.29 | | | | | | | | | |
| 3.0 | 2.26 | 2.25 | | | | | | | | | |
| 3.2 | 2.23 | 2.22 | | | | | | | | | 9.62 |
| 3.4 | 2.20 | 2.19 | | | | | | | | 9.01 | 9.59 |
| 3.6 | 2.16 | 2.15 | | | | | | | | 8.97 | 9.55 |
| 3.8 | 2.14 | 2.13 | 4.61 | | | | | | | 8.95 | 9.53 |
| 4.0 | 2.11 | 2.10 | 4.58 | | | | | 7.60 | | 8.92 | 9.50 |
| 4.2 | 2.09 | 2.08 | 4.56 | | | | | 7.58 | | 8.90 | 9.48 |
| 4.4 | 2.06 | 2.06 | 4.53 | | | | | 7.55 | 8.45 | 8.87 | 9.45 |
| 4.6 | 2.03 | 2.03 | 4.50 | | | | | 7.52 | 8.42 | 8.84 | 9.42 |
| 4.8 | 2.01 | 2.00 | 4.48 | | | | 6.80 | 7.50 | 8.40 | 8.82 | 9.40 |
| 5.0 | 1.99 | 1.98 | 4.46 | | | | 6.78 | 7.48 | 8.38 | 8.80 | 9.38 |
| 5.2 | 1.96 | 1.95 | 4.43 | | 6.43 | | 6.75 | 7.45 | 8.35 | 8.77 | 9.35 |
| 5.4 | 1.94 | 1.93 | 4.41 | 5.10 | 6.41 | | 6.73 | 7.42 | 8.32 | 8.75 | 9.32 |
| 5.6 | 1.92 | 1.91 | 4.39 | 5.08 | 6.39 | | 6.71 | 7.41 | 8.31 | 8.73 | 9.31 |
| 5.8 | 1.90 | 1.89 | 4.37 | 5.06 | 6.37 | | 6.69 | 7.39 | 8.29 | 8.71 | 9.29 |
| 6.0 | 1.88 | 1.87 | 4.35 | 5.04 | 6.35 | | 6.67 | 7.37 | 8.27 | 8.69 | 9.27 |
| 6.2 | 1.86 | 1.85 | 4.33 | 5.02 | 6.33 | | 6.65 | 7.35 | 8.25 | 8.67 | 9.25 |
| 6.4 | 1.84 | 1.83 | 4.31 | 5.00 | 6.31 | | 6.63 | 7.33 | 8.23 | 8.65 | 9.23 |
| 6.6 | 1.82 | 1.81 | 4.29 | 4.98 | 6.29 | | 6.61 | 7.31 | 8.21 | 8.63 | 9.21 |
| 6.8 | 1.80 | 1.79 | 4.27 | 4.96 | 6.27 | | 6.59 | 7.29 | 8.19 | 8.61 | 9.19 |
| 7.0 | 1.78 | 1.77 | 4.25 | 4.94 | 6.25 | | 6.57 | 7.27 | 8.17 | 8.59 | 9.17 |
| 7.2 | 1.76 | 1.75 | 4.23 | 4.92 | 6.23 | 6.41 | 6.55 | 7.25 | 8.15 | 8.57 | 9.15 |
| 7.4 | 1.74 | 1.73 | 4.21 | 4.90 | 6.21 | 6.39 | 6.53 | 7.23 | 8.13 | 8.55 | 9.13 |
| 7.6 | 1.72 | 1.71 | 4.19 | 4.88 | 6.19 | 6.37 | 6.51 | 7.21 | 8.11 | 8.53 | 9.11 |
| 7.8 | 1.70 | 1.69 | 4.17 | 4.86 | 6.17 | 6.35 | 6.49 | 7.19 | 8.09 | 8.51 | 9.09 |
| 8.0 | 1.69 | 1.68 | 4.16 | 4.85 | 6.16 | 6.34 | 6.48 | 7.18 | 8.08 | 8.50 | 9.08 |
| 8.2 | 1.67 | 1.66 | 4.14 | 4.83 | 6.14 | 6.32 | 6.46 | 7.16 | 8.06 | 8.48 | 9.06 |
| 8.4 | 1.65 | 1.64 | 4.12 | 4.81 | 6.12 | 6.30 | 6.44 | 7.14 | 8.04 | 8.46 | 9.04 |
| 8.6 | 1.63 | 1.62 | 4.10 | 4.79 | 6.10 | 6.28 | 6.42 | 7.12 | 8.02 | 8.44 | 9.02 |
| 8.8 | 1.61 | 1.60 | 4.08 | 4.77 | 6.08 | 6.26 | 6.40 | 7.10 | 8.00 | 8.42 | 9.00 |
| 9.0 | 1.60 | 1.59 | 4.06 | 4.76 | 6.07 | 6.25 | 6.39 | 7.09 | 7.99 | 8.41 | 8.99 |
| 9.2 | 1.58 | 1.57 | 4.05 | 4.74 | 6.05 | 6.23 | 6.37 | 7.07 | 7.97 | 8.39 | 8.97 |
| 9.4 | 1.56 | 1.55 | 4.03 | 4.72 | 6.03 | 6.21 | 6.35 | 7.05 | 7.95 | 8.37 | 8.95 |
| 9.6 | 1.54 | 1.53 | 4.01 | 4.70 | 6.01 | 6.19 | 6.33 | 7.03 | 7.93 | 8.35 | 8.93 |
| 9.8 | 1.53 | 1.52 | 4.00 | 4.69 | 6.00 | 6.18 | 6.32 | 7.02 | 7.92 | 8.34 | 8.92 |
| 10.0 | 1.51 | 1.50 | 3.98 | 4.67 | 5.98 | 6.16 | 6.30 | 7.00 | 7.90 | 8.32 | 8.90 |

TABLE 47. READINGS FOR BALANCING TYPE COLORIMETER WHEN STANDARD COLUMN IS 20 MM.—*Continued*

| Colorimeter Readings in mm. | pH m-Cresol Purple | pH Thymol Blue (acid) | pH Bromophenol Blue | pH Bromocresol Green | pH Chlorophenol Red | pH Bromophenol Red | pH Bromocresol Purple | pH Bromothymol Blue | pH Phenol Red | pH m-Cresol Purple | pH Thymo Blue |
|---|---|---|---|---|---|---|---|---|---|---|---|
| 10.2 | 1.49 | 1.48 | 3.96 | 4.65 | 5.96 | 6.14 | 6.28 | 6.98 | 7.88 | 8.30 | 8.88 |
| 10.4 | 1.47 | 1.46 | 3.94 | 4.64 | 5.94 | 6.12 | 6.26 | 6.96 | 7.86 | 8.28 | 8.86 |
| 10.6 | 1.46 | 1.45 | 3.93 | 4.62 | 5.93 | 6.11 | 6.25 | 6.95 | 7.85 | 8.27 | 8.85 |
| 10.8 | 1.44 | 1.43 | 3.91 | 4.60 | 5.91 | 6.09 | 6.23 | 6.93 | 7.83 | 8.25 | 8.83 |
| 11.0 | 1.42 | 1.41 | 3.89 | 4.58 | 5.89 | 6.07 | 6.21 | 6.91 | 7.81 | 8.23 | 8.81 |
| 11.2 | 1.40 | 1.39 | 3.88 | 4.57 | 5.87 | 6.05 | 6.19 | 6.89 | 7.79 | 8.21 | 8.79 |
| 11.4 | 1.39 | 1.38 | 3.86 | 4.55 | 5.86 | 6.04 | 6.18 | 6.88 | 7.78 | 8.20 | 8.78 |
| 11.6 | 1.37 | 1.36 | 3.84 | 4.53 | 5.84 | 6.02 | 6.16 | 6.86 | 7.76 | 8.18 | 8.76 |
| 11.8 | 1.35 | 1.34 | 3.82 | 4.51 | 5.82 | 6.00 | 6.14 | 6.84 | 7.74 | 8.16 | 8.74 |
| 12.0 | 1.33 | 1.32 | 3.81 | 4.50 | 5.80 | 5.98 | 6.12 | 6.82 | 7.72 | 8.14 | 8.72 |
| 12.2 | 1.32 | 1.31 | 3.79 | 4.48 | 5.79 | 5.97 | 6.11 | 6.81 | 7.71 | 8.13 | 8.71 |
| 12.4 | 1.30 | 1.29 | 3.77 | 4.46 | 5.77 | 5.95 | 6.09 | 6.79 | 7.69 | 8.11 | 8.69 |
| 12.6 | 1.28 | 1.27 | 3.75 | 4.44 | 5.75 | 5.93 | 6.07 | 6.77 | 7.67 | 8.09 | 8.67 |
| 12.8 | 1.26 | 1.25 | 3.73 | 4.42 | 5.73 | 5.91 | 6.05 | 6.75 | 7.65 | 8.07 | 8.65 |
| 13.0 | 1.24 | 1.23 | 3.71 | 4.40 | 5.71 | 5.89 | 6.03 | 6.73 | 7.63 | 8.05 | 8.63 |
| 13.2 | 1.22 | 1.21 | 3.69 | 4.38 | 5.69 | 5.87 | 6.01 | 6.71 | 7.61 | 8.03 | 8.61 |
| 13.4 | 1.20 | 1.19 | 3.67 | 4.36 | 5.67 | 5.85 | 5.99 | 6.69 | 7.59 | 8.01 | 8.59 |
| 13.6 | 1.18 | 1.17 | 3.65 | 4.34 | 5.65 | 5.83 | 5.97 | 6.67 | 7.57 | 7.99 | 8.57 |
| 13.8 | | | 3.63 | 4.32 | 5.63 | 5.81 | 5.95 | 6.65 | 7.55 | 7.97 | 8.55 |
| 14.0 | | | 3.61 | 4.30 | 5.61 | 5.79 | 5.93 | 6.63 | 7.53 | 7.95 | 8.53 |
| 14.2 | | | 3.59 | 4.28 | 5.59 | 5.77 | 5.91 | 6.61 | 7.51 | 7.93 | 8.51 |
| 14.4 | | | 3.57 | 4.26 | 5.57 | 5.75 | 5.89 | 6.59 | 7.49 | 7.91 | 8.49 |
| 14.6 | | | 3.55 | 4.24 | 5.55 | 5.73 | 5.87 | 6.57 | 7.47 | 7.89 | 8.47 |
| 14.8 | | | 3.53 | 4.22 | 5.53 | 5.71 | 5.85 | 6.55 | 7.45 | 7.87 | 8.45 |
| 15.0 | | | 3.50 | 4.19 | 5.50 | 5.68 | 5.82 | 6.52 | 7.42 | 7.84 | 8.42 |
| 15.2 | | | 3.48 | 4.17 | 5.48 | 5.66 | 5.80 | 6.50 | 7.40 | 7.82 | 8.40 |
| 15.4 | | | 3.45 | 4.14 | 5.45 | 5.63 | 5.77 | 6.47 | 7.37 | 7.79 | 8.37 |
| 15.6 | | | 3.43 | 4.12 | 5.43 | 5.61 | 5.75 | 6.45 | 7.35 | 7.77 | 8.35 |
| 15.8 | | | 3.40 | 4.09 | 5.40 | 5.58 | 5.72 | 6.42 | 7.32 | 7.74 | 8.32 |
| 16.0 | | | 3.38 | 4.07 | 5.38 | 5.56 | 5.70 | 6.40 | 7.30 | 7.72 | 8.30 |
| 16.2 | | | 3.35 | 4.04 | 5.35 | 5.53 | 5.67 | 6.37 | 7.27 | 7.69 | 8.27 |
| 16.4 | | | 3.32 | 4.01 | 5.32 | 5.50 | 5.64 | 6.34 | 7.24 | 7.66 | 8.24 |
| 16.6 | | | 3.29 | 3.98 | 5.29 | 5.47 | 5.61 | 6.31 | 7.21 | 7.63 | 8.21 |
| 16.8 | | | 3.26 | 3.95 | 5.26 | 5.44 | 5.58 | 6.28 | 7.18 | 7.60 | 8.18 |
| 17.0 | | | 3.23 | 3.92 | 5.23 | 5.41 | 5.55 | 6.25 | 7.15 | 7.57 | 8.15 |
| 17.2 | | | 3.19 | 3.88 | 5.19 | 5.37 | 5.51 | 6.21 | 7.11 | 7.53 | 8.11 |
| 17.4 | | | 3.16 | 3.85 | 5.16 | 5.34 | 5.48 | 6.18 | 7.08 | 7.50 | 8.08 |
| 17.6 | | | 3.12 | 3.81 | 5.12 | 5.30 | 5.44 | 6.14 | 7.04 | 7.46 | 8.04 |
| 17.8 | | | 3.07 | 3.76 | 5.07 | 5.25 | 5.39 | 6.09 | 6.99 | 7.41 | 7.99 |
| 18.0 | | | 3.03 | 3.72 | 5.03 | 5.21 | 5.35 | 6.05 | 6.95 | 7.37 | |
| 18.2 | | | 2.97 | 3.66 | 4.97 | 5.15 | 5.29 | 5.99 | 6.89 | | |
| 18.4 | | | | | 4.92 | | 5.24 | | 6.84 | | |
| 18.6 | | | | | 4.86 | | 5.18 | | 6.78 | | |
| 18.8 | | | | | 4.78 | | | | | | |
| 19.0 | | | | | 4.70 | | | | | | |

Thus, to illustrate,[16] the amount of diluted indicator added to the standard is 1 ml., equivalent to 0.1 ml. of undiluted. The indicator is p-nitrophenol, of pK value 7.18. Substitution in the formula gives

$$pH = 7.18 + \log(0.1/0.9)$$
$$pH = 7.18 + (\log 0.1 - \log 0.9)$$
$$pH = 7.18 + (-1 - (-0.05))$$
$$pH = 7.18 - 0.95 = 6.23$$

In a more general application of the formula given above, the value $C$ may be substituted by $a$, representing the degrees of dissociation in solution. Values for $\dfrac{C}{1-C}$ may be obtained as the log by reference to Table 48.

### DILUTION METHOD

This standard technic [17] is applicable with suitable modification for pH determination. Monochromatic indicators are required.

Satisfactory cells for the determination are a pair of matched test tubes. To one add 10 ml. of the sample solution. To the other add 9 ml. of the sample solution and 1 ml. of approximately 0.1 $N$ sodium hydroxide or hydrochloric acid according to whether the sample is acid or alkaline.

Add a measured volume of standard indicator to the sample, a volume which will give a distinct color but not an intense one. Add the identical volume of indicator to the standard where it will be completely converted to alkaline form or acid form as the case may be. Add distilled water to the standard until the intensity of color matches that of the sample.

*Calculation.* For purposes of calculation the factor $D$ will be taken as the ratio of initial and final volumes of the standard. Thus, if the original 5 ml. of standard were diluted to 12.5 ml., $D = 2.5$. Then the formula is

$$pH = pK - \log (D - 1).$$

Assume the indicator to have been p-nitrophenol and this becomes

$$pH = 7.18 - \log 1.5$$
$$pH = 7.18 - 0.18$$
$$pH = 7.00$$

---

16 Philip B. Hawk, Olaf Bergeim, Bernard L. Oser and Arthur G. Cole, *Practical Physiological Chemistry*, 11th Ed., p. 30. The Blakiston Co., Philadelphia, Pa. (1937).
17 J. McCrae, *Analyst*, **68**, 183 (1943).

TABLE 48. VALUES OF LOG $\dfrac{a}{1-a}$, AND OF LOG $\dfrac{a}{1-a}$ MULTIPLIED BY THE TEMPERATURE FACTORS FOR CONCENTRATION CELLS AT 20°, 25°, 30° AND 37.5° C.

| $a$ | Log $\dfrac{a}{1-a}$ | Log $\dfrac{a}{1-a}$ Multiplied by | | | |
|---|---|---|---|---|---|
| | | 0.058128 (20) | 0.059120 (25) | 0.060111 (30) | 0.061599 (37.5) |
| 0.001 | −2.9996 | −0.1744 | −0.1773 | −0.1803 | −0.1848 |
| 0.005 | −2.2989 | −0.1336 | −0.1359 | −0.1382 | −0.1416 |
| 0.01 | −1.9956 | −0.1160 | −0.1180 | −0.1200 | −0.1229 |
| 0.02 | −1.6902 | −0.0982 | −0.0999 | −0.1016 | −0.1041 |
| 0.03 | −1.5096 | −0.0878 | −0.0892 | −0.0907 | −0.0930 |
| 0.04 | −1.3802 | −0.0802 | −0.0816 | −0.0830 | −0.0850 |
| 0.05 | −1.2788 | −0.0743 | −0.0756 | −0.0769 | −0.0788 |
| 0.06 | −1.1950 | −0.0695 | −0.0706 | −0.0718 | −0.0736 |
| 0.07 | −1.1234 | −0.0653 | −0.0664 | −0.0675 | −0.0692 |
| 0.08 | −1.0607 | −0.0617 | −0.0627 | −0.0638 | −0.0653 |
| 0.09 | −1.0048 | −0.0584 | −0.0594 | −0.0604 | −0.0619 |
| 0.10 | −0.9542 | −0.0555 | −0.0564 | −0.0574 | −0.0588 |
| 0.11 | −0.9080 | −0.0528 | −0.0537 | −0.0546 | −0.0559 |
| 0.12 | −0.8653 | −0.0503 | −0.0512 | −0.0520 | −0.0533 |
| 0.13 | −0.8256 | −0.0480 | −0.0488 | −0.0496 | −0.0509 |
| 0.14 | −0.7884 | −0.0458 | −0.0466 | −0.0474 | −0.0486 |
| 0.15 | −0.7533 | −0.0438 | −0.0445 | −0.0453 | −0.0464 |
| 0.16 | −0.7202 | −0.0419 | −0.0426 | −0.0433 | −0.0444 |
| 0.17 | −0.6886 | −0.0400 | −0.0407 | −0.0414 | −0.0424 |
| 0.18 | −0.6585 | −0.0383 | −0.0389 | −0.0396 | −0.0406 |
| 0.19 | −0.6297 | −0.0366 | −0.0372 | −0.0379 | −0.0388 |
| 0.20 | −0.6021 | −0.0350 | −0.0356 | −0.0362 | −0.0371 |
| 0.21 | −0.5754 | −0.0334 | −0.0340 | −0.0346 | −0.0354 |
| 0.22 | −0.5497 | −0.0320 | −0.0325 | −0.0330 | −0.0339 |
| 0.23 | −0.5248 | −0.0305 | −0.0310 | −0.0315 | −0.0323 |
| 0.24 | −0.5006 | −0.0291 | −0.0296 | −0.0301 | −0.0308 |
| 0.25 | −0.4771 | −0.0277 | −0.0282 | −0.0287 | −0.0294 |
| 0.26 | −0.4543 | −0.0264 | −0.0269 | −0.0273 | −0.0280 |
| 0.27 | −0.4320 | −0.0251 | −0.0255 | −0.0260 | −0.0266 |
| 0.28 | −0.4102 | −0.0238 | −0.0243 | −0.0247 | −0.0253 |
| 0.29 | −0.3888 | −0.0226 | −0.0230 | −0.0234 | −0.0239 |
| 0.30 | −0.3680 | −0.0214 | −0.0218 | −0.0221 | −0.0227 |
| 0.31 | −0.3475 | −0.0202 | −0.0205 | −0.0209 | −0.0214 |
| 0.32 | −0.3274 | −0.0190 | −0.0194 | −0.0197 | −0.0202 |
| 0.33 | −0.3076 | −0.0179 | −0.0182 | −0.0185 | −0.0189 |
| 0.34 | −0.2880 | −0.0167 | −0.0170 | −0.0173 | −0.0177 |
| 0.35 | −0.2688 | −0.0156 | −0.0159 | −0.0162 | −0.0166 |
| 0.36 | −0.2499 | −0.0145 | −0.0148 | −0.0150 | −0.0154 |
| 0.37 | −0.2311 | −0.0134 | −0.0137 | −0.0139 | −0.0142 |
| 0.38 | −0.2126 | −0.0124 | −0.0126 | −0.0128 | −0.0131 |
| 0.39 | −0.1943 | −0.0113 | −0.0115 | −0.0117 | −0.0120 |
| 0.40 | −0.1761 | −0.0102 | −0.0104 | −0.0106 | −0.0108 |
| 0.41 | −0.1581 | −0.0092 | −0.0093 | −0.0095 | −0.0097 |
| 0.42 | −0.1402 | −0.0081 | −0.0083 | −0.0084 | −0.0086 |
| 0.43 | −0.1224 | −0.0071 | −0.0072 | −0.0074 | −0.0075 |
| 0.44 | −0.1047 | −0.0061 | −0.0062 | −0.0063 | −0.0064 |
| 0.45 | −0.0871 | −0.0051 | −0.0051 | −0.0052 | −0.0054 |
| 0.46 | −0.0696 | −0.0040 | −0.0041 | −0.0042 | −0.0043 |
| 0.47 | −0.0522 | −0.0030 | −0.0031 | −0.0031 | −0.0032 |
| 0.48 | −0.0347 | −0.0020 | −0.0021 | −0.0021 | −0.0021 |
| 0.49 | −0.0174 | −0.0010 | −0.0010 | −0.0010 | −0.0011 |
| 0.50 | ±0.0000 | ±0.0000 | ±0.0000 | ±0.0000 | ±0.0000 |
| 0.51 | +0.0174 | +0.0010 | +0.0010 | +0.0010 | +0.0011 |
| 0.52 | +0.0347 | +0.0020 | +0.0020 | +0.0021 | +0.0021 |

For values beyond $a = 0.50$ the table progresses inversely as above but with sign +. Example: $a = 0.53$, $(1 − a = 0.47)$, read row for $a = 0.47$, i.e., log $\dfrac{a}{1-a} = +0.0522$, etc. If $a = 0.80$, $(1 − a = 0.20)$, read row for $a = 0.20$, i.e., log $\dfrac{a}{1-a} = +0.6021$, etc.

That method of calculation is not applicable to phenolphthalein and Salicyl yellow but data for use with them are given in Table 49.[18]

TABLE 49. VALUES FOR pH BY DILUTION METHOD

| Proportion of Indicator Transformed | Dilution Value | pH |
|---|---|---|
| PHENOLPHTHALEIN | | |
| 0.01 | 100 | 8.45 |
| 0.014 | 71 | 8.50 |
| 0.030 | 33 | 8.60 |
| 0.047 | 21 | 8.70 |
| 0.069 | 14.5 | 8.80 |
| 0.090 | 11 | 8.90 |
| 0.12 | 8.3 | 9.00 |
| 0.16 | 6.25 | 9.10 |
| 0.21 | 4.75 | 9.20 |
| 0.27 | 3.7 | 9.30 |
| 0.34 | 2.95 | 9.40 |
| 0.40 | 2.5 | 9.50 |
| 0.45 | 2.22 | 9.60 |
| 0.50 | 2.0 | 9.70 |
| 0.55 | 1.82 | 9.80 |
| 0.60 | 1.67 | 9.90 |
| 0.65 | 1.54 | 10.00 |
| 0.70 | 1.43 | 10.10 |
| 0.75 | 1.33 | 10.20 |
| 0.80 | 1.25 | 10.30 |
| 0.845 | 1.18 | 10.40 |
| 0.873 | 1.145 | 10.50 |
| SALICYL YELLOW | | |
| 0.13 | 7.7 | 10.00 |
| 0.16 | 6.25 | 10.20 |
| 0.22 | 4.55 | 10.40 |
| 0.29 | 3.45 | 10.60 |
| 0.36 | 2.78 | 10.80 |
| 0.46 | 2.17 | 11.00 |
| 0.56 | 1.79 | 11.20 |
| 0.66 | 1.51 | 11.40 |
| 0.75 | 1.33 | 11.60 |
| 0.83 | 1.20 | 11.80 |
| 0.88 | 1.14 | 12.00 |

[18] L. Michaelis and A. Gyemant, *Biochem. Z.*, **109**, 165-210 (1920).

## COLORED SOLUTIONS

The estimation of pH in colored solutions requires one additional step. Buffer solutions may be used, alternatively either the variation in concentration of indicator in the acid and alkaline tubes or the balancing method. The procedure is applicable only if the color is not too intense and the turbidity slight.

**Procedure Using Buffers.** Treat 10 ml. of sample in 1 tube by the usual procedure. In another tube place 10 ml. of untreated sample. For estimation of the pH compare the total color of the sample tube and one tube of distilled water with the total color of the standard and the untreated sample. In every case, therefore, the sum of two tubes is compared.

**Procedure without Buffers.** By the usual procedure 2 tubes are usually compared with 2 others. For colored solutions 3 are compared: the treated sample and 2 tubes of distilled water with the 2 standard tubes and 1 tube of untreated sample.

**Balancing Method.** Auxiliary cups of fixed depth are used below the cups previously described. In the right-hand auxiliary cup place the unknown with the indicator, instead of in the next cup above. In the left-hand auxiliary cup place the unknown without the indicator. Fill the right-hand large cup with distilled water and lift the next cup to touch the plunger. Place indicator solutions in the left-hand cups as before.

The depth adjusted for the large cups from the plunger must be the same as the depth of the auxiliary cups. On the left side the light goes through a layer of fixed depth of sample without indicator and then through an equal depth of acid and alkaline form of indicator in distilled water. On the right, the light passes through the sample with color developed with an indicator, then through the same depth of distilled water. From that point on the manipulation is the same as for a colorless sample.

**Extrapolation.**[19] In order to determine the pH of a colored solution, dilute to 2, 4, 6, 8, etc. times the original volumes. Determine the pH of each according to one of the usual procedures. Plot the pH found against the logarithm of the dilution. The points should fall on a straight line and when extrapolated to zero dilution will give the pH of the

---

[19] F. C. Thompson and W. R. Atkins, *J. Intern. Soc. Leather Trades Chem.*, **13**, 297-9 (1929).

original solution. Data with tan liquors check the electrometric method within about 0.05 pH unit.

Table 50 gives the pH ranges and wave lengths for readings of the photometer with common indicators covering the normal range.

TABLE 50. WAVE LENGTHS FOR READING INDICATORS BY PHOTOMETER

| Indicator | pH Range | Wave Lengths mμ |
|---|---|---|
| Thymol blue | 1.0–3.0 | 530–430 |
| Bromophenol blue | 3.0–4.4 | 430–570 |
| Methyl red | 4.4–6.27 | 530–430 |
| Bromothymol blue | 6.0–8.0 | 430–610 |
| Thymol blue | 8.0–10.0 | 430–570 |

Determinations may be made photoelectrically,[20] and recorded in terms of transmittance or absorbency values.[21]

**Procedure.** Add 1 ml. of standard neutral indicator to 10 ml. of test solution. Measure the transmittance at a suitable wave length and relate to pH by a calibration curve. Apply correction data for temperature and the presence of salts,[22] if necessary, after the apparent pH has been read.

The spectrophotometer provides a more dependable means of judging these indicators than the human eye.[23] Evaluation is based on the matching of the intensity of light of the same color in contiguous fields. Turbidity and excessive color of the solution may be surmounted by increasing the concentration of the indicator and decreasing the thickness of the layer of solution measured. The ideal indicators for spectrographic investigation have two bands occurring in spectral regions in which variations of intensity are perceptible to the human eye.[24] An accuracy of 0.05 pH is obtainable in the determination of pH by some spectrophotometric methods.

COMPARISON WITH TEST STRIPS

For rough approximations the colors of test papers moistened with various pH indicators are used. Complex sets of pH papers are avail-

---

[20] G. F. Lothian, *Trans. Faraday Soc.*, **33**, 1239 (1937).

[21] György Goll, *Magyar Chem. Folyóirat*, **64**, 92-9 (1938).

[22] John Rae, Jr., and V. W. Meloche, *Trans. Wisconsin Acad. Sci.*, **34**, 195-212 (1942).

[23] S. E. Q. Ashley, *Ind. Eng. Chem., Anal. Ed.*, **11**, 72-9 (1939).

[24] Walter C. Holmes, *J. Am. Chem. Soc.*, **46**, 627-31 (1924).

able.[25] Individual pH papers in these sets have a very short range, so that an accuracy of 0.1 pH unit is obtainable. Sets have also been made from special blotting paper impregnated with 8 indicators covering the pH range from 1-14. The pH may be estimated with an accuracy of 0.1 unit.[26]

A series of mixed indicators used on test papers show a neutral gray, varied to a color in each direction from the standard value.[27] Instead of paper, thin films of colorless cellulose acetate carrying the indicator are also used.[28] The pH of those colored solutions which do not stain the strips, and of turbid solutions, can be estimated by dipping for 1 to 2 minutes, rinsing and comparing with a scale. The indicator is not readily leached out. The entire range is not equally accurate.

### COMPARISON BY DROP METHODS

Small glass cells are made by cementing round 15 mm. cover slips to one edge of small glass rings. Fill one of these glass cells with distilled water, and add one or two drops of fluid to be tested. Add one drop of the appropriate indicator solution. When the range of the reaction of the fluid is obtained, prepare a series of similar glass cells containing buffer solutions of known hydrogen-ion concentrations to match the color of the unknown. Measurement with an accuracy of 0.1 pH is possible. This method is particularly useful where, as in biological samples, the amount of sample is limited.[29] Another approximate method is by comparison of single drops on a vaselined plate [30] or of a few drops in a depression in a porcelain plate. The method, comparing with a chart of colors, is used for soil acidity.[31]

---

[25] Anachemia, 70 East 45th Street, New York, N. Y.; R. P. Cargille, 118 Liberty Street, New York, N. Y.

[26] Karl Höll, *Chem. Fabrik*, **1935**, 218-19.

[27] W. U. Behrens, *Z. anal. Chem.*, **73**, 129-37 (1928).

[28] Peter Wulff, *Kolloid Z.*, **40**, 341-2 (1926).

[29] J. H. Brown, *J. Lab. Clin. Med.*, **9**, 239-44 (1924).

[30] Oscar W. Richards, *Science*, **68**, 185 (1928).

[31] M. F. Morgan, *Ecology*, **8**, 387-8 (1927).

# AUTHOR INDEX

# SUBJECT INDEX